Quantum Mechanics of
Particles and Wave Fields

Quantum Mechanics of Particles and Wave Fields

ARTHUR MARCH

Professor of Theoretical Physics
University of Innsbruck

JOHN WILEY & SONS, INC., NEW YORK
CHAPMAN & HALL, LIMITED, LONDON

Preface

Since its inception nearly a quarter of a century ago, quantum mechanics has been the subject of many books. Notwithstanding this abundance of books, if someone, not a theoretical physicist and not thoroughly acquainted with modern methods of analysis, were to attempt to digest a current article dealing with nuclear forces or cosmic rays, relying for help on the available books on the subject, he would discover to his dismay that modern quantum mechanics differs radically from that which he finds in the textbooks. Even the terminology is different. What, for example, is the pseudoscalar field which in some obscure way seems to be intimately associated with a particle? He will not find the answer in the information at his disposal. More confusing to him is the interpretation of a field in the new mechanics. It seems evident that what is meant is a real field possessing energy and momentum. Yet the textbooks attach a purely symbolic meaning to the wave field of a particle, picturing the field concept merely as a probability function.

The whole difficulty arises from the fact that in recent years quantum mechanics, following relativistic laws, has reached certain conclusions which are not in accord with its original ideas. It is true that the idea of representing the state of a system by a vector and any observable quantity by a linear operator is still the same, there being a special interpretation of both. But in relativistic quantum mechanics the vector representing a certain state is no longer determined with the aid of a wave equation. It was this belief in non-relativistic theory that led to the common belief—one still upheld by the textbooks—that the waves encountered in wave mechanics have a purely constructive character. In relativistic theory this is not true. Only by the association of the particle with a real field, that is, one possessing energy and momentum, was it possible to establish equations satisfying the requirements of relativity theory. It is assumed that this field is related to the particle in a way similar to the association of the photon with the electromagnetic field; that is, it is of importance only for those cases wherein the particle displays the properties of a wave motion. It is essential to realize that, as long as the field is not quantized, it is completely dissociated from the concept of a particle; it neither consists of particles nor admits of any quantity which might have a corpuscular interpretation. In order to achieve this distinctly one-sided description of the phenomena it is necessary to quantize the field, this being accomplished by transcribing the field quantities into matrices. This process brings about the appearance of particles and leads to that formalism which, making use of the property of non-commutability of certain matrices, unites the undulatory and the corpuscular nature into one consistent scheme.

It is impossible to understand the methods of modern quantum mechanics without a knowledge of the way in which the theory has been developing. It is precisely for this reason that I have adopted as the main purpose of this book the presentation of the theory in such a manner that the reader will have adequate information whenever it is needed. To achieve this purpose, I felt that it was necessary to devote almost one half of the book to relativistic quantum mechanics, that is, the quantum mechanics of wave fields, the knowledge of which is indispensable for any physicist engaged in modern research work. As this part of quantum mechanics is considered especially difficult, I have taken the utmost care in explaining the fundamental ideas as clearly and understandably as possible. The reader should not only become acquainted with the mathematical formalism of the theory but also should first of all acquire a real understanding of its foundation. Criticism may be made that many important applications of the theory and methods of calculation are omitted, but the book was so planned as not to exceed a certain size and it seemed preferable to use the space for a thorough exposition of principles rather than for examples and methods which can be found in many existing textbooks.

As the last chapter deals with the concept of a fundamental length, I feel that a word of justification for its introduction is needed. The method therein suggested for contending with the well-known fundamental difficulties arising in quantum mechanics does not form a part of the currently adopted theory. Neither is there general agreement among physicists as to whether the concept of a constant is really indispensable for reaching a reasonable theory, nor is there agreement among those who support the idea as to how this new constant should be introduced into the theory. Thus it might seem that the introduction into the text of the concept of a constant which would limit the possibilities of observation is premature. And yet there is not the slightest doubt that in its present form quantum mechanics is of little or no use in the evaluation of nuclear processes unless the formalism is complemented with instruction as to how the divergent results of the theory can be made convergent. The universal length seems to be the simplest means that can be used to attain this end. Since I first introduced the idea of the universal length, an idea developed in several papers as early as 1936, I feel justified in presenting my views in this book. The procedure suggested in Chapter 10 has the advantages of being simple and permitting a plausible interpretation. Moreover, in all those cases which are subject to calculation, it is in good agreement with the experimental facts. It is quite true that the method removes only those divergences which arise from the quantum-mechanical formalism; it does not affect those which are caused by the assumed punctiformity of the particles, a condition which already existed in classical theory. However, it certainly represents a step forward if we can handle successfully the difficulties first mentioned, difficulties by which theory is most hampered in its practical applications.

Writing a book in a language which is not one's mother tongue is always a venture. That it could succeed is due to Professor William Hurley of Fordham University, New York, who was kind enough to revise the wording and the formulas of the manuscript most carefully. I take this opportunity of expressing my deep gratitude to Professor Hurley. I am also indebted to my colleague, Mr. J. McDonaugh of the University of Innsbruck, who assisted me with valuable advice.

A.M.

Innsbruck, Austria
March, 1951

Contents

1. Wave Mechanics of a Single Particle   1

1. The fundamental idea of quantum mechanics. 2. Heisenberg's uncertainty relations. Coordinate and momentum. 3. Heisenberg's uncertainty relations. Method of Doppler effect. 4. The new mechanics and the principle of causality. 5. de Broglie waves. 6. The method of wave packets. 7. Reconciliation of wave and classical mechanics. 8. The wave mechanics of a particle moving in a field of force. 9. The geometrical method of wave mechanics. 10. The scattering of probability waves by a nucleus.

2. Wave Mechanics of Stationary States   35

11. Schroedinger's wave equation. 12. The experimental possibilities. 13. States of undefined energy. 14. Wave mechanics and Bohr's theory. 15. Expectation values of mechanical entities. 16. The principle of transformation. 17. The linear oscillator. 18. The hydrogen atom. 19. Discussion of the solution. Comparison with Bohr's theory. 20. Wave mechanics and the correspondence principle. Transition probabilities.

3. Wave Mechanics in Matrix Form   83

21. The idea of matrix mechanics. 22. The Hilbert space. Concept of matrix. 23. Addition and multiplication of matrices. 24. Dual, unitary, Hermitean matrices. 25. Transformation to principal axes. 26. Functions of matrices. 27. The quantum-mechanical interpretation of matrices. 28. The commutation relations. 29. Hermitean forms and expectation values. 30. Coordinate systems with a continuous infinity of axes. 31. The passage from matrix to wave mechanics. The fundamental problem of matrix mechanics. 32. Unique nature of the solution. 33. The dynamical law of quantum mechanics. The principle of causality. 34. Systems with many degrees of freedom.

4. Perturbation Theory   127

35. Perturbation of non-degenerated systems. 36. Perturbation of degenerated systems. 37. Perturbation as causing transitions.

5. Systems of Many Particles   136

38. Schroedinger's equation for the many-body problem. 39. Symmetric and antisymmetric solutions. 40. The exclusion principle relative to a combination of symmetric and antisymmetric states. 41. The helium atom. 42. Systems of many similar particles. Method of particle picture. 43. Systems of many similar particles. Method of wave picture. 44. Statistics of Bose-Einstein and Fermi-Dirac.

6. Relativistic Wave Equations   **165**

45. Particles with spin $\frac{1}{2}$. Dirac's equation. 46. A particle in an electromagnetic field. Dirac's hole theory. 47. Particles with spin 0. The equation of Klein and Gordon. 48. Digression on tensor calculus. Pseudoscalar wave field. 49. Particles with spin 1. de Broglie and Proca's equation. 50. The pseudovector field.

7. Quantization of Wave Fields   **191**

51. The idea of quantization. 52. Quantization of a scalar field. 53. Quantization of a vector field.

8. Quantum Electrodynamics   **204**

54. Classical theory. The field as a superposition of plane waves. 55. Transformation of the Hamiltonian. 56. Quantization of the field. 57. Quantization of a system consisting of field and particles. 58. Interaction between radiation and matter. 59. Emission and absorption of a light quantum by an atom. 60. The divergences occurring in the higher approximations.

9. Wave Fields and Nuclear Matter   **231**

61. The Lagrangian of the interaction. 62. Scalar and pseudoscalar fields. 63. Vector and pseudovector fields. 64. The potential of the nuclear forces. 65. Nuclear scattering of mesons. 66. Magnetic moment of proton and neutron. 67. Mesons in an electromagnetic field.

10. Introduction of a Fundamental Length   **267**

68. The idea of a fundamental length. 69. Introduction of l_0 into the interaction terms. 70. Application to electrodynamics. 71. *Bremsstrahlung*—transversal self-energy of an electron. 72. Application to the nuclear forces. 73. Nuclear scattering of mesons. Magnetic moment of proton and neutron. 74. Decay of negative mesons in light elements.

Index   **291**

1

WAVE MECHANICS

OF A SINGLE PARTICLE

1. The Fundamental Idea of Quantum Mechanics. Quantum mechanics was developed because of the failure of classical physics to account for atomic phenomena. According to classical physics, the state of a physical system can be determined to any desired degree of accuracy by measuring certain quantities, such as coordinates and velocities, with ideal apparatus and applying to these measurements certain principles by means of which the future states of the system can be predicted. However, when a system of exceedingly small mass is considered, the following difficulty is encountered: in the measuring of any observable quantity, the state of the object is disturbed by the measuring process in an unpredictable way and the state loses its determinacy relative to other quantities. If an attempt is made to compensate for this loss by measuring one of the other observable quantities, the knowledge of the first is lost. Thus we can never succeed in determining the simultaneous values of all the quantities that define the state of the system.

Such a situation, which finds its expression in what are called the uncertainty relations, has frequently been interpreted as being due to an interaction between the observing subject and the object observed, which prevents a distinct separation of observer and object, thus depriving the object of its determinacy. Such an interpretation is inaccurate in that it is not the observer that interacts with the object but rather the measuring apparatus itself. This interaction implies that the state of the object cannot be measured without being changed by the process of that measurement, a fact which of itself is not new. Prior to quantum mechanics it was known that the value of an observable is influenced by the introduction of an instrument, for example a thermometer, into the system. This complication involved no difficulty, since the disturbance caused by the instrument was considered an effect that could be compensated for with the aid of classical theory. The viewpoint of quantum mechanics is different.

It is based on the fundamental idea that any phenomenon that occurs in nature consists of elementary processes which, by virtue of a natural law, cannot be analyzed. The emission or absorption of light and the scattering of a photon by an electron are examples of elementary processes which resist any attempt to analyze them. We do not know, and if quantum mechanics is correct we shall never know, what happens in an atom during the process that leads to the production or annihilation of a photon. As a result, we cannot apply the principle of causality to the process, and it appears to us as a discontinuity in the course of events. Hence there is an atomicity in nature, not only for matter but for events as well, and Planck's constant h has the significance that it determines the size of an atomic event, if by size we mean the quantity of action involved in an elementary process.

The above leads us to conclude that the uncertainty relations arise from the fact that, since any observation consists of an indeterminate interaction between object and measuring apparatus, the object is left in a state which escapes our control to an extent given by the constant h. Therefore it is impossible for us to determine the exact state of a system. As an example, consider a particle the x coordinate of which is to be measured. As will be seen, we are confronted with the following situation: if a measurement made at time t gives the value of x with an uncertainty Δx, meaning that x lies somewhere between the limits x and $x + \Delta x$, the simultaneous value of the momentum p_x of the particle cannot be determined more accurately than with a possible deviation Δp_x, which is related to Δx by the expression $\Delta p_x = h/\Delta x$. Thus, the more accurately we measure x, the less accurate becomes the measurement of p_x, and vice versa. This follows from the fact that with every measurement is associated an effect on the system which cannot be predicted, because it lies outside the domain of causality due to Planck's constant h. Thus, whereas classical physics has assumed that all observables of a system can be measured simultaneously to any desired degree of accuracy, there is in fact a limit to this accuracy. On principle, it is impossible to ascertain the exact initial state of a system, and consequently it must also be impossible to infer unique values of the observables at time t from measurements made at t_0. An exact prediction of the future is impossible without exact knowledge of the present. Therefore quantum mechanics refuses to ascribe a physical meaning to equations that refer to an exactly measured initial state, there being no experiment to which such equations can be applied. The question, adequate to the possibilities of observation, is not what will develop from an exactly known state, but what will occur if the initial state is not exactly defined. Evidently there is no unique answer to this question, for the state, being indeterminate, offers a variety of possibilities. Only a prediction based on probability can be made. To work out this prediction we must start always at the same indeterminate initial state and then measure the state after a time t. The result will be a statistical one from which we can determine the probability that a measurement on the system at time t will furnish a given value.

Thus only probability relations exist between present and future, a fact that implies the essentially statistical nature of the new mechanics. The problem then is to determine how to formulate these relations in a general set of equations that will supply us with a description of atomic phenomena. As will be seen, this problem is solved satisfactorily by quantum mechanics.

2. Heisenberg's Uncertainty Relations.   Coordinate and Momentum.   As a beginning, it will be proved that the state of a system can be determined only within certain limits of accuracy even with ideal apparatus. For simplicity we shall consider first a single particle, for example an electron. Let the problem be to determine the position and momentum of the particle at a given instant of time t. Let us assume that from a previous measurement we know the velocity with which the particle has been moving up to the instant t. We assume also that the velocity is directed along the x axis and denote the corresponding momentum by p. All we wish to determine here is the position of the particle at time t. Following Heisenberg's method, we could use a microscope for this purpose, but we prefer to use a simple pinhole camera, proceeding as follows. Let the opaque screen S have a small circular aperture of radius r. At time t let the particle be at a distance a from S. Direct a beam of light of wavelength λ along the x axis to illuminate the particle. Of the light scattered by the particle, let us observe that which passes through the aperture. This light will produce a diffraction pattern on a screen S', the bright central spot having a radius $\lambda b/r$, where b is the distance between the two screens. Under ideal observation, this spot is the region within which the screen S' is hit by the light quanta. Now let us suppose that it is a single light quantum which hits the particle at the instant t and is reflected in the direction of the aperture. The position of the particle now can be located by the projection of the point of incidence of the quantum through the aperture, which is assumed to be infinitely small, onto the plane in which the particle lies. If the quantum passes through the aperture without deflection, the incidence on S' will be the center of the central diffraction circle and the projection will be on the particle itself. In general, however, the quantum may strike the circle at a distance anywhere up to $\lambda b/r$ from center.   This means that the projection onto the particle plane may be at points up to $(\lambda b/r)(a/b) = \lambda a/r$ from the particle's position.   Thus the observer can determine the x and y coordinates of the particle's position with possible errors Δx and Δy each equal to $\lambda a/r$.   By using light of sufficiently short wavelength this error can be made as small as desired.

Now let us consider how the momentum is affected by the act of observation.   The original momentum of the quantum was $h\nu/c$.

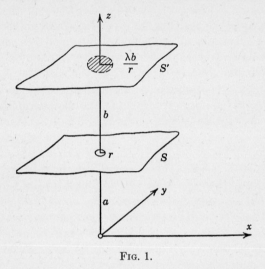

Fig. 1.

The reflection of the quantum leaves the amount of momentum nearly the same, the small reduction due to the Compton effect being negligible.   However, the direction is changed in such a way that after reflection it deviates from the z axis by a small angle θ.   This deviation must be $\leqq \alpha$, where α is the semi-angle subtended at the particle by the aperture; it is defined by $\sin \alpha = r/a$.   Specifying the direction of the quantum after reflection from the particle by the polar angles θ and ϕ and denoting the momentum of the particle after reflection by $\mathbf{p}$, the components of which are p_x, p_y, p_z, we can write, from the principle of the conservation of momentum,

$$P + \frac{h\nu}{c} = \frac{h\nu}{c} \sin \theta \cos \phi + p_x$$

$$0 = \frac{h\nu}{c} \sin \theta \sin \phi + p_y$$

If θ and ϕ were known, the components of momentum p_x and p_y could be calculated from the above equations. Actually, however, ϕ is unknown and the most that can be said about θ is that it must be smaller than α. Therefore we can maintain only that the first terms on the right-hand sides of the equations cannot exceed $h\nu \sin \alpha/c = (h/\lambda)(r/a)$. Thus the components of momentum p_x and p_y after the measurement of position are given by $P + h\nu/c$ and 0 respectively, the possible error being $\Delta p_x = \Delta p_y = (h/\lambda)(r/a)$.

Thus it turns out that we can make the error of position as small as desirable by using sufficiently short wavelength, but the more accurately we determine the position the less we know about the momentum of the particle after the observation. Conversely, if we proceed to make Δp_x as small as desirable, as, from the expression above, we can by using sufficiently long wavelength, we increase the position error Δx. Thus an exact simultaneous measurement of coordinates and momenta proves to be impossible. Heisenberg's uncertainty principle expresses this fact by the fundamental relations

$$\Delta x \, \Delta p_x \geqq h \qquad \Delta y \, \Delta p_y \geqq h \qquad \Delta z \, \Delta p_z \geqq h \qquad (1)$$

The equality sign is used in these relations if the interaction between measurement and state has been checked as far as possible. Otherwise the greater-than sign is employed.

In what we have been discussing above, the velocity was assumed to be known. We must investigate now how we can measure the velocity with which the particle was moving up to the instant t, at which time the position was determined. For this purpose we must compare the position P of the particle at time t with its position P' at time $t' < t$, known from a previous measurement. The desired velocity then is given in magnitude and direction by $(P - P')/(t - t')$. By making the interval $t - t'$ sufficiently great we can determine the velocity to any desired accuracy, since the errors in the determinations of P and P' are outweighed by the great value of the denominator $t - t'$.

It might be supposed that this procedure ultimately would provide a method for determining the exact simultaneous values of coordinate and momentum in contradiction to the uncertainty relations. Actually the particle no longer moves with the velocity $(P - P')/(t - t')$, however, for, at the instant t when the position of P was ascertained, the velocity was changed by the process of measurement, and it is this changed motion on which the future of the system depends.

For some purposes it is useful to formulate relations (1) as follows: the observed state of a system cannot be represented in the phase space by a definite point but, rather, corresponds to a space element. The dimensions of an element depends on the special kind of experiment by means of which the measurement is made. For a moving particle, these would be given by $\Delta x\, \Delta y\, \Delta z\, \Delta p_x\, \Delta p_y\, \Delta p_z$. Under no circumstance can it be less than h^3 and, if the system in question has n degrees of freedom, it can be no smaller than h^n.

3. Heisenberg's Uncertainty Relations. Method of Doppler Effect. On the basis of the preceding discussion, we are not yet sure whether relations (1) hold for all methods of measuring coordinates and momenta since, a priori, we cannot exclude the possibility of a procedure furnishing a more accurate measurement of the quantities than the method of the pinhole camera. Actually, though, no one has found a method, at least up to the present, that invalidates Heisenberg's relations. Whatever method we adopt to observe the state of a system, a precise measurement of the simultaneous values of two conjugate observables always turns out to be impossible. For example, we might think of measuring the velocity of a particle by means of the Doppler effect in the following way. Let us assume that the position x_0, y_0, z_0 of a particle at time t_0 is known, and that from this point the particle is moving with an unknown velocity the components of which are v_x, v_y, v_z. In order to determine v_x, a light wave of frequency ν is caused to collide with the particle in the direction of the x axis. Let the energy of the light wave be that of a quantum $h\nu$. Now let us measure the frequency ν' of the light which is reflected by the particle in the negative x direction. From the theory of the Doppler effect, the frequencies ν and ν' are related by the equation

$$\nu' = \nu \left(1 - \frac{2v_x}{c} \right)$$

Solving this for v_x gives

$$v_x = \frac{\nu - \nu'}{2\nu}\, c$$

Now, to obtain the real velocity of the particle, we also must consider the recoil of the particle due to the reflection of the light quantum. This involves a change in momentum of $2h\nu/c$, and therefore v_x is increased by $2h\nu/mc$, where m is the mass of the particle. Thus, assuming that we are able to measure the frequencies ν and ν' with sufficient accuracy, we could represent the exact value of v_x by the equation

$$v_x = \frac{(\nu - \nu')}{2\nu}\, c + \frac{2h\nu}{mc}$$

Now ν and ν' can be measured, but the following situation introduces a

difficulty. Light can be produced only in wave trains of a finite
length which require a finite time Δt to pass a given point in space.
A finite wave train is never monochromatic—as will be pointed out in
Section 6—but is always resolvable into a multitude of partial waves
by a Fourier analysis. These partial waves superpose in such a way
that they interfere destructively outside the train. The frequencies of
the harmonic components of the train spread over a certain interval
$\Delta \nu$, which is wider the shorter the wave train, the spectral determinacy
being the less, the broader the interval $\Delta \nu$. It will be demonstrated
in Section 6 that $\Delta \nu \, \Delta t \sim 1$, where Δt is the interval of time required
by the wave train to pass a fixed point in space.

On principle, therefore, we can determine the velocity v_x of a particle
at time $t_0 + \Delta t$ to any desired degree of accuracy by using a sufficiently
long wave train. For then the spectral indeterminacy $\Delta \nu = 1/\Delta t$
becomes very small, and the same holds for the uncertainty Δv_x since
this is represented by

$$\Delta v_x = \frac{\Delta \nu}{2\nu} c + \frac{2h \, \Delta \nu}{mc}$$

Since the second term is very small relative to the first, Δv_x can be
represented by $c/2\nu \, \Delta t$. But, the greater the interval Δt, the less
accurately can we locate the particle at $t_0 + \Delta t$, because we are
ignorant of the instant at which the recoil of the particle occurs. If
the light quantum is reflected at the beginning of Δt, that is, at t_0,
the position of the particle at $t_0 + \Delta t$ will be

$$x = x_0 + \left[\frac{(\nu - \nu_0)}{2\nu} c + \frac{2h\nu}{mc} \right] \Delta t$$

But, if the quantum is reflected at the instant $t_0 + \Delta t$,

$$x = x_0 + \frac{(\nu - \nu_0)}{2\nu} c \, \Delta t$$

Thus we only can know the position with the possible error $\Delta x = (2h\nu/mc) \, \Delta t$, and again we obtain

$$\Delta x \, \Delta p_x = \left(\frac{2h\nu}{mc} \, \Delta t \right) \left(\frac{mc}{2\nu \, \Delta t} \right) = h$$

Thus it seems that relations (1) are independent of the choice of
both the experiment and the coordinates. Accordingly we propose
the following theorem as fundamental to the new mechanics.

There is no experiment by means of which two canonically conjugate observables can be measured with a greater accuracy than is foreseen by relations (1).

Should such an experiment be discovered unexpectedly, all that follows would be wrong. It is not very likely, however, that the proposed theorem will be disproved because, if we go to the very root of the uncertainty relations, we find that they originate in the fact that the course of all elementary processes evades our control. The method of the pinhole camera does not permit an exact measurement because we are unable to say in what direction the light quantum will be deflected. The Doppler effect method fails because we do not know the instant of time at which the reflection of the quantum will occur. The question then is whether we shall be able some day to predict the course of elementary reactions. Shall we ever, for example, learn how to direct a light quantum so that it will be reflected by the struck particle exactly in a given direction? Should this turn out to be possible in the future, the supposition of the quantum theory, that, on principle, the elementary processes under investigation cannot be analyzed, would be incorrect and a new theory that could dispense with the constant h would have to be sought. The facts, however, undoubtedly favor the quantum theory, and therefore the current viewpoint is that the processes governed by h are not subject in any way to a space-time description. They appear to our observation as discontinuities in the course of events and cannot be interpreted on the basis of causality. The question whether they are, for that reason, acausal or whether their causal character only escapes our limited powers of observation is, for the physicist, meaningless because, if the supposition that the elementary processes cannot be analyzed is true, then there is no experiment by means of which the question can be answered. The only thing the physicist can maintain is that there is no possibility for him to apply the principle of causality to elementary micro processes as he experiences them, and to him experience alone counts. If when causality fails to explain an event we call it chance, then we may say that in all elementary reactions chance, or something we cannot distinguish from it, is at work.

4. The New Mechanics and the Principle of Causality. It turns out, then, that in quantum physics a concept, namely that of chance, plays a role for which, taken in its full significance, there has been no room in the methods of classical physics. Although it is true that this concept has been employed because of its usefulness in surveying events that are composed of a great number of non-controll-

able single processes, it was never assumed that chance actually, anywhere and at any time, could interfere with the course of events.   In
contrast to this, quantum mechanics considers it an established fact
that in the observable world something is at work which can be
designated only as chance.   Does this mean, therefore, that we must
deny the principle of causality in the physical world?

Before answering this question let us adopt the principle that the
physicist must be concerned only with the things he can observe.
Accordingly a question is meaningless to him if there is no possibility
of answering it on the basis of experiment.   Therefore, when we ask
him his opinion of causality, it is necessary first to formulate the
principle so that he can test it by experiment.   A formulation that
fulfills this requirement is: in an isolated system, an identical initial
state always leads to an identical sequence of later states.   This is a
statement that is proved by observation to be either true or false,
and the physicist has only the choice of accepting or denying.   Actually he has to deny it, for when he performs a great number of experiments on a system, starting always from the same initial state—the
word "same" meaning as far as the possibilities of observation are
concerned—he finds the system changing every time in a different
way.   It is true that the objection could be offered that this does not
disprove causality because the initial states only seem to be identical
to us whereas in reality they may differ one from the other.   Such an
argument, however, leads to metaphysics.   It is not the business of
the physicist to speculate on what would be if this or that condition,
which is incapable of fulfillment, were realized.   The physicist concerns himself only with what can be observed and therefore is compelled to consider two states as identical if no experiment can prove
them to be different.   Therefore he is not in a position to agree with
the statement by which we have defined causality.

Thus the physicist is not interested in the question whether the
world "in itself," that is, as it exists independently of our observa-
tions, may be governed by causality in the defined sense of the word.
He is concerned only with the world as it presents itself to his observation, and he feels that chance enters into certain aspects of it.

We do not mean by this that there is nothing but anarchy in nature.
We deny only the possibility of predicting in a unique way the future
behavior of a system from its present state.   As we have seen, such
predictions cannot be made and there remains only the need to explain
how classical physics can reconcile its determinacy of events with this
fact.   The explanation is that, when we measure the position of a
body, the Compton effect, owing to the smallness of Planck's constant

h, cannot change the velocity by a measurable amount unless the mass of the body is extremely small. We have seen from relations (1) that the uncertainty Δv_x of v_x, which is due to the Compton effect, is given by $\Delta v_x \geqq h/m\,\Delta x$. From this it is clear that, for a body with great mass, chance has too small a scope to have a noticeable effect. The effect is of importance for extremely light particles, which are so sensitive that they withstand observation. For instance, consider an electron. In order to determine its position within an atom we have to strive for an accuracy of at least 10^{-8} cm. Hence for the velocity this means an uncertainty

$$\Delta v_x \geqq \frac{6.62 \times 10^{-27}}{(10^{-27})(10^{-8})} \sim 10^8 \text{ cm/sec}$$

On the other hand, if we consider a small macroscopic body of 1 gram mass, an accuracy of the order 10^{-2} cm in determining its position is quite sufficient. The uncertainty here is

$$\Delta v_x \geqq \frac{6.62 \times 10^{-27}}{10^{-2}} \sim 10^{-25} \text{ cm/sec}$$

a value which lies far below the limit of any measurability. Chance is at work in the macro as well as in the micro world, but it is important only in micro world. The situation would be quite different if the magnitude of h were great, for then chance would prevail in the macro world also and it would be difficult to recognize any law as valid because of it. For example, a body that is moving subject to no force would change its velocity every time we observed it, and thus it would be impossible to conceive the law of inertia in this seeming disorder.

However, it must not be concluded that quantum mechanics maintains complete indeterminism. Such a view is out of the question because it excludes the possibility of physics altogether. If there were nothing but chance, nothing could be said about the future. In reality, besides chance, there are also laws, and the doctrine of quantum mechanics is not that causality does not exist but only that it must not be interpreted as in classical mechanics. We cannot conclude exactly the future of a system from a given initial state because the data of this state do not suffice. They do, however, suffice for determining the probability of finding the system in a given state at a future time. It is in this statistical sense of future prediction that quantum mechanics expresses the principle of causality. It should not be maintained that we do not know anything about the future but rather that in many respects we do not know it exactly. The qualification "in many respects" is necessary because in quantum mechanics there are certain observables also the values of which can be predicted exactly for the future if the initial values are known exactly. The principle of the conservation of energy holds in the new mechanics as it does in the old. If we know that a system has an energy E at $t = 0$, we may be sure that measurements of energy made later will furnish the same value for E if the system has not been disturbed in the meantime. Deferring until later a precise statement of causality from the viewpoint of quantum mechanics, it is sufficient for our present purposes to express it as follows: a given initial state does not determine the future development of a system, but it does determine the probability that the development will take a given course.

5. de Broglie Waves. Let us consider the problem of a free particle and investigate how quantum mechanics attempts to solve it. From a measurement at t_0, it is concluded that the particle lies within the space element $\Delta x\, \Delta y\, \Delta z$ and at that instant has momentum components within $\Delta p_x, \Delta p_y, \Delta p_z$. At $t > t_0$, another very precise measurement is made. What is the probability of finding the particle at a given point xyz at this time? The question is reasonable, for it can be decided experimentally. In many experiments we start from the same initial conditions and determine the exact position of the particle at time t. However, we must not presume that such experiments would verify classical mechanics. If this were so, we would have to apply the methods of classical statistics to determine the desired probability. But this would not explain how it is possible for electrons to be diffracted when they pass through a crystal. We may take this phenomenon as proof that the principles of classical mechanics are approximations that may be used for macroscopic systems and do not hold for bodies of extremely small mass. In this search for the principles of a new mechanics which would hold for microscopic bodies, Louis de Broglie proposed a solution of the problem. His theory may be characterized as an attempt to interpret a mechanical event by means of a wave representation. Two facts suggested this idea to de Broglie. The first was the fundamental relation, $E = h\nu$, wherein a certain frequency ν, being associated with the energy, points to some connection between a mechanical event and wave motion. The second fact was that in the Hamiltonian form of classical mechanics such an interpretation had already been used.

To carry out the plan of a wave mechanics, de Broglie associated a harmonic wave motion with every moving particle, the frequency ν of this wave motion being that given in the energy relation $E = h\nu$.

This association does not mean that the motion of the particle is actually that of a wave. Whether such an interpretation is plausible will be discussed in Chapter 6. For the present discussion the wave is used as a figurative description of a certain function of coordinate and time by means of which we can learn about the behavior of the particle. Thus, since the wave has a purely symbolic significance, there need be no question about the medium of propagation.

To clarify further the idea of wave mechanics, let us consider a particle moving relative to a coordinate system K in the direction of the x axis with a momentum which, we assume, has been measured accurately. According to relations (1), we cannot know anything about the position of the particle since an infinitely small Δv_x introduces an infinitely great uncertainty Δx. The total energy of the particle, kinetic as well as rest energy, is given by $E = mc^2/\sqrt{1 - \beta^2}$, and its momentum by $p = mv/\sqrt{1 - \beta^2}$, where m is the rest mass of the particle and $\beta = v/c$. If, on the other hand, we refer the motion not to K but to a coordinate system K_0 in which the particle is at rest, its momentum vanishes and its energy reduces to $E_0 = mc^2$. Now imagine that the whole space is filled with a fictitious medium, and associate a vibration of this medium with the motion of the particle. Assume that all the particles of the medium vibrate with a frequency ν_0 relative to K_0, where $\nu_0 = E_0/h$, and that all the particles are in the same phase of vibration. Then for an observer in the K_0 system this motion may be described by $a \cos 2\pi\nu_0 t_0$. But to an observer in the K system, relative to which the particle is moving with a velocity v, the motion of the medium is that of a wave in the x direction. The Lorentz transformation for the transition from K_0 to K is

$$t_0 = \frac{(t - vx/c^2)}{\sqrt{1 - \beta^2}}$$

and thus the motion of the medium in K can be represented by

$$a \cos 2\pi\nu_0 \frac{\left(t - \dfrac{vx}{c^2}\right)}{\sqrt{1 - \beta^2}} = a \cos 2\pi\nu \left(t - \frac{x}{V}\right) \qquad (2)$$

where $\nu = \nu_0/\sqrt{1 - \beta^2}$, $c^2/v = V$. Thus there is observed in the system K a wave whose frequency is

$$\nu = \frac{\nu_0}{\sqrt{1 - \beta^2}} = \frac{E_0}{h\sqrt{1 - \beta^2}} = \frac{E}{h} \qquad (3)$$

and a velocity of propagation V which is related to the velocity v of the particle by

$$Vv = c^2 \tag{4}$$

The wavelength is

$$\lambda = \frac{V}{\nu}$$

Therefore from (4)

$$\lambda = \frac{c^2}{\nu v}$$

But $p = vE/c^2 = vh\nu/c^2$; therefore

$$\lambda = \frac{h}{p} \tag{5}$$

The relations

$$\nu = \frac{E}{h} \quad \text{and} \quad \lambda = \frac{h}{p} \tag{6}$$

hold for any coordinate system, for, in transforming from reference system K to a new system K' relative to which the particle moves with a velocity v' in the x direction, we obtain $\nu' = E'/h$ and $\lambda' = h/p'$. Thus in any coordinate system the wave can be represented by

$$a \cos \frac{2\pi}{h} (Et - px)$$

or, on letting $h/2\pi = \hbar$,

$$a \cos \frac{1}{\hbar} (Et - px) \tag{7}$$

However, no relation exists between the wave and the positions of the particle during its motion because a clear-cut measurement of momentum excludes the knowledge of position.

Suppose that the particle is moving in the direction $\alpha\beta\gamma$ and with a momentum the components of which are p_x, p_y, p_z. The wave expression (7) must be modified to read

$$a \cos \frac{1}{\hbar} [Et - (p_x x + p_y y + p_z z)] \tag{8}$$

The components of momentum may be expressed as

$$p_x = \alpha p \qquad p_y = \beta p \qquad p_z = \gamma p$$

But $p = h/\lambda$; therefore

$$p_x = \alpha \frac{h}{\lambda} \qquad p_y = \beta \frac{h}{\lambda} \qquad p_z = \gamma \frac{h}{\lambda}$$

Now, since $V = c^2/v$ with $v < c$, the de Broglie waves are propagated with a velocity that can never be less than the velocity of light, and thus they cannot be real waves but are purely symbolic in character.

That the velocity V depends on the frequency can be demonstrated by

$$hv_0 = mc^2 \quad \text{and} \quad hv = \frac{mc^2}{\sqrt{1 - \beta^2}}$$

Therefore $v_0/v = \sqrt{1 - \beta^2}$; $\beta = \sqrt{1 - v_0^2/v^2}$. Therefore, since $V = c^2/v$ and $\beta = v/c$, we have

$$V = \frac{c}{\sqrt{1 - v_0^2/v^2}} \tag{9}$$

And, if n is the index of refraction c/V, we obtain

$$n = \sqrt{1 - v_0^2/v^2} \tag{10}$$

6. The Method of Wave Packets.   Since the de Broglie waves are symbolic only, their usefulness might be questioned. To answer this question, let us refer once more to our original problem, namely the probability of locating a particle at a given point and given time, assuming that initially the particle was within the element $\Delta x\, \Delta y\, \Delta z\, \Delta p_x\, \Delta p_y\, \Delta p_z$. It is the aim of wave mechanics to determine this probability by making use of the de Broglie wave motion, which can be associated in a certain way with the observed initial state of the particle. Obviously a single wave of definite frequency and direction will not be sufficient because the momentum of the particle is known only with an uncertainty $\Delta p_x\, \Delta p_y\, \Delta p_z$. Hence it becomes necessary to represent the initial state by an ensemble of waves so that for each vector $\mathbf{p}$ within $\Delta p_x\, \Delta p_y\, \Delta p_z$ there is a corresponding wave. When the components p_x, p_y, p_z are replaced by ξ, η, ζ, the expression for the wave associated with the momentum becomes

$$a(\xi, \eta, \zeta)e^{(i/\hbar)[Et-(x\xi+y\eta+z\zeta)]} \tag{11}$$

This expression can represent the wave by either its real or its imaginary part. Here both the amplitude and the phase may depend on ξ, η, ζ. By writing a similar expression for every vector $\mathbf{p}$ within the uncertainty element we can represent the state by

$$u(xyzt) = \int \int \int ae^{(i/\hbar)[Et-(x\xi+y\eta+z\zeta)]} \, d\xi \, d\eta \, d\zeta \tag{12}$$

the integration being extended over the whole element. The ensemble of waves represented by (12) is called a wave packet.

In order that equation (12) may have physical meaning in describing the given state, the amplitude function $a(\xi\eta\zeta)$ must be chosen so that there is a definite relation between the wave group and the space element $\Delta x\,\Delta y\,\Delta z$ in which the particle initially is situated. Such a relation can be established by making use of the following theorem due to Rayleigh: if in an ensemble of waves of the form (11) the parameters ξ, η, ζ vary continuously within certain intervals $\Delta\xi\,\Delta\eta\,\Delta\zeta$, the amplitude function $a(\xi\eta\zeta)$ can be chosen always in such a way that the total intensity of the waves is greater than zero only within a space the dimensions of which are

$$\Delta x \geqq \frac{h}{\Delta\xi} \qquad \Delta y \geqq \frac{h}{\Delta\eta} \qquad \Delta z \geqq \frac{h}{\Delta\zeta}$$

and outside of this space the waves interfere destructively; that is, the intensity there is zero.

A rigorous proof of this theorem will not be given here. That it is plausible will be clear from the following example. Consider two parallel waves of infinite extension, the waves being characterized by $E_1\xi_1\eta_1\zeta_1$ and $E_2\xi_2\eta_2\zeta_2$ respectively. Let us assume that the waves are in phase at time t_0 at a point which we shall choose as origin of coordinates. As the waves move away from the origin in the direction of the x axis, a difference in phase continuously develops so that at a certain distance x this difference will be π and hence $x\xi_1 = x\xi_2 \pm h/2$. Therefore at this point there is destructive interference. As the propagation along x continues, we pass through a series of maxima and minima depending on whether $x(\xi_1 - \xi_2)$ is an even or odd multiple of $h/2$. Now add to these two waves a group of wave motions the parameters of which vary continuously between those of the two given ones. Let the whole ensemble be in phase at the origin at time t_0. The excitation caused by the waves is increased between $x = 0$ and $x = h/[2(\xi_1 - \xi_2)]$, but all outside maxima disappear because the waves meet there in all possible phases. It appears then that a group of waves in which ξ varies within the limits ξ_1 and $\xi_2 = \Delta\xi$ can be superposed so that it has a non-vanishing intensity only within a space $\Delta x = h/\Delta\xi$. This excitation cannot be confined to a smaller space, but, by introducing suitable phase differences at the origin, we can make $\Delta x > h/\Delta\xi$. Since the same reasoning applies to the y and z directions, it follows that the behavior of the wave group is in accord with Rayleigh's theorem.

In addition, we can prove that the interval of time Δt, during which positive excitation occurs at a certain point, is related to an energy interval $E_1 - E_2 = \Delta E$ by the relation $\Delta t\,\Delta E \geqq h$. For, if we start out with the same two waves which are in phase at the origin and then plot the oscillation against time, we observe a sequence of maxima and minima, the first minima being obtained when $E_1 t = E_2 t \pm h/2$. During the interval $t = 0$ and $t = \pm h/[2(E_1 - E_2)]$, the effect of the additional waves, the energies of which lie between E_1 and E_2, will be one of excitation with all outside maxima removed. Thus the excitation caused by the wave group lasts for an interval Δt which is related to ΔE by $\Delta t \geqq h/\Delta E$. Since $h\nu = E$, we obtain the relation $\Delta t \, \Delta \nu \geqq 1$.

Let us apply the theorem to the wave group represented by (12) and try to find a relation between this group and the uncertainties, Δx, Δy, Δz. We must superpose the waves in such a way that they destroy each other outside the element $\Delta x \, \Delta y \, \Delta z$, giving a total intensity only within this element. We have seen that this is possible only when the conditions $\Delta x \, \Delta \xi \geqq h$, $\Delta y \, \Delta \eta \geqq h$, $\Delta z \, \Delta \zeta \geqq h$ are satisfied. This is precisely what is defined by the uncertainty relations (1). By virtue of the above, the following theorem can be stated:

We always can associate a wave packet with the observed initial state of a particle. The spectral composition of the packet describes our knowledge of the momentum of the particle, whereas the manner of its superposition describes our knowledge of the position.

We are able now to give an answer to the question of the probability of locating the position of the particle. Leaving the wave packet which symbolizes the initial state of the particle undisturbed, we determine the distribution of the waves at time t. Then the probability in question for any point in space is given by the square of the resultant amplitude. This statement brings out the essential idea of the statistical nature of wave mechanics as it is applied to a free particle. It is not to be considered a purely formal statement but rather a real one which can be confirmed or disproved by experiments. We shall refer to these experiments later.

When we do not disturb the waves, the phase differences at a certain point will change because of difference in frequencies. This being the case, the resultant amplitude will change. The interference phenomena produced by the waves keep changing, and wave mechanics uses this fact to establish a relationship between the motion of the particle and the propagation of the waves. Originally the approach to the problem was to identify directly the wave packet with a corpuscle, an idea chiefly proposed by Schroedinger. Such an interpretation would be practicable if the wave packet remained intact during the motion (that is, the space within which the intensity is greater than zero remains unchanged in size). Apart from an exception discussed below, this space does change, because after a certain time the wave packet gradually loosens and spreads out in all directions, thus making the position of the particle more and more uncertain.

7. Reconciliation of Wave and Classical Mechanics. Here we consider a macroscopic body, wishing to find out how wave mechanics can furnish us with information of future events when this information is, if not exactly precise, at least exact enough for all practical purposes. It is quite certain that by applying classical mechanics to this problem we can determine the position of the particle uniquely at time t from its state of motion at t_0. Actually, in their application to macroscopic bodies, the new and old mechanics lead to the same results. Consider, for example, the motion of a small macroscopic particle. In determining the position of the center of the particle at time t, there will be a possible error of some fractions of a millimeter in the measurement. When compared with h this is an extremely great inaccuracy, but it is compensated for by the possibility of a very accurate measurement of the momentum. Thus the observed state can be represented by a wave packet which occupies a macroscopic space $\Delta x \, \Delta y \, \Delta z$ of nearly point dimensions and which corresponds to the very small element $\Delta \xi \, \Delta \eta \, \Delta \zeta$ of the momentum space between $\xi_0 \eta_0 \zeta_0$ and $\xi_0 + \Delta \xi$, $\eta_0 + \Delta \eta$, $\zeta_0 + \Delta \zeta$. In equation (12) replace ξ, η, ζ by

$$\xi = \xi_0 + \xi' \qquad \eta = \eta_0 + \eta' \qquad \zeta = \zeta_0 + \zeta' \tag{13}$$

These new variables are very small quantities. The limits of integration will be 0 and $\Delta \xi$, $\Delta \eta$, $\Delta \zeta$. Making these substitutions, we obtain

$$u(xyzt) = \int\int\int a(\xi'\eta'\zeta') \times$$
$$e^{\frac{i}{\hbar}\left\{\left[E_0 + \left(\frac{\partial E}{\partial \xi}\right)_0 \xi' + \left(\frac{\partial E}{\partial \eta}\right)_0 \eta' + \left(\frac{\partial E}{\partial \zeta}\right)_0 \zeta'\right]t - x(\xi_0+\xi') - y(\eta_0+\eta') - z(\zeta_0+\zeta')\right\}} d\xi' \, d\eta' \, d\zeta'$$

E_0 is the energy corresponding to the momentum $\xi_0\eta_0\zeta_0$, and $(\partial E/\partial \xi)_0$, $(\partial E/\partial \eta)_0$, $(\partial E/\partial \zeta)_0$ are the derivatives of E relative to ξ, η, ζ at point ξ_0, η_0, ζ_0. Since ξ', η', ζ' are small quantities, it is sufficient to keep only the first-order terms in the expansion of E. Placing outside the integral sign those factors not subject to the integration, we obtain

$$u(xyzt) = e^{\frac{i}{\hbar}[E_0t - (x\xi_0 + y\eta_0 + z\zeta_0)]} \int\int\int ae^{\frac{i}{\hbar}\left\{\left[\left(\frac{\partial E}{\partial \xi}\right)_0 t - x\right]\xi' + \cdots\right\}} d\xi' \, d\eta' \, d\zeta'$$

from which complex expression the real part is to be used. Thus, if we let $Ae^{i\Delta}$ represent the complex integral in the above equation, both A and Δ being real, u becomes

$$u = A \cos\left\{\frac{i}{\hbar}[E_0t - (x\xi_0 + y\eta_0 + z\zeta_0)] + \Delta\right\} \tag{14}$$

where A is the amplitude of the motion and A^2 represents the probability of locating the particle at time t at point xyz.

To determine A^2 we find the product of the two conjugate integrals

$$Ae^{i\Delta} = \int \int \int ae^{\frac{i}{\hbar}\{[(\frac{\partial E}{\partial \xi})_0 t - x]\xi' + \cdots\}} \, d\xi' \, d\eta' \, d\zeta'$$

$$Ae^{-i\Delta} = \int \int \int ae^{-\frac{i}{\hbar}\{[(\frac{\partial E}{\partial \xi})_0 t - x]\xi' + \cdots\}} \, d\xi' \, d\eta' \, d\zeta'$$

In each of the integrals on the right it will be observed that x, y, z, and t appear only in the terms $(\partial E/\partial \xi)_0 t - x$, $(\partial E/\partial \eta)_0 t - y$, $(\partial E/\partial \zeta)_0 t - z$. The same must be true for the product of the two, which gives us A^2. Thus we can conclude that the resultant amplitude will remain unaltered when x, y, z, and t change in such a way that

$$\left(\frac{\partial E}{\partial \xi}\right)_0 t - x = \text{constant} \qquad \left(\frac{\partial E}{\partial \eta}\right)_0 t - y = \text{constant}$$

$$\left(\frac{\partial E}{\partial \zeta}\right)_0 t - z = \text{constant} \tag{15}$$

From this we see that the amplitudes are propagated in straight lines with a velocity the components of which are $(\partial E/\partial \xi)_0$, $(\partial E/\partial \eta)_0$, $(\partial E/\partial \zeta)_0$. Evidently the relative space distribution of the amplitudes is not altered by this displacement, and at every instant of time the wave packet maintains a constant size and a form which is nearly point-shaped. This packet moves through space with a velocity c, the components of which are given above. So, in the case being considered, the position of the particle can be predicted for every instant of time with certainty. Thus, when wave mechanics is applied to macroscopic systems, it loses its characteristic uncertainty, which is its distinguishing mark when microscopic systems are involved. Of greater import is the fact that the new and old mechanics are in complete agreement on proving that the velocity c of the packet is identical with the velocity v of the particle corresponding to the packet. The energy E is given by $E = (\xi^2 + \eta^2 + \zeta^2)/2m$. Then

$$\left(\frac{\partial E}{\partial \xi}\right)_0 = \frac{\xi_0}{m} = \frac{mv_{x0}}{m} = v_{x0}$$

Similarly

$$\left(\frac{\partial E}{\partial \eta}\right)_0 = v_{y0} \qquad \text{and} \qquad \left(\frac{\partial E}{\partial \zeta}\right)_0 = v_{z0}$$

Thus c and v are identical.

This identity of motion of the particle and the packet for a time inspired the belief that the particle and the packet were identical. Such an interpretation is, of course, incorrect because the packet cannot be the particle.   It must be considered solely as a description of the probability function from which can be drawn certain knowledge about the future behavior of the particle.   We have already noted how the packet soon begins to spread outward, a fact that would make the identification of the particle and the packet impracticable.   Even for a macroscopic particle the stability of the packet is a limited one, for in the expansion of E above we have retained only first-order terms.   If we had retained terms of higher order in the expansion we would have had

$$\left(\frac{\partial E}{\partial \xi}\right)_0 t + \left(\frac{\partial^2 E}{\partial \xi^2}\right)_0 \frac{t\xi'}{2} + \cdots - x$$

Only as long as t is not too great can the second- and higher-order terms be considered negligible.   But if t becomes sufficiently great these terms become of importance, and the packet ceases to maintain its size and form.   To show this let us subdivide the element $\Delta\xi \, \Delta\eta \, \Delta\zeta$ of the momentum space into elements $d\xi'$, $d\eta'$, $d\zeta'$ which are small enough to consider ξ', η', ζ' constant within the element.   The whole packet then is made up of parts each of which contains the momentum of an element $d\xi' \, d\eta' \, d\zeta'$.   Thus A will now be expressed by $\sum A_i$, where by A_i we mean the integral

$$\int\int\int ae^{\frac{i}{\hbar}\left\{\left[\left(\frac{\partial E}{\partial \xi}\right)_0 t + \left(\frac{\partial^2 E}{\partial \xi^2}\right)_0 \frac{t\xi'}{2} + \cdots - x\right]\xi' + \cdots\right\}} d\xi' \, d\eta' \, d\zeta'$$

the integration being extended over the ith element $d\xi' \, d\eta' \, d\zeta'$.   From this it is seen that this particular sub-packet moves through space according to the equation

$$\left(\frac{\partial E}{\partial \xi}\right)_0 t + \left(\frac{\partial^2 E}{\partial \xi^2}\right)_0 \frac{t\xi'}{2} + \cdots x = \text{constant}$$

with corresponding forms for y and z.   Hence the different amplitudes move with different velocities depending on ξ', η', ζ'.   Consequently the sum of these amplitudes $\sum A_i$ as a function of xyz represents something that is changing in size and form, and as a result the wave packet will dissolve.   The smaller we take $\xi'\eta'\zeta'$, that is, the more accurately the momentum of the particle is defined, the later will this dissolution occur, for, according to the equations above, the relative displacement of two amplitudes A_k and A_m will be $(\partial^2 E/\partial \xi^2)_0$

$(\xi_k' - \xi_m')(t/2) + \cdots$. This will be smaller the smaller we take ξ'. But, no matter how small we choose ξ', if we let t assume sufficiently great values, this relative displacement increases and dissolution sets in. Therefore the connection between the old and the new mechanics can be expressed as follows:

> *In the application of wave mechanics to macroscopic systems predictions can be made which for all practical purposes do not differ from those of classical mechanics provided that a certain magnitude of time is considered, which magnitude will depend on the accuracy with which the momentum has been measured.*

In order to describe the connection between the propagation of the wave and the motion of the particle, the authors of wave mechanics frequently have used the concept of *group velocity*, which deals with the displacement of a point in space at which all the waves of a given group are in phase. Thus the group velocity is identical with the velocity with which a wave packet moves through space. Therefore the components of the group velocity are $(\partial E/\partial \xi)_0$, $(\partial E/\partial \eta)_0$, and $(\partial E/\partial \zeta)_0$. Replacing E by $h\nu$ and p by h/λ,

$$\frac{\partial E}{\partial \xi} = \frac{dE}{dp}\frac{\partial p}{\partial \xi} = \frac{d\nu}{d(1/\lambda)}\frac{\partial p}{\partial \xi}$$

Now $p^2 = \xi^2 + \eta^2 + \zeta^2$; therefore $\partial p/\partial \xi = \xi/p = \alpha$, the direction cosine of p relative to the x axis. Therefore

$$\frac{\partial E}{\partial \xi} = \frac{d\nu}{d(1/\lambda)}\alpha \qquad \frac{\partial E}{\partial \eta} = \frac{d\nu}{d(1/\lambda)}\beta \qquad \frac{\partial E}{\partial \zeta} = \frac{d\nu}{d(1/\lambda)}\gamma \qquad (16)$$

from which it follows that the group velocity is $d\nu/d(1/\lambda)$. Generally this velocity differs from V, the velocity with which the waves are propagated and which is called the phase velocity. The two velocities will be identical only if V is independent of ν. In that case we obtain $d(1/\lambda) = d(\nu/V) = d\nu/V$, and thus $d\nu/d(1/\lambda) = V$.

Finally, it is well to make clear the following point. In Section 4 we saw that wave mechanics does not subscribe to a strict causality of events, a viewpoint that should not be misconstrued as complete indeterminism. Now, however, we can interpret the point of view more precisely. The answer to the question about the future of a mechanical system can be a definite or an indefinite one, depending on what we wish to know. The answer is an indefinite one if knowledge of the exact state of a system at a future time t is desired. As we have seen this cannot be predicted precisely because the initial state is not precisely known. On the other hand, if we seek only the probability of finding the system in a given configuration at that time, a definite answer can be given because this probability is determined uniquely by the propagation of a wave packet. Thus we assert that *mechanical events can take a determinate or an indeterminate course depending on whether the concepts of corpuscular or wave mechanics are used for their description.*

8. The Wave Mechanics of a Particle Moving in a Field of Force. Up to this point we have considered a particle subject to no force. We now consider a particle moving in a field of force in which a potential function $V(xyz)$ exists. To apply the method of wave mechanics to such a particle, it seems that there must be some relation between the wave motion and this potential function, otherwise there could be no connection between the waves and the motion of the particle. Consideration of the case brings up the idea of waves in a heterogeneous medium, this heterogeneity being defined by the function $V(xyz)$. However, it was not easy to develop the idea. As we know now, the credit for overcoming this difficulty belongs to Schroedinger. de Broglie had pointed out that there was a significant connection between the principles of Maupertuis and Fermat. Following this suggestion, Schroedinger undertook the further development of the mechanical-optical relations which had been known to Hamilton and might now be used for the purposes of wave mechanics.

To make Schroedinger's idea clear, let us confine ourselves to classical mechanics first. Consider a function S representing the action of a particle that moves in a field of force. S is defined by the integral $\int (p_x\, dx + p_y\, dy + p_z\, dz)$, which is taken over the path between the space points $P(x_0 y_0 z_0)$ and $P(xyz)$. According to classical mechanics the motion starting at P_0 is determined uniquely by $x_0 y_0 z_0$ and $\dot{x}_0 \dot{y}_0 \dot{z}_0$. Thus S can be considered a function of these quantities and time or, for brevity, of q_0, $\dot{q}_0$, and t. The coordinates of P are also functions of q_0, $\dot{q}_0$, and t. Furthermore the energy E of the particle can be calculated from q_0 and $\dot{q}_0$, this energy remaining constant throughout the motion. Therefore S can be given as a function of $x_0 y_0 z_0 xyzE$. Thus, when a particle moves with an energy E by suitable projection from P_0 to P, S gives the action $\int (p_x\, dx + p_y\, dy + p_z\, dz)$ as a function of P_0, P_1 and E.

From the way in which S has been defined, we see that the vector momentum $\mathbf{p}$ is the gradient of S, for the components of $\mathbf{p}$ are

$$p_x = \frac{\partial S}{\partial x} \qquad p_y = \frac{\partial S}{\partial y} \qquad p_z = \frac{\partial S}{\partial z} \qquad (17)$$

Now the energy of the particle is

$$\frac{1}{2m}(p_x{}^2 + p_y{}^2 + p_z{}^2) + V(xyz) = E$$

Introducing the components of the gradient, we obtain

$$\frac{1}{2m}\left[\left(\frac{\partial S}{\partial x}\right)^2 + \left(\frac{\partial S}{\partial y}\right)^2 + \left(\frac{\partial S}{\partial z}\right)^2\right] + V(xyz) = E \tag{18}$$

Thus S satisfies the fundamental differential equation of Hamilton. From this equation can be derived the whole of the possible motions of a particle. Now assume that we are able to solve the equation by means of a function $S(xyz)$ which contains as parameters—aside from an unimportant additive constant—besides E two constants α and β so that $S = S(xyzE\alpha\beta)$. The solution then associates with every point in space a certain vector $\mathbf{p} = \text{grad } S$. The composition of these vectors results in a twice-infinite manifold of curves each one of which represents a possible path of the particle. If we are interested in a particular motion with the initial state $q_0\dot{q}_0$, then the constants E, α, β of the solution have to be chosen so that for $x_0 = x$, $y_0 = y$, $z_0 = z$, grad $S = \mathbf{p}$. The path is then given by that member of the manifold which passes through $x_0y_0z_0$. According to Jacobi every motion of the particle can be described by

$$\frac{\partial S}{\partial \alpha} = \alpha_1 \qquad \frac{\partial S}{\partial \beta} = \beta_1 \qquad \frac{\partial S}{\partial E} = t - t_0 \tag{19}$$

where α_1, β_1, and t_0 are three new constants. Since two equations in xyz determine a curve, the first two equations of (19) select a certain curve from the manifold. The third equation fixes the position of the particle at time t.

Let us compare an optical problem with the mechanical one by investigating the propagation of light in a heterogeneous medium. This propagation is defined by the wave equation

$$\frac{\partial^2 u}{\partial x^2} + \frac{\partial^2 u}{\partial y^2} + \frac{\partial^2 u}{\partial z^2} = \frac{1}{v^2}\frac{\partial^2 u}{\partial t^2} \tag{20}$$

where v is the velocity of light and is a function of xyz. Assume a solution of the form

$$u = a(xyz) \sin 2\pi[\nu t - k\phi(xyz)] \tag{21}$$

where $a(xyz)$ is the unknown amplitude and u represents the excitation produced by the light. The significance of the function ϕ is that, for every surface represented by ϕ = constant, such a surface is one of constant phase.   With the above value of u, equation (20) becomes

$$\left[\sum \frac{\partial^2 a}{\partial x^2} - 4\pi^2 k^2 a \sum \left(\frac{\partial \phi}{\partial x}\right)^2 + \frac{4\pi^2 \nu^2}{v^2} a\right] \sin 2\pi(\nu t - k\phi)$$
$$- 2\pi k \left(2 \sum \frac{\partial a}{\partial x} \frac{\partial \phi}{\partial x} + a \sum \frac{\partial^2 \phi}{\partial x^2}\right) \cos 2\pi(\nu t - k\phi) = 0$$

This equation is satisfied only if the factors of the sine and cosine vanish.   From this result the equations

$$k^2 \sum \left(\frac{\partial \phi}{\partial x}\right)^2 = \frac{\nu^2}{v^2} + \frac{1}{4\pi^2 a} \sum \frac{\partial^2 a}{\partial x^2} \tag{22}$$

$$\sum \frac{\partial a}{\partial x} \frac{\partial \phi}{\partial x} + \frac{a}{2} \sum \frac{\partial^2 \phi}{\partial x^2} = 0 \tag{22'}$$

Now assume that the wavelength λ is sufficiently small so that $a(xyz)$ may be considered nearly constant within a distance comparable in magnitude to λ.   A sufficiently short wavelength undergoes no noticeable diffraction, and under this condition the postulates of geometric optics apply.   Therefore equation (22) must permit a corresponding simplification.

To determine the wavelength at a given point we must find the distance measured along a normal l to the surface ϕ = constant, which will introduce a change of 2π into the argument of the sine.   Thus $k\lambda(\partial\phi/\partial l) = 1$, or, on defining the direction of the normal l by α, β, γ,

$$\lambda = \frac{1}{k\left(\dfrac{\partial \phi}{\partial x}\alpha + \dfrac{\partial \phi}{\partial y}\beta + \dfrac{\partial \phi}{\partial z}\gamma\right)}$$

Now

$$\alpha = \frac{\dfrac{\partial \phi}{\partial x}}{\sqrt{\sum \left(\dfrac{\partial \phi}{\partial x}\right)^2}} \qquad \beta = \frac{\dfrac{\partial \phi}{\partial y}}{\sqrt{\sum \left(\dfrac{\partial \phi}{\partial x}\right)^2}} \qquad \gamma = \frac{\dfrac{\partial \phi}{\partial z}}{\sqrt{\sum \left(\dfrac{\partial \phi}{\partial x}\right)^2}}$$

Therefore

$$\lambda = \frac{1}{k\sqrt{\sum \left(\dfrac{\partial \phi}{\partial x}\right)^2}}$$

On the assumption that $(\partial a/\partial x)\lambda \ll a$, on differentiation we obtain

$$\frac{\partial^2 a}{\partial x^2}\lambda + \frac{\partial a}{\partial x}\frac{\partial \lambda}{\partial x} \ll \frac{\partial a}{\partial x}$$

or

$$\frac{\partial^2 a}{\partial x^2}\lambda \ll \frac{\partial a}{\partial x}\left(1 - \frac{\partial \lambda}{\partial x}\right) \sim \frac{\partial a}{\partial x}$$

Multiply both sides by λ,

$$\frac{\partial^2 a}{\partial x^2}\lambda^2 \ll \frac{\partial a}{\partial x}\lambda \ll a$$

Finally we can write

$$\frac{1}{a}\sum \frac{\partial^2 a}{\partial x^2} \ll \frac{1}{\lambda^2} = k^2 \sum \left(\frac{\partial \phi}{\partial x}\right)^2$$

Thus we observe that, when λ is sufficiently small, the last term in equation (22) is negligible and the equation takes the simpler form

$$\sum \left(\frac{\partial \phi}{\partial x}\right)^2 = \frac{\nu^2}{k^2 v^2} \tag{23}$$

which agrees in form with equation (18). It appears then that the phase function ϕ in the domain of geometric optics satisfies Hamilton's differential equation and becomes identical with it if we set $\nu^2/k^2v^2 = 2m(E - V)$. Thus the same differential equation

$$\sum \left(\frac{\partial \phi}{\partial x}\right)^2 = 2m(E - V) \tag{24}$$

can account for the motion of a particle of energy E in a field of force $V(xyz)$ according to classical mechanics as well as for the propagation of light in a heterogeneous medium described optically by the relation

$$v(xyz) = \frac{\nu}{k\ \sqrt{2m(E - V)}} \tag{25}$$

Equation (24) has, therefore, a mechanical as well as an optical interpretation. For the mechanical case a complete integral, $\phi(xyzE\alpha\beta)$, has the significance of the action function from which a twice-infinite manifold of paths can be derived with grad ϕ giving for all points in space the direction of the momentum with which the particle passes the point. In the optical case the same solution determines the phase surfaces of the wave motion, and the components of grad ϕ are proportional to the direction cosines of the light beam at a given point P.

Thus, with every motion of the particle in the field $V(xyz)$, a beam of light in a heterogeneous medium can be associated so that the beam takes the same way as the particle.

In order that equation (25) may have a physical meaning, we must assign to the constant k the dimension of a reciprocal action because $v/[k \sqrt{2m(E - V)}]$ must have the dimension of a velocity. Thus arises the idea of a relationship between k and h, and we shall see that it is possible to develop a consistent theory on the assumption that $k = 1/h$. Equation (25) then takes the form

$$v(xyz) = \frac{h\nu}{\sqrt{2m(E - V)}} \tag{26}$$

And so it turns out that this close connection between the classical motion of a particle and a beam of light in a heterogeneous medium conforms with the aims of wave mechanics, although at first it is purely formal in character, for that which we wish is the representation of the state $\Delta x \, \Delta y \, \Delta z \, \Delta \xi \, \Delta \eta \, \Delta \zeta$ by a wave group the propagation of which will supply us with information about the future behavior of the particle. We can achieve this aim by associating with every point $xyz\xi\eta\zeta$ within the element $\Delta x \, \cdot \, \cdot \, \cdot \, \Delta \zeta$ a certain solution of the wave equation

$$\nabla^2 u + \frac{4\pi^2\nu^2}{v^2}\, u = \nabla^2 u + \frac{2m}{\hbar^2}\, (E - V)u = 0 \tag{27}$$

where E is the energy corresponding to the point and $\nu = E/h$. If the wave under consideration satisfies the assumptions of geometric optics, there is no doubt about the procedure. We have seen that equation (27) can have a solution of the form

$$a(xyz) \sin 2\pi[\nu t - k\phi(xyz)]$$

wherein the function ϕ satisfies Hamilton's equation (24). Accordingly we shall identify ϕ with the action function $S(xyzE\alpha\beta)$ specified by the point $xyz\xi\eta\zeta$. The amplitude a can be calculated from equation (22'), ϕ being replaced by S. This procedure is permitted only if λ is sufficiently small so that $a(xyz)$ is nearly constant within an interval of the same order of magnitude as λ. If this condition is satisfied, we can use a wave mechanics method which, although of only a limited validity, proves very valuable in many applications.

9. The Geometrical Method of Wave Mechanics. The purpose of this section is to describe, with the help of a wave packet, the initial state of a particle according to the plan discussed in the preceding section. To accomplish this let us consider first all the points $xyz\xi\eta\zeta$ lying within the element $\Delta x \cdot \cdot \cdot \Delta\zeta$ to which the same function $S(xyzE\alpha\beta)$ applies. We mean by this that the equations

$$\frac{\partial S}{\partial x} = \xi \qquad \frac{\partial S}{\partial y} = \eta \qquad \frac{\partial S}{\partial z} = \zeta$$

give the same values of α, β, and E for all the points. Then a wave can be associated with all these points; this wave will be given by the real part of the expression

$$a(xyz)e^{i/\hbar[Et-S(xyzE\alpha\beta)]} \tag{28}$$

The frequency of the wave is defined, as before, by $\nu = E/h$, where E comprises the rest energy m_0c^2 as well as the kinetic and potential energy. The complex amplitude $a(xyz)$ is assumed to be a solution of equation (22′) if we substitute $S(xyzE\alpha\beta)$ for ϕ. Thus the amplitude will be dependent also on the variables E, α, and β and will be expressed by $a(xyzE\alpha\beta)$. Because of the homogeneity of equation (22′) in $a(xyz)$, a complex factor remains arbitrary. We are then permitted to multiply the amplitude of the wave by any real number and to add an arbitrary phase constant to the argument of the cosine, a possibility that is important in the construction of the wave packet.

The wave packet is now formed of waves represented by equation (28) in such a way that, if the parameters E, α, β are varied within suitable intervals ΔE, $\Delta\alpha$, and $\Delta\beta$, all points in the element $\Delta x \cdot \cdot \cdot \Delta\zeta$ are considered. Hence is obtained a manifold of waves which are represented by

$$u(xyzt) = \int\int\int a(xyzE\alpha\beta)e^{i/\hbar[Et-S(xyzE\alpha\beta)]}\, dE\, d\alpha\, d\beta \tag{29}$$

the integration being extended over the intervals ΔE, $\Delta\alpha$, $\Delta\beta$. However, the above equation is deficient still because with each $a(xyz)$ there is an arbitrary factor $\gamma e^{i\delta}$. To remedy this we must try to select the factors $\gamma e^{i\delta}$ so as to superpose the waves with such amplitudes and in such phases as to have all of them related to the space element $\Delta x\, \Delta y\, \Delta z$. This can be done by making use of the uncertainty relation (1) which make it possible to superpose the waves so that at time t the resultant intensity differs from zero only within the limits Δx, Δy, Δz. As noted above, this can be accomplished by a suitable choice of amplitudes and phases. Again it should be pointed out that the procedure is to leave the constructed wave packet undisturbed. Then the intensity at a point P at time t can be taken as a measure of the probability of locating the particle at that time and position.

It can be proved easily that, when this method is applied to a particle upon which no force is acting, the result agrees with that of Section 6. For in this case the action function S of such a particle is given by

$$S = \int (\xi\, dx + \eta\, dy + \zeta\, dz)$$
$$= \xi x + \eta y + \zeta z$$

In this expression, ξ, η, and ζ are to be taken as parameters, any two of which, say ξ and η, may be identified with the constants α and β. Then the relations between E, α, β and ξ, η, ζ can be expressed by

$$\alpha = \xi \qquad \beta = \eta \qquad E = \frac{\xi^2 + \eta^2 + \zeta^2}{2m} + \text{constant}$$

For $a(xyz)$ in equation (29), with $\phi = S$, the solution $a = \text{constant}$ follows, it being possible for the constant to depend on ξ, η, ζ. Equation (29) can be transformed by substituting, in the integral, ξ, η, and ζ for the variables E, α, and β. This gives

$$u(xyzt) = \int \int \int a(\xi\eta\zeta) e^{i/\hbar[Et-(x\xi+y\eta+z\zeta)]}\, d\xi\, d\eta\, d\zeta \tag{30}$$

which is equation (12).

It should be clear at once that the different velocities with which the members of the ensemble represented by (29) travel through space must, before long, dissolve the initially sharply defined packet. The points at which the waves are in phase agreement will begin to separate and diverge outward in space. Thus the uncertainty of the initial state gives rise to an increasing uncertainty in future states. Only in the case of a particle of sufficiently large mass can wave mechanics agree with classical mechanics and supply information that is, for all practical purposes, certain. Here the probability function described by the wave packet is confined to a very small space at any time, so that the prediction assumes the character of certainty and the predicted position agrees with that which results from the initial state according to classical calculation. In other words, for large mass, the requirement is that the wave group remain intact and carry out a motion corresponding to the laws of classical mechanics.

To show this let us consider a particle the momentum of which has been measured with great accuracy. For a macroscopic body this measurement does not affect the accurate measurement of position. The initial state is represented by a group of waves of the form $ae^{i/\hbar(Et-S)}$ in which the constants E, α, and β vary so slightly that their values are confined to the immediate neighborhood of certain values, E_0, α_0, and β_0. This limitation arises in the case under discussion because E, α, and β at a point depend on the components of momentum, hence the variation will be small. Thus if E, α, and β become $E_0 + E'$, $\alpha_0 + \alpha'$, $\beta_0 + \beta'$, then E', α', and β' lie between zero and ΔE, $\Delta \alpha$, and $\Delta \beta$. Therefore we have for S

$$S(xyz, E_0 + E', \alpha_0 + \alpha', \beta_0 + \beta')$$
$$= S(xyzE_0\alpha_0\beta_0) + \left(\frac{\partial S}{\partial E}\right)_0 E' + \left(\frac{\partial S}{\partial \alpha}\right)_0 \alpha' + \left(\frac{\partial S}{\partial \beta}\right)_0 \beta'$$

where the subscript 0 of the derivatives means that the operation is to be performed at the point $E_0\alpha_0\beta_0$. On the other hand, in the case of the amplitude a, which depends on E, α, β, these constants can be considered the constants E_0, α_0, β_0, that is $a = a(xyzE_0\alpha_0\beta_0)$. The same thing cannot be permitted in the case of S because it appears in the wave expression together with the factor $1/h$. With these changes the equation for u becomes

$$u(xyzt) = \int\int\int a(xyzE_0\alpha_0\beta_0)e^{\frac{i}{\hbar}\left\{(E_0+E')t-\left[S_0+\left(\frac{\partial S}{\partial E}\right)_0 E'+\left(\frac{\partial S}{\partial \alpha}\right)_0\alpha'+\left(\frac{\partial S}{\partial \beta}\right)_0\beta'\right]\right\}}$$
$$dE'\,d\alpha'\,d\beta'$$

$$= a(xyzE_0\alpha_0\beta_0)e^{\frac{i}{\hbar}(E_0 t - S_0)}\int\int\int e^{\frac{i}{\hbar}\left\{\left[t-\left(\frac{\partial S}{\partial E}\right)_0\right]E'-\left(\frac{\partial S}{\partial \alpha}\right)_0\alpha'-\left(\frac{\partial S}{\partial \beta}\right)_0\beta'\right\}}$$
$$dE'\,d\alpha'\,d\beta'$$

where $S_0 = S(xyzE_0\alpha_0\beta_0)$. Finally, setting the triple integral equal to A,

$$A = \int\int\int e^{\frac{i}{\hbar}\left\{\left[t-\left(\frac{\partial S}{\partial E}\right)_0\right]E'-\left(\frac{\partial S}{\partial \alpha}\right)_0\alpha'-\left(\frac{\partial S}{\partial \beta}\right)_0\beta'\right\}} dE'\,d\alpha'\,d\beta' \tag{31}$$

we have

$$u(xyzt) = aAe^{(i/\hbar)(E_0 t - S_0)} \tag{32}$$

from which we see that $|aA|$ represents the resultant amplitude. Thus the probability is given by $|a^2 A^2|$ which, for any time t, furnishes the probability of finding the particle at P.

Let us consider first the factor A of the probability function. From the way in which the wave packet has been formed, it follows that, at time t, A differs from zero within the element $\Delta x \, \Delta y \, \Delta z$, vanishing elsewhere. Now, according to equation (31), A depends on x, y, z, and t only in the terms $t - (\partial S/\partial E)_0$, $(\partial S/\partial \alpha)_0$, and $(\partial S/\partial \beta)_0$. Hence, if x, y, and z change with time in such a way that

$$t - \left(\frac{\partial S}{\partial E}\right)_0 = \text{constant} \qquad \left(\frac{\partial S}{\partial \alpha}\right)_0 = \text{constant} \qquad \left(\frac{\partial S}{\partial \beta}\right)_0 = \text{constant}$$

$$\tag{33}$$

the amplitude must remain the same.   And so the amplitude, at any time, differs from zero only at those points which satisfy relation (33). In other words, if at some point $P_0(x_0y_0z_0)$ of the space $\Delta x \, \Delta y \, \Delta z$ the functions $t - (\partial S/\partial E)_0$, $(\partial S/\partial \alpha)_0$, and $(\partial S/\partial \beta)_0$ equal a, b, and c respectively at t_0, then in an interval of time $t - t_0$ the amplitude shifts to a point P, determined by

$$t - \left(\frac{\partial S}{\partial E}\right)_0 = a \qquad \left(\frac{\partial S}{\partial \alpha}\right)_0 = b \qquad \left(\frac{\partial S}{\partial \beta}\right)_0 = c$$

On comparing these equations with those of (19), we find them to be identical with Jacobi's solution of the mechanical problem.   They describe the motion carried out by a point mass according to classical mechanics, the motion starting at point P_0 and the initial momentum being given by grad $S(xyzE_0\alpha_0\beta_0)$ taken at P_0.

In this case there is no difficulty in following the motion of the wave packet.   Let us imagine that all space is filled with a fluid the molecules of which are moving with a momentum $\mathbf{p} = \text{grad } S(xyzE_0\alpha_0\beta_0)$ at every point xyz.   The behavior of the wave packet is described by the motion of that part of the fluid which at the instant t lies within the space $\Delta x \, \Delta y \, \Delta z$.   Consequently, since the corresponding fluid moves within a certain stream tube, the wave packet holds together. Even though there are small changes in volume due to variations in cross section of tube, the volume remains extremely small in a macroscopic sense.   And thus, to a particle moving in space according to the laws of classical mechanics, the wave packet will assign at each instant of time a definite position, the term "definite" being used in the macroscopic sense.   From this we see that when heavy particles are involved the old and new mechanics are in full agreement.

It should be pointed out that the limitation mentioned in Section 7 applies here as well.   Hence, if time assumes a sufficiently great value, the wave packet will begin to lose its stability.   For, if the terms of higher order are retained in the development of S, the wave packet defined by equation (29) disperses into parts moving with different velocities, causing the region of phase agreement to become more and more indefinite.   We see then that classical mechanics is true only to a certain approximation which is closer the more accurately the momentum of the particle has been measured.

It must be emphasized again that all the waves in the packet defined by equation (29) are supposed to have a sufficiently short wavelength. Only on this assumption can we apply the laws of geometric optics to the propagation of waves.   As we have seen, the wavelength is inversely proportional to the momentum of the particle, and therefore the geometric method is adequate for the treatment of a rapidly moving particle provided that its momentum satisfies the condition that $v(xyz) = h\nu/\sqrt{2m(E - V)}$ does not change noticeably within the distance $\lambda = h/p$.

What must the procedure be if the above supposition is not fulfilled? In the theory of the atom this is precisely the situation in which we are interested. Under these circumstances we cannot neglect the last terms in equation (22'), and thus there is removed from consideration any connection with geometric optics and therefore with classical mechanics which, up to this point, we could have maintained. The only alternative is to consider the waves that are to be associated with the particle by the wave equation

$$\nabla^2 u + \frac{4\pi^2 \nu^2}{v^2} u = 0$$

in which $h\nu/\sqrt{2m(E - V)}$ is to replace $v(xyz)$. In other words, we must return to Schroedinger's equation

$$\nabla^2 u + \frac{2m}{\hbar^2} (E - V)u = 0$$

and attempt to find a rigorous solution of that equation. This will be considered in detail in the following Chapter 2.

10. The Scattering of Probability Waves by a Nucleus. The geometric method may be used in dealing with the deflection of α particles by a nucleus if we limit ourselves to those deflections wherein the particle does not come too close to the nucleus. Consider an alpha particle moving in the direction of the x axis, a nucleus of charge Ze being at the origin. In the experiments of Rutherford the velocity of the particle was 2×10^9 cm sec. This corresponds to a de Broglie wavelength, $\lambda = h/p = (6.62 \times 10^{-27})/(2 \times 10^9 \times 6.6 \times 10^{-24})$, which is almost 5×10^{-13} cm, or about the linear dimension of the nucleus. Thus, if we disregard the immediate neighborhood in which the strongest deflections occur, the Coulomb field of the nucleus may be considered nearly constant within a range of the order λ. Hence we can treat at least the smaller deflections by the method of the preceding section.

Let us assume that the velocity with which the particle approaches the nucleus was measured with great accuracy. Then according to Heisenberg's relations (1) our knowledge of the initial position is very inaccurate. All we know is that at time t_0 the particle was somewhere in a large space $\Delta x\, \Delta y\, \Delta z$ around the x axis. Accordingly the initial state must be represented by a probability packet filling this space uniformly.   The problem then is to determine the history of this packet during the interval $t - t_0$.

For this purpose we make use of the theorem proved in the preceding section.   That theorem states that, if the initial momentum of the particle is known very accurately, the amplitude factor A of a point P_0 will be at the same point P after the interval $t - t_0$ as a particle which starts from P_0 at time t_0, with the given initial velocity and subject to classical mechanics, would be at time t.   To determine the classical path of such a particle we proceed as follows.   Let the initial velocity be v, and b the initial distance of the particle from the x axis.   Then the angular momentum relative to O at this instant is mbv.   When the particle passes a point M in its path, its angular momentum is given by $-mr^2(d\theta/dt)$, where θ is the angle between OM and the x axis.   Since angular momentum is conserved, we have $-r^2(d\theta/dt) = bv$.   Furthermore, if v_y is the y component of the velocity at M, then, from Coulomb's law,

$$m\frac{dv_y}{dt} = 2\frac{Ze^2}{r^2}\sin\theta$$

$$= -\frac{2Ze^2}{bv}\sin\theta\frac{d\theta}{dt}$$

which on integrating gives (the initial conditions $v_y = 0$, $\theta = \pi$ being kept in mind)

$$mv_y = \frac{2Ze^2}{vb}(\cos\theta + 1) \tag{34}$$

When the particle has passed the domain within which the nucleus exerts a noticeable repulsion, it resumes its original velocity v along a straight line.   If α is the angle between this straight line and the x axis—α depends on b—we have $v_y = v\sin\alpha$ and $\theta = \alpha$.   Equation (34) then becomes

$$mv\sin\alpha = \frac{2Ze^2}{vb}(\cos\alpha + 1)$$

Therefore

$$b = \frac{2Ze^2}{mv^2}\frac{(\cos\alpha + 1)}{\sin\alpha} = \frac{2Ze^2}{mv^2}\cot\frac{\alpha}{2} \tag{35}$$

Equation (35) determines the angle α through which a particle, incident at a distance b from the axis, will be deflected by the nucleus.

Let us determine now the probability of finding the particle at a point P from measurements made at time t.   This probability is given by the intensity $C^2 = |aA|^2$ of the wave packet at that time and position. This intensity is compared with the intensity $C_0^2 = 1$, the value at the point P_0 at time t_0. Since the factor A is transferred without change from P_0 to P, then C^2 and C_0^2 differ only on account of the factor $|a(xyz)|^2$. If the value of this factor at P_0 and t_0 is $|a_0|^2$, then $C_0^2 = |a_0|A^2$ and therefore $C^2 = |a|^2A^2$ becomes $|a^2/a_0^2|$. To determine the ratio $|a^2/a_0^2|$ we make use of equation (22)', according to which

$$\sum \frac{\partial \phi}{\partial x} \frac{\partial a}{\partial x} + \frac{a}{2} \nabla^2 \phi = 0$$

In this equation the action function S must be substituted for ϕ. Therefore grad ϕ is proportional to the classical velocity $\mathbf{v}$ with which the particle is moving. Thus we get

$$\sum v_x \frac{\partial a}{\partial x} + \frac{a}{2} \operatorname{div} \mathbf{v} = 0$$

On multiplying the above equation by a we obtain

$$\sum v_x \frac{\partial a^2}{\partial x} + a^2 \operatorname{div} \mathbf{v} = \operatorname{div} a^2\mathbf{v} = 0 \tag{36}$$

Hence the vector $a^2\mathbf{v}$ is solenoidal, and this enables us to determine $|a^2/a_0^2|$ in the following way. At point P_0 an annular ring of radii b and $b + db$ is described around the x axis. If we follow the stream tube that issues from this ring, we find that when it passes through the field of the nucleus its walls are no longer parallel but diverge at an angle $d\alpha$. The relation between this angle and db is found, from equation (35), to be

$$db^2 = \left(\frac{2Ze^2}{mv^2}\right)^2 \frac{d}{d\alpha} \cot^2 \frac{\alpha}{2} \, d\alpha$$

Thus a cross section of the tube at point P will be a ring of radius $r \sin \alpha$ and breadth $r \, d\alpha$. The area of this ring is $2\pi r^2 \sin \alpha \, d\alpha$, whereas that at point P_0 has an area $2\pi b \, db = \pi \, db^2$. As the particle has a velocity $\mathbf{v}$ at the two points and as $\operatorname{div} a^2\mathbf{v} = 0$,

$$a_0^2\pi \, db^2 = a^2 2\pi r^2 \sin \alpha \, d\alpha$$

Therefore

$$\frac{a^2}{a_0^2} = C^2 = \frac{db^2}{2r^2 \sin \alpha \, d\alpha}$$

$$= \left(\frac{2Ze^2}{mv^2}\right)^2 \frac{1}{2r^2 \sin \alpha} \frac{d \cot^2 \alpha/2}{d\alpha}$$

$$= \left(\frac{Ze^2}{rmv^2}\right)^2 \frac{1}{\sin^4 \alpha/2} \tag{37}$$

C^2 evidently may be considered as the probability of the alpha particle being deviated from its original direction by the angle α; it corresponds to Rutherford's deduction from classical mechanics.

We might take this agreement as a matter of course, since we have made ample use of classical mechanics in our calculations. Such would be misunderstanding the result, for the calculation is based essentially on wave equation (27), and the use of classical mechanics has been possible only because of the close connection between the two mechanics when the de Broglie wavelength is sufficiently short.

For the alpha particles this condition is fulfilled because their great mass has a diminishing effect on the wavelength. For electrons, however, the method fails because, as they have a mass about 7000 times smaller than the alpha particles, their wavelength is of the order of 10^{-8} cm. The assumptions of geometric optics hold only at distances from the nucleus which are far greater than 10^{-8} cm. At such distances the force field is very weak, and geometric methods are inadequate for explaining the observed deflections of the electrons. For the treatment of such problems we must determine, with the help of equation (27), the change which a plain wave undergoes when it meets an atomic scatterer such as a nucleus, atom, or molecule. The calculations of this change follow a procedure developed by Born on the basis of perturbation theory (Chapter 4).

The deflection of particles by a charged nucleus is interpreted in the new mechanics as a scattering process involving probability waves. The originally plane de Broglie waves that are incident in a given direction are scattered by the nucleus in all directions. If we disregard the region immediately around the nucleus, the scattering takes place in a manner quite similar to the penetration of the earth's atmosphere by light. This is observed at once from equation (26) for the phase velocity:

$$v(xyz) = \frac{E}{\sqrt{2m[E - V(xyz)]}}$$

in which $V(xyz)$ is the field potential and E the constant energy of the particle. At a great distance from the nucleus $V = 0$, and therefore $v = \sqrt{E/2m}$. In the neighborhood of the nucleus, V is greater or less than zero, depending on whether the charge on the particle is positive or negative. For small values of r, v is greater than v_0 when the charge is positive but less than v_0 when it is negative. If we consider the ratio $v_0/v(xyz)$, which depends only on r, as the index of refraction of a hypothetical medium, then for a positive charge it becomes less than unity as the nucleus is approached, but for a negative charge it becomes greater than unity.   Thus probability waves are affected by a nucleus as if the nucleus were surrounded by an atmosphere consisting of spherical shells which become optically denser in the outward direction for a positive corpuscle but optically thinner for a negative one. When the rays penetrate this atmosphere, they are refracted from and toward the normal respectively and thus leave the domain of the nucleus in all directions.   A wave packet that passes through the field of a nucleus must, therefore, begin to disperse.

PROBLEMS

1. Verify relations (1) by discussing the accuracy Δx with which the position of a particle can be determined with the aid of a microscope.

2. By representing the motion of a particle by a de Broglie wave, show that the diffraction of the wave by a slit of width Δx is in agreement with the uncertainty relation.

3. A beam of monochromatic light illuminates a diaphragm A containing two slits.   A diffraction pattern then appears on a screen B set behind A.   Imagine that the experiment is carried out with but one photon, and show that, owing to the uncertainty relations, the diffraction pattern is destroyed by any attempt to determine the slit through which the photon passed.   (Set up an indicator behind each slit, and take into account the fact that the reaction of the indicator must not shift the photon from a maximum of the diffraction pattern to a neighboring minimum.)

4. Show that the expression $d\nu/[d(1/\lambda)]$ for the group velocity can be put in the form $V - \lambda(dv/d\lambda)$, where v is the phase velocity.

5. How must the phase velocity v be chosen as a function of ν in order that the group velocity become inversely proportional to v^2?

6. Apply the equation $\nabla^2 u + (2m/\hbar)^2(E - V)u = 0$ to the case wherein the potential at a certain surface varies discontinuously, and show by using the integral theorem of Gauss that the component of grad u, normal to the surface, behaves continuously.   The same holds for the function u itself.

7. When a plane wave $u = a_1 e^{i\mathbf{k_1 \cdot r}}$ falls on a surface at which V is discontinuous, the wave is partly reflected $(a_2 e^{i\mathbf{k_2 \cdot r}})$ and partly refracted $(a_3 e^{i\mathbf{k_3 \cdot r}})$.   Find the relations between the normal and tangential components of $\mathbf{k_1}$, $\mathbf{k_2}$, and $\mathbf{k_3}$.

8. A plane wave $a e^{i\mathbf{k_1 \cdot r}}$ is moving in the direction of the x axis against a potential wall, $V = $ constant, extending from $x = 0$ to $x = a$.   The wall V is assumed to be so high as to be impenetrable for the particle according to classical mechanics. Show that the boundary conditions can be fulfilled only if there exists for $x < 0$ a reflected wave $a_2 e^{i\mathbf{k_2 \cdot r}}$, and for $x > a$ a wave $a_3 e^{i\mathbf{k_3 \cdot r}}$ which has penetrated the wall ("tunnel effect").

2

WAVE MECHANICS

OF STATIONARY STATES

11. Schroedinger's Wave Equation. In the preceding chapter wave mechanics was developed on the supposition that the field of force does not change noticeably within a distance of the order of magnitude λ. Under this condition the application of the principles of geometric optics to the propagation of probability waves permits the maintenance of a close connection with classical mechanics, the formalism of geometric optics being identical with the treatment of mechanics according to the Hamilton-Jacobi method.

We lose this connection when we try to apply the methods of wave mechanics to an electron bound to an atom. The field of force acting on such an electron varies so rapidly in the immediate neighborhood of the nucleus that the application of geometric optics is out of the question even when the wavelength is extremely short. For example, let us consider the electron of a H atom. According to Bohr's theory, in the ground state of this atom the electron moves with a momentum $p = mv = 2\pi me^2/h$ in a circular orbit of radius $a_1 = h^2/4\pi^2 me^2$. Should we for the moment disregard all doubts as to the admissibility of this conception, there would remain an essential difficulty. Should it be true that there actually are states of the electron that fall within the above-mentioned values of momentum and radius, there would be no way in which to describe the motion by using classical mechanics, for the de Broglie wavelength associated with this motion would be $\lambda = h/p = h^2/2\pi me^2 = 2\pi a_1$. Within a space of these dimensions, at a distance a_1 from the nucleus, the potential of the Coulomb field can by no means be considered even approximately constant, and thus the methods of geometric optics no longer apply.

Here we must make use of the rigorous solutions of Schroedinger's wave equation

$$\nabla^2 u + \frac{2m}{\hbar^2}(E - V)u = 0 \qquad (27)$$

As we have seen, the purpose of wave mechanics is to represent the

35

motion of a particle starting from a given initial state $\Delta q\, \Delta p$ by a sum of solutions of (27). In Section 9 this plan was used successfully by combining into a wave packet approximate solutions of the form

$$a(xyzE\alpha\beta)e^{(i/\hbar)[Et-S(xyzE\alpha\beta)]} \tag{38}$$

which satisfy equation (27) when the potential is nearly constant within a distance of the order of magnitude λ. In this way we obtained a probability function $u(xyzt)$ by which the behavior of the particle can be described correctly.

As approximations are permissible no longer, our procedure must be to seek rigorous solutions of equation (27) and construct linear aggregates from these which will represent the analogue to the wave packet. A priori, we cannot say whether this procedure will have meaning. At any rate it is worth-while to investigate whether the coefficients of the aggregate can be connected with the measurements so that the sum will have the same significance as the function u, which represented a wave packet.

In attempting the integration of equation (27), we immediately discover a most striking peculiarity of that equation. It turns out that a differential equation of that type can be solved by a regular function $\psi(xyz)$, that is, one that is everywhere finite, continuous, and single-valued, only if the energy parameter E of the equation has a value belonging to a definite discrete set, $E_0, E_1, \cdots, E_n, \cdots$. The values of this set depend on the nature of the function $V(xyz)$ and are called *eigenvalues* of the differential equation. The corresponding solutions, $\psi_0, \psi_1, \cdots, \psi_n, \cdots$, are called *eigenfunctions*. These functions are uniquely defined, that is, they contain no arbitrary constants aside from an arbitrary factor by which they can be multiplied by virtue of the homogeneity of the equation.

Thus the attempt to apply Schroedinger's equation to an atom defined by a given potential function V starts out with the promising discovery that there exists a set of energy values which have a distinct significance relative to the atom. They are, as we shall see, identical with the energies belonging to the various states of the atom according to Bohr's theory and are connected with the frequencies of the emitted spectrum by the relation $h\nu = E_i - E_k$. It is a decisive success that wave mechanics, of itself, is able to provide the critical energy values without supplementary assumptions. However, for the present we are interested in another point. Our intention is to combine the solutions of equation (27) with indefinite coefficients with a linear aggregate, taking into account the time t in such a way that, following the wave packet method, we multiply every eigenfunction by the factor $e^{(i/\hbar)Et}$. Then, instead of equation (29), we shall have the function

$$u(xyzt) = \sum c_i \psi_i e^{(i/\hbar)E_i t} \tag{39}$$

The function u is represented now by a sum because the eigenfunctions ψ_i form an infinite discrete† set, whereas in the continuous solutions (38) u was represented by an integral.

It is a question now of how to choose the coefficients c_i in the summation (39) so that u may be regarded as a probability function which will give information about the position of the electron. Obviously this choice can be made only on the basis of certain experiments, and therefore we are bound to undertake a careful examination of the experimental possibilities.

12. The Experimental Possibilities. First of all, we are interested in experiments that enable us to measure the energy of an atom. If we want the measurement to be exact, experiments that involve the coordinates and momentum of the electron are of no use. Only if the exact simultaneous values of q and p could be measured would the exact determination of the energy $E = V(xyz) + p^2/2m$ be possible. Hence the only appropriate experiments for our purpose are those which deal directly with the energy of the atom. Of special importance are the experiments of Franck and Hertz dealing with the energy transfer in the collision of an atom with an electron. They have the advantage that the energy of the colliding electron can be measured exactly both before and after the collision; hence the energy which the atom acquires because of the collision can be determined. It is true that we do not gain any information about the absolute energy of the atom in this way. What we do learn from the measurements is that this energy is always changed by an amount ΔE, corresponding exactly with the difference $E_i - E_k$ of two eigenvalues. From the measured ΔE we are able to infer the energy levels between which the passage takes place. To do this we must find those levels of the set of values the difference of which just equals ΔE. Thus the collision method informs us about the energy belonging to the atom both before and after the measurement.

Now suppose that the energy of a given atom is known. Will we be able to find out further details about the motion of the electron in the given stationary state? Evidently not, because when we try to examine the motion we are bound to perturb the state by that act of observation in such a way that the state is changed into another. For

---

† For the present we assume a set of discrete eigenvalues. The case of a continuous spectrum is discussed in Section 36.

example, a single measurement of the position is sufficient to throw the electron out of its orbit. The reason for this failure is that the energy and phase of the rotational motion are conjugate quantities and as such cannot be measured simultaneously. An exact knowledge of the energy is possible only if we renounce any knowledge of the phase. From our point of view, therefore, we cannot agree with the old atomic theory in which a certain motion was correlated with the electron in every stationary state. Such a conception is not in accordance with the principle that theory must not make use of concepts that have no observational meaning. On principle, we cannot know the motion the electron is undergoing when the atom is in a given stationary state, and therefore the question concerning the motion cannot be included in a correct theory.

This does not mean, however, that a stationary state is definable only with respect to its energy. We can analyze the state more adequately if we confine ourselves to questions that can be answered on the basis of experiments. Such a question is the following: Let us assume that we have a great number of atoms of the same kind and under the same conditions. We pick samples at random out of the assemblage and examine their behavior when colliding with electrons. From this behavior we judge the energy levels of the atoms, so that from a sufficiently great number of tests a probability that an atom is at a given energy level can be inferred.

First let us consider the case in which the experiments furnish a probability of unity for a certain energy E_i. Then we are certain that any atom chosen at random from the assemblage is in the ith stationary state, and we imagine that this atom is subjected to a measurement by which the position of the rotating electron is determined. Of course, by such a measurement the state is destroyed, but every atom examined provides a datum belonging to the description of the state. After carrying out a great number of such measurements we are in possession of a statistical ensemble which can give us information about the probability of finding the electron at the point xyz relative to the nucleus. This ensemble provides the limit of experimental possibilities, and we see that, although on principle there is no way of knowing the motion of the electron in a given stationary state of the atom, we can at least in a mental experiment make sure of all the positions corresponding to the state together with the probabilities of finding the electron in these positions.

Our purpose now is to give to the eigenfunctions ψ_i an interpretation that is guaranteed by experimental possibilities. The idea that ψ_i may be connected with the probabilities defined above suggests itself;

also the idea that we should try to establish a theory on the following assumption: the square of the modulus of $\psi_i(xyz)$, taken as a function of xyz, will, when multiplied by $dx\,dy\,dz$, give the relative probability that a measurement of position made on an atom in the ith stationary state will find the electron within the volume element $dx\,dy\,dz$. Whether $|\psi_i|^2$ really has this meaning cannot be decided by direct experiments (feasible only in our imagination); it can be proved only by an examination of the consequences.

Thus the question of how to determine the coefficients c_i of the summation in equation (39) is to be answered for a special case as follows. If we know for certain that the atom has an energy E_k, we take $c_k = 1$, with all the others being zero. The state then is represented by

$$u(xyzt) = \psi_k(xyz)e^{(i/\hbar)E_k t} \tag{40}$$

which is a wave of amplitude ψ_k and frequency $\nu_k = E_k/h$. The interpretation of this wave according to our theory is that the square of u, uu^*, where u^* denotes the conjugate complex to u, gives the probability that the electron is to be found at xyz at time t. In the case defined by equation (40) the probability is independent of time, since t is eliminated in performing the operation uu^*.

13. States of Undefined Energy. Now let us consider the general case in which the measurement of energy does not supply the same value for all the atoms in the assemblage. Assume that the values $E_0E_1 \cdots$ are found with the probabilities $c_0{}^2c_1{}^2 \cdots$ respectively, where, for formal reasons, the probabilities are written as squares the sum of which equals unity. This case requires careful consideration.

At first we might imagine that the meaning of the measured statistics is perfectly clear. If we adopt the viewpoint of the old quantum theory wherein the atoms could exist only in the states $0, 1, 2 \cdots$, we can interpret the statistics only in the sense that there are, in the assemblage of N atoms, $Nc_0{}^2$ atoms having an energy E_0, $Nc_1{}^2$ atoms with an energy E_1, and so on. In short, the assemblage is a mixture of different stationary states.

Now, in a given case it is very easy to decide whether this interpretation is correct. The method is to refine the statistical investigation by removing from the whole assemblage a sufficiently great section and ascertain its statistics. The test is this: if the whole assemblage is really a mixture, it should be possible, by repeating the above procedure, to find a partial assemblage which is statistically different from the whole. When once we happen to find atoms of the same energy E_k only, the statistics will show $c_k = 1$ and all the others zero.

If such experiments prove that the assemblage is a mixture, the probability of finding the electron of an atom picked at random from the assemblage at the point xyz evidently is given by

$$\sum c_i{}^2 \psi_i \psi_i{}^* \qquad (41)$$

for the probability that the atom is in the ith stationary state is $c_i{}^2$, and for this state the xyz probability is $\psi_i(xyz)\psi_i{}^*(xyz)$. If it is a single atom existing under given conditions, rather than an assemblage, with which we are dealing, expression (47) still applies if an assemblage under exactly the same conditions proves to be a mixture containing the different states in the ratio $c_0{}^2 : c_1{}^2 : \cdots$.

Accordingly quantum mechanics does not deny the possibility of mixtures. But, contrary to conventional opinion, it maintains that not any assemblage may be considered a mixture. It may be that there is a statistical identity for any sufficiently large partial assemblage taken from the whole. Then the assemblage can be considered a mixture no longer, and we have to assume that all the atoms are in the same state, which is quite as well defined as a stationary state in the sense of Bohr but with the difference, however, *that no definite energy value can be assigned to the atom.* For the understanding of quantum mechanics it is of decisive importance to become familiar with this strange idea of a defined state without a defined energy. What is meant is not an atom with definite energy which is not known. Nor must we think of an atom the energy of which varies with time. In fact we must adopt the idea of a state not energetically defined. This concept is characteristic of quantum mechanics and cannot be understood on the basis of classical mechanics. There is no contradiction between the idea of undefined energy and the fact that we are always in a position to ascertain a definite energy value by means of a measurement. Since by an act of measurement we destroy the state being investigated, the atom is compelled to seek a new energy level, that is, to assume a certain stationary state of definite energy. From this we can understand the significance of the numbers c_i which characterize the state in question; that is, $c_i{}^2$ is the probability of the atom favoring the ith state.

Let us assume now an assemblage of atoms which is not a mixture but which, by statistical analysis, has been proved homogeneous. We state that the conditions to which the atoms are subject guarantee a *pure case.* The question in this case is what function $u(xyz)$ gives the probability of locating the electron at xyz by the product uu^*. Quantum mechanics assumes that this function is given by

$$u(xyzt) = \sum c_i \psi_i(xyz) e^{(i/\hbar)E_i t} \tag{42}$$

Hence the probability in question is

$$uu^* = \sum_i c_i \psi_i e^{(i/\hbar)E_i t} \sum c_k{}^* \psi_k{}^* e^{-(i/\hbar)E_k t} \tag{43}$$

$$= \sum_{ik} c_i c_k{}^* \psi_i \psi_k{}^* e^{(i/\hbar)(E_i - E_k)t}$$

This probability does not agree with that of a mixture. The essential difference between equations (41) and (43) is that in (41) all the terms are independent of time, whereas in (43) the terms with $i \neq k$ are periodic functions of time. To understand the meaning of this difference we must refer to the electron on which no force acts. We saw in Section 5 that for such an electron the motion of definite energy is described by a de Broglie wave

$$u = ae^{(i/\hbar)[Et - (x\xi + y\eta + z\zeta)]}$$

and, since uu^* is independent of both time and coordinates, it follows that, when the energy of an electron is known exactly, any position in space has the same probability and therefore it becomes impossible to localize the particle. But, if we renounce an exact determination of energy, we have to substitute a wave packet for the single wave, the effect being that now the probability has a maximum in a certain domain of space. Then uu^* depends on time; that is, the maximum is not stationary but moves through space. Thus, if the state loses its energetical determinacy, the motion of the particle, in its successive phases, becomes visible with a distinctness that increases with decreasing definition of energy.

Thus the time-dependence of equation (43) is to be interpreted as the way in which the phases of motion of the electron are pictured in the propagation of the de Broglie waves. The phase, as a function of time, is canonically conjugate to the energy, and hence, according to the uncertainty relations, exact simultaneous measurement of these is impossible. Any indication of phase must vanish from the wave picture when the energy has an exact value; this is the reason why the element of time does not appear in equation (41). Only when the energy becomes indefinite does phase enter the picture, and then it represents a compensation by which the state gains in the definition of one entity what it loses in the definition of another. Now we see how the concept of the motion of rotation is to be treated. In quantum mechanics this concept has a meaning only when, in the definition of the state, the energy recedes in favor of the phase. Under this condition equation (43) consists of a very great number of eigenfunctions superposed in such a way that uu^* represents a nearly point-shaped domain. It is to be expected that the domain will hold together, at least for a certain time, performing during this interval a motion according to the laws of classical mechanics.

Whether quantum mechanics is correct in representing a pure case, characterized by given numbers c_i, by a function of the type (43), of course, can be proved only by experiments. The application of the theory to given systems will afford us the opportunity to test it. One point, however, must be made clear beforehand. The assumption that equation (43), when multiplied by $dx\, dy\, dz$, furnishes the probability of the electron being found within $dx\, dy\, dz$ at time t can be correct only if the integration of equation (43) over the whole space has a value that does not change with time, for that integral gives the probability that the electron is found anywhere in space and is always equal to unity.

In order to show that this requirement really can be fulfilled, let us consider first the time-independent integral

$$\int\int\int \psi_i\psi_i{}^*\, dx\, dy\, dz \;=\; \int \psi_i\psi_i{}^*\, dv \tag{44}$$

The function ψ_i is a solution of equation (27), and, since that equation is homogeneous in ψ_i, ψ_i remains a solution when multiplied by an arbitrary factor. This factor is chosen so that the integral in (44) has a value of unity. We then call the function ψ_i "normalized." It can be shown further that all integrals $\int \psi_i\psi_k{}^*\, dv$ vanish for $i \neq k$. To prove this let us consider the equations

$$\frac{\hbar^2}{2m}\, \nabla^2\psi_i + (E_i - V)\psi_i = 0$$

$$\frac{\hbar^2}{2m}\, \nabla^2\psi_k{}^* + (E_k - V)\psi_k{}^* = 0$$

On multiplying the first by $\psi_k{}^*$ and the second by ψ_i and subtracting, we get

$$\frac{\hbar^2}{2m}\, (\psi_k{}^*\nabla^2\psi_i - \psi_i\nabla^2\psi_k{}^*) = (E_k - E_i)\psi_i\psi_k{}^*$$

This equation is integrated over the whole space. The integral on the left vanishes according to Green's theorem, and, since $E_i \neq E_k$,

$$\int \psi_i\psi_k{}^*\, dv = 0 \qquad (i \neq k)$$

Thus the functions ψ_i are orthogonal. The conditions for normalization and orthogonality are contained in the equation

$$\int \psi_i \psi_k{}^* \, dv = \delta_{ik} \qquad (45)$$

δ_{ik} having a value unity when $i = k$ and a value zero when $i \neq k$. Now, by using equation (45), we can transform the integral of (43) into

$$\sum c_i c_k{}^* e^{(i/\hbar)(E_i - E_k)t} \int \psi_i \psi_k{}^* \, dv = \sum c_i{}^2$$

from which it follows that the integral is independent of time and has the value unity since $\sum c_i{}^2 = 1$, this because $c_i{}^2$ represents the probability of the ith state.

14. Wave Mechanics and Bohr's Theory. It is instructive to compare the statistical manner in which wave mechanics describes the stationary states of an atom with the theory of Bohr, according to which an electron should be performing an orbital motion that can be determined on the basis of classical mechanics. In quantum mechanics we cannot adopt this viewpoint because there is no experiment by means of which the motion can be observed. We cannot carry out more than one measurement on an atom which is known to be in a given stationary state, because this one measurement is sufficient to destroy the state completely. The concept "orbit of an electron" has no meaning, therefore, for a state of definite energy, and thus, depending on the experimental possibilities, we must substitute a statistical ensemble of the positions in which the electron can be found for that concept.

A priori, it is conceivable that statistics might furnish a probability which differs from zero only for points that define a certain orbit. However, according to quantum mechanics this is not true. As will be seen in applying the theory to an oscillator or to the H atom, the values of the functions ψ_i differ from zero *everywhere* in space except for certain "nodal surfaces." In other words, for any stationary state it is possible that, in the determination of its position, the electron can be found at any distance from the nucleus. The orbits, which in Bohr's theory play so predominant a role, are indicated in the wave-mechanical model of the atom only in so far as the maxima of the functions $\psi_i(xyz)$ make recognizable a surface that has a certain resemblance to Bohr's elliptical and circular orbits. Thus we may characterize the new theory figuratively by saying that every orbit is dissolved into a *statistical cloud* in which the orbit can be recognized only in the form of a diffuse condensation.

However, the relationship between wave mechanics and Bohr's atomic theory requires a deeper analysis. The great success of Bohr's theory makes it rather obvious that the application of classical mechanics to the atom cannot be wholly wrong but to a certain extent must be justifiable. As we saw in the preceding section there certainly is a connection between the old and the new mechanics which becomes conspicuous only when we are dealing with states the energy of which is undefined. In order to bring out this connection more clearly, let us consider an atom which is known to be in a stationary state of high energy. Let us suppose that there is made a measurement which furnishes, within the accuracy afforded by the uncertainty relations, the position and velocity of the electron at a given moment. If the number i of the state is sufficiently high, it is most probable that we shall find the electron at a great distance from the nucleus since the maximum of the function ψ_i moves outward as i increases. When the measurement is completed, the atom, of course, is no longer in the ith state because this state has been changed into another of undefined energy which, according to equation (42), is represented by $\sum c_k \psi_k e^{(i/\hbar)E_k t}$. Now, if we assume that light of a great wavelength has been used for the measurement, the state cannot have been changed very much, and therefore we can suppose that the sum contains only ψ_k which belong in the neighborhood of ψ_i. On the other hand, the initial state, defined within the limits $\Delta x \cdot \cdot \cdot \Delta \zeta$, can be represented by a wave packet as well, for, because of the great distance from the nucleus, the force field acting on the electron varies slowly and hence we can apply the methods of geometric optics to the problem. Then as a representation we obtain a wave packet defining a function of coordinates and time which must be equivalent to the function $\sum c_k \psi_k e^{(i/\hbar)E_k t}$, for both of them have the same physical meaning, namely, both give the probability of finding the particle at the point xyz at time t. We know that in the case of a very accurately measured momentum the wave packet contracts nearly to a point the motion of which agrees with that of a material point in classical mechanics. Thus in quantum mechanics also there are states of the atom which can be described approximately by the picture of an electron moving in an elliptical or circular orbit, provided, however, that the energy of the states is not assumed to be exactly defined. From this viewpoint the fact that classical mechanics was able to solve the problem of the atom, at least to a certain extent, seems surprising no longer. The theory was not altogether wrong. It was only the application of it to definite energy states that was incorrect.

Luckily, however, this did not prevent the theory from arriving at results, for example those concerning energy terms, which were at least partly correct.

15. Expectation Values of Mechanical Entities. From the definition of the function $u_i = \psi_i e^{(i/\hbar)E_i t}$, upon differentiation relative to t we obtain

$$\frac{\hbar}{i} \frac{\partial u_i}{\partial t} = E_i u_i$$

Therefore the wave equation

$$\frac{\hbar^2}{2m} \nabla^2 u_i + (E_i - V)u_i = 0$$

can be transformed into

$$\frac{\hbar^2}{2m} \nabla^2 u_i - V u_i = -\frac{\hbar}{i} \frac{\partial u_i}{\partial t} \qquad (46)$$

This equation, which may be called the time equation and no longer contains the energy parameter, holds for all u functions simultaneously, and consequently for any linear aggregate $\sum c_i u_i = \sum c_i \psi_i e^{(i/\hbar)E_i t}$, in contrast to equation (27), which does not possess this property. With Schroedinger, we assume that equation (46) holds also when the potential V depends not only on coordinates but on time as well; this case has been omitted from our previous considerations. The derivation of equation (27) then loses its validity, since it is based on the supposition that equation (20) can be solved by an expression of the form $\psi(xyz)e^{i2\pi\nu t}$.

For the present, however, we shall restrict ourselves to a potential V which is independent of time, and use equation (46) to determine the probable velocity of the electron. Let us write the latter equation in the form

$$-\frac{\partial u}{\partial t} = \frac{\hbar i}{2m} \left(\nabla^2 - \frac{2m}{\hbar^2} V \right) u \qquad (47)$$

Replacing u in this equation by its conjugate complex, we obtain

$$-\frac{\partial u^*}{\partial t} = -\frac{\hbar i}{2m} \left(\nabla^2 - \frac{2m}{\hbar^2} V \right) u^* \qquad (48)$$

Multiplying (47) by u^* and (48) by u and adding, we get

$$-\frac{\partial(uu^*)}{\partial t} = \frac{\hbar i}{2m} (u^* \nabla^2 u - u \nabla^2 u^*)$$

$$= \frac{\hbar i}{2m} \left[\frac{\partial}{\partial x} \left(u^* \frac{\partial u}{\partial x} - u \frac{\partial u^*}{\partial x} \right) + \cdots \right]$$

and in vector notation

$$\frac{\partial}{\partial t}(uu^*) = -\frac{\hbar i}{2m} \operatorname{div}(u^* \operatorname{grad} u - u \operatorname{grad} u^*) \tag{49}$$

If we multiply both sides of this equation by the volume element $dx\, dy\, dz = dv$, on applying the theorem of Gauss we obtain

$$\frac{\partial}{\partial t}(uu^*)\, dv = -\frac{\hbar i}{2m} \int\int (u^* \operatorname{grad}_n u - u \operatorname{grad}_n u^*)\, df$$

where the integral on the right is to be extended over the surface of the space element considered and the subscript n signifies the normal to the surface outward. The following interpretation can be given to the above relation. According to Section 13, $uu^*\, dv$ is the probability that at time t the particle can be found within dv. The product uu^* can change with time only if there is a certain probability of the particle entering or leaving the element. From this it can be inferred that the vector

$$\mathbf{s} = \frac{\hbar i}{2m}(u^* \operatorname{grad} u - u \operatorname{grad} u^*) \tag{50}$$

must be the probability that the particle will in unit time pass through a unit surface normal to the direction of the vector. Equation (49) has the exact form of the equation of continuity in hydrodynamics,

$$\frac{\partial \rho}{\partial t} + \operatorname{div}(\rho \mathbf{v}) = 0$$

and with which it agrees also in sense, the only difference being that in wave mechanics $\rho = uu^*$ and $\rho \mathbf{v} = \mathbf{s}$ must not be interpreted as density and current but as probabilities.

The analogy of $\mathbf{s}$ with $\rho \mathbf{v}$ suggests the assumption that the vector

$$\frac{\mathbf{s}}{\rho} = \frac{\mathbf{s}}{uu^*} = \frac{\hbar i}{2m}\left(\frac{\operatorname{grad} u}{u} - \frac{\operatorname{grad} u^*}{u^*}\right) \tag{51}$$

represents the probable velocity with which the particle is moving at time t at the point xyz. It is true that this interpretation cannot be tested directly, because the uncertainty relations do not permit an experiment by which the velocity of a particle can be measured at a given point. The only thing we can measure is the velocity itself, a simultaneous measurement of position being impossible. However, we can arrive at a statement about the velocity by the following consideration.   Since the probability of the particle being in dv is uu^*, in which case it is moving with a velocity s/uu^*, the contribution of dv to the velocity is given in magnitude and direction by

$$\frac{suu^* \, dv}{uu^*} = s \, dv$$

Therefore

$$\int s \, dv = \frac{\hbar i}{2m} \int (u^* \operatorname{grad} u - u \operatorname{grad} u^*) \, dv \tag{52}$$

is the *expectation value of velocity* at time t.   This value has nothing to do with the position of the particle at time t and can be determined experimentally by taking a great number of atoms which are under identical conditions so that they are described by the same function u. We measure the velocity of the electron at time t for every atom and from these take the mean value.

If we multiply equation (52) by m, we get the expectation value of the momentum:

$$\bar{p} = \frac{\hbar i}{2} \int (u^* \operatorname{grad} u - u \operatorname{grad} u^*) \, dv \tag{53}$$

In what follows, expectation values are indicated by a bar over the quantity.

Equation (53) can be simplified by taking into account the fact that the integral

$$\int (u^* \operatorname{grad} u + u \operatorname{grad} u^*) \, dv = \int \operatorname{grad} (uu^*) \, dv$$

$$= \int uu^* \mathbf{n} \, df$$

where $\mathbf{n}$ is a unit vector in the direction of the outward drawn normal, tends towards zero for an infinitely remote surface since the probability uu^* vanishes there.   Then, upon multiplying the integral by $\hbar i/2$ and adding it to the equation for $\bar{p}$, we obtain

$$\bar{p} = \hbar i \int u^* \operatorname{grad} u \, dv \tag{54}$$

and therefore

$$\bar{p}_x = \hbar i \int u^* \frac{\partial u}{\partial x} \, dv \tag{55}$$

If a stationary state of definite energy is given, we have to substitute $\psi_i e^{(i/\hbar)E_i t}$ for u, and, from equation (53), we obtain

$$\bar{p}_x = \frac{\hbar i}{2} \int \left(\psi_i^* \frac{\partial \psi_i}{\partial x} - \psi_i \frac{\partial \psi_i^*}{\partial x} \right) dv$$

from which it follows that $\bar{p}_x$ vanishes when the wave equation (27) is solved by real eigenfunctions, since then $\psi_i = \psi_i{}^*$.

The expectation values of other observables can be evaluated in the same manner as that for **p**. For example, that for the coordinate x is given by

$$\bar{x} = \int uu^*x \, dv \tag{56}$$

or, in general, for an arbitrary function $f(xyz)$,

$$\overline{f(xyz)} = \int uu^*f(xyz) \, dv \tag{57}$$

Thus the expectation value of the potential is

$$\bar{V} = \bar{E}_{\text{pot}} = \int uu^*V(xyz) \, dv$$

and that for $\mathbf{K} = -\text{grad } V$ is given by

$$\bar{\mathbf{K}} = - \int uu^* \text{ grad } V \, dv$$

To evaluate $\bar{E}$, let us refer to the interpretation of the coefficients c_i in the expression $u = \sum c_i\psi_i e^{(i/\hbar)E_i t}$. According to Section 13, the product $c_ic_i{}^*$ gives the probability of the energy value E_i, so that $\bar{E} = \sum c_ic_i{}^*E_i$. This expression can be transformed. From the equation

$$\frac{\partial u}{\partial t} = \frac{i}{\hbar} \sum c_i\psi_i E_i e^{(i/\hbar)E_i t}$$

it follows that

$$\frac{\hbar}{i} u^* \frac{\partial u}{\partial t} = \sum c_i{}^*\psi_i{}^*e^{-(i/\hbar)E_i t} \sum_k c_k\psi_k E_k e^{(i/\hbar)E_k t}$$

Upon integrating this over the whole space and taking relations (45) into account, we obtain

$$\frac{\hbar}{i} \int u^* \frac{\partial u}{\partial t} \, dv = \sum c_ic_i{}^*E_i$$

so that we get

$$\bar{E} = \frac{\hbar}{i} \int u^* \frac{\partial u}{\partial t} \, dv$$

We now obtain for the expectation value of kinetic energy

$$\bar{E}_{kin} = \bar{E} - \bar{E}_{pot} = \int \left(\frac{\hbar}{i} u^* \frac{\partial u}{\partial t} - V u u^* \right) dv$$

and therefore, because of equation (46),

$$\bar{E}_{kin} = - \frac{\hbar^2}{2m} \int u^* \nabla^2 u \, dv \qquad (58)$$

from which it follows that, since $E_{kin} = (p_x^2 + p_y^2 + p_z^2)/2m$,

$$\overline{p_x^2} = - \hbar^2 \int u^* \frac{\partial^2 u}{\partial x^2} \, dv \qquad (58')$$

Finally let us determine the expectation value of the angular momentum, $\mathbf{d} = \mathbf{r} \times \mathbf{p}$. We have

$$\bar{\mathbf{d}} = \frac{\hbar i}{2} \int \mathbf{r} \times (u^* \, \text{grad} \, u - u \, \text{grad} \, u^*) \, dv$$

Transforming as for $\mathbf{p}$, we get

$$\bar{\mathbf{d}} = \hbar i \int (\mathbf{r} \times \text{grad} \, u) u^* \, dv \qquad (59)$$

Therefore

$$\bar{d}_x = \hbar i \int u^* \left(y \frac{\partial u}{\partial z} - z \frac{\partial u}{\partial y} \right) dv \qquad (59')$$

For the expectation value of $\mathbf{M} = \mathbf{r} \times \mathbf{K}$, we find

$$\bar{\mathbf{M}} = - \int u u^* \mathbf{r} \times \text{grad} \, V \, dv$$

As we shall see in Chapter 3, all expectation values are real automatically. We could show that the expectation values of the various entities are connected by the relations of classical mechanics $\overline{d\mathbf{p}}/dt = \bar{\mathbf{K}}$ and $\overline{d\mathbf{d}}/dt = \bar{\mathbf{M}}$. However, we shall derive these relations in a more general way in the next chapter.

16. The Principle of Transformation. In order to discover the meaning of ψ_i, in Section 13 we considered an assemblage of atoms, all in the ith stationary state. By measuring the position of the electron for every atom, we can determine the probability of any position xyz, and we assumed that this probability, as a function of xyz, could be expressed by $\psi_i \psi_i^*$. We may, however, choose, instead of xyz, the momentum of the particle and inquire about the probability that a measurement of $\mathbf{p}$ will furnish a vector with the components ξ, η, ζ. Wave mechanics maintains that this probability is given by the norm

$\chi_i(\xi\eta\zeta)\chi_i{}^*(\xi\eta\zeta)$ of a function $\chi_i(\xi\eta\zeta)$ which is connected to $\psi_i(xyz)$ by the relation

$$\chi_i(\xi\eta\zeta) = h^{-3/2} \int \psi_i(xyz)e^{(i/h)\,(x\xi+y\eta+z\zeta)}\,dv \qquad (60)$$

To prove this we show first that the integral of $\chi_i\chi_i{}^*$ over the whole momentum space has the value unity, as is necessary if $\chi_i\chi_i{}^*$ is to satisfy the stated interpretation. Letting $dp = d\xi\,d\eta\,d\zeta$, we write

$$\int_{-\infty}^{+\infty} \chi_i\chi_i{}^*\,dp$$
$$= h^{-3}\int_{-\infty}^{+\infty} dp \int \psi_i{}^*(xyz)\,dv \int \psi_i(x'y'z')e^{(i/h)[(x'-x)\xi+(y'-y)\eta+(z'-z)\zeta]}\,dv'$$
$$\qquad (61)$$

To evaluate the right-hand side, let us consider an expression of the form

$$\int_{-\infty}^{+\infty} f(x)\,dx \int_{-g}^{+g} e^{ix\xi/h}\,d\xi = h\int_{-\infty}^{+\infty} f(x)\,\frac{2\sin gx/h}{x}\,dx$$

When the limits $\pm g$ of the second integral tend to $\pm\infty$, $\sin gx/h$ becomes a rapidly oscillating function of x, permitting the integrand to be effective only in the immediate neighborhood of $x = 0$, whereas in any other interval dx the oscillation causes a zero result. Thus we have

$$\int_{-\infty}^{+\infty} f(x)\,dx \int_{-\infty}^{+\infty} e^{ix\xi/h}\,d\xi = 2hf(0)\int_{-\infty}^{+\infty} \frac{\sin x'}{x'}\,dx' = 2\pi hf(0)$$

This equation can be generalized to give

$$\int_{-\infty}^{+\infty} f(xyz)\,dv \int_{-\infty}^{+\infty} e^{(i/h)\,(x\xi+y\eta+z\zeta)}\,dp = 8\pi^3h^3f(000) = h^3f(000) \qquad (62)$$

Equation (61) can be transformed by making use of the above equation. First write (61) in the form

$$\int_{-\infty}^{+\infty} \chi_i\chi_i{}^*\,dp$$
$$= h^{-3}\int \psi_i{}^*(xyz)\,dv \int \psi_i(x'y'z')\,dv' \int_{-\infty}^{+\infty} e^{(i/h)[(x'-x)\xi+(y'-y)\eta+(z'-z)\zeta]}\,dp$$

In the dv' integral set $x'' = x' - x$, $y'' = y' - y$, $z'' = z' - z$. Then $\psi_i(x'y'z')$ changes to a function $\phi(x''y''z'')$. Thus

$$\int \psi_i(x'y'z')\,dv' \int_{-\infty}^{+\infty} e^{(i/h)[(x'-x)\xi+\cdots]}\,dp$$
$$= \int \phi(x''y''z'')\,dv'' \int_{-\infty}^{+\infty} e^{(i/h)\,(x''\xi+\cdots)}\,dp$$

But, according to equation (62), the last expression is $h^3\phi(000) =$

$h^3\psi_i(xyz)$, and so we find that

$$\int_{-\infty}^{+\infty} \chi_i\chi_i^* \, dp = \int \psi_i\psi_i^* \, dv$$

As the integral has the value unity, the theorem is proved.

The next step is to show that

$$\int_{-\infty}^{+\infty} \chi_i\chi_i^*\xi \, dp = \bar{\xi} = \bar{p}_x$$

which is necessary if $\chi_i\chi_i^*$ is to represent the momentum probability within dp. Now

$$\int \chi_i\chi_i^*\xi \, dp = h^{-3} \int dp \int \psi_i^*(xyz) \, dv \int \psi_i(x'y'z')\xi e^{(i/\hbar)[(x'-x)\xi+\cdots]} \, dv'$$

If we transform $\xi e^{(i/\hbar)[(x'-x)\xi+\cdots]}$ into $(\hbar/i)(\partial/\partial x')e^{(i/\hbar)[(x'-x)\xi+\cdots]}$, the integral relative to dv' becomes

$$\int \psi_i(x'y'z') \frac{\hbar}{i} \frac{\partial}{\partial x'} e^{(i/\hbar)(\cdots)} \, dv'$$
$$= \left[\frac{\hbar}{i} \psi_i(x'y'z')e^{(i/\hbar)(\cdots)} \right]_{-\infty}^{+\infty} - \frac{\hbar}{i} \int \frac{\partial\psi_i}{\partial x'} e^{(i/\hbar)(\cdots)} \, dv'$$

Let us suppose that ψ_i vanishes when x becomes very great. Then we have

$$\int_{-\infty}^{+\infty} \chi_i\chi_i^*\xi \, dp = -h^{-3} \int dp \int \psi_i^*(xyz) \, dv \frac{\hbar}{i} \int \frac{\partial\psi_i}{\partial x'} e^{(i/\hbar)(\cdots)} \, dv'$$
$$= -\frac{\hbar}{i} \int \psi_i^* \frac{\partial\psi_i}{\partial x} \, dv$$

which according to equation (55) is truly the expectation value $\bar{p}_x$.

Evidently equation (60) represents nothing but a Fourier expansion of the function $\chi_i(\xi\eta\zeta)$ and permits the inversion

$$\psi_i(xyz) = h^{-3/2} \int \chi_i(\xi\eta\zeta)e^{-(i/\hbar)(x\xi+y\eta+z\zeta)} \qquad (60')$$

Thus the same stationary state can be represented in q space by a function $\psi_i(xyz)$ as well as in p space by a function $\chi_i(\xi\eta\zeta)$, wherein ψ_i and χ_i are connected by relations (60) and (60'). This means that any state of undefined energy can be described either in q space by

$$u(xyzt) = \sum c_i\psi_i e^{(i/\hbar)E_i t} \qquad (63)$$

or in p space by

$$w(\xi\eta\zeta t) = \sum c_i\chi_i e^{(i/\hbar)E_i t} \qquad (63')$$

Thus we get two equivalent descriptions of the state which are related by the equations

$$u(xyzt) = h^{-\frac{3}{2}} \int w(\xi\eta\zeta t)e^{-(i/\hbar)(x\xi+y\eta+z\zeta)}\, dp \qquad (64)$$

$$w(\xi\eta\zeta t) = h^{-\frac{3}{2}} \int u(xyzt)e^{(i/\hbar)(x\xi+y\eta+z\zeta)}\, dv \qquad (64')$$

These equations furnish a good example of a principle which plays an important part in quantum mechanics. Let us consider an atom the momentary state of which in q space is described by a certain function $u(xyz)$, dispensing from consideration the time-dependence. We know the meaning of the function, for uu^* gives the probability that a measurement will locate the electron at xyz. In order to arrive at equation (64), which expresses the connection between u and the representation of the same state in p space, consider the operator $-(\hbar/i)(\partial/\partial x)$. If a function of x is subject to this operator, we get another function which we may call the image of the first. Generally the operator changes the character of the function completely. For example, x^2 is changed by $-(\hbar/i)(\partial/\partial x)$ into $-(2\hbar/i)x$. However, there exist certain functions $f(xyz)$ which are changed by the operator into a multiple of themselves, so that we can write

$$-\frac{\hbar}{i}\frac{\partial f}{\partial x} = \alpha f$$

where α denotes a constant parameter. The functions which satisfy the above equation are given by $f = \phi(yz)e^{(i/\hbar)\alpha x}$, α being an arbitrary function of y and z. These functions f are called eigenfunctions of the operator $-(\hbar/i)(\partial/\partial x)$. Every eigenfunction corresponds to a certain eigenvalue α. With the help of these concepts, we now can assign the following meaning to equations (64) and (64'). In order to determine the probability that a measurement of momentum will furnish a value $p_x = \xi$, we must express the function $u(xyz)$ in terms of the eigenfunctions belonging to the operator $-(\hbar/i)(\partial/\partial x)$, that is, in terms of the functions $e^{-(i/\hbar)\alpha x}$. When this is performed by the Fourier expansion,

$$u(xyz) = h^{-\frac{1}{2}} \int w'(yz\xi)e^{-(i/\hbar)x\xi}\, d\xi \qquad (65)$$

the coefficient $w'(yz\xi)$ of a definite $e^{-(i/\hbar)x\xi}$ is the probability amplitude for $p_x = \xi$, or ww^* is the probability that we shall find ξ for p_x.[†] It is

† Strictly speaking, the coefficient of $e^{-(i/\hbar)x\xi}$ in (65) is not w' but $w'h^{-\frac{1}{2}}$. The factor $h^{-\frac{1}{2}}$ is due to the failure of the normalization rule (45) in the case of a continuous spectrum. The rule must be replaced then by another. Cf. Section 30.

seen that the probability, through y and z, depends on the place where the measurement is carried out. This does not contradict the experimental possibilities since p_x, y, and z can be measured simultaneously with precision.

Now we take into consideration p_y as well as p_x and look for the probability of a measurement furnishing ξ and η for p_x and p_y respectively. We consider the function $u(xyz)$ in its dependence on y and expand it in terms of the eigenfunctions belonging to the operator $-(\hbar/i)(\partial/\partial y)$, that is, in terms of the functions $e^{-(i/\hbar)\alpha y}$. This means an expansion of the coefficient $w'(yz\xi)$ in equation (65) and leads to the equation

$$u(xyz) = h^{-1} \int \int w''(z\xi\eta)e^{-(i/\hbar)(x\xi+y\eta)} \, d\xi \, d\eta \qquad (65')$$

In this expansion the product of two eigenfunctions appears with the factor $w''(z\xi\eta)$, and this factor gives, by means of $w''w''^*$, the probability we seek. Finally a third expansion performed by using the eigenfunctions of the operator $-(\hbar/i)(\partial/\partial z)$ provides equation (64).

Thus, when a state of the atom is represented in q space by a function $u(xyz)$, we find the statistics of the momentum components by expressing u in terms of the eigenfunctions of the operator $-(\hbar/i)(\partial/\partial q)$ or, in other words, by resolving u into the spectrum defined by the eigenfunctions. We generalize this theorem by maintaining that any mechanical entity can be represented by an operator with eigenfunctions $f_0 f_1 \cdots$ and eigenvalues α_0, α_1, $\cdots$, which are related to the entity in such a way that (1) the eigenvalues α represent the possible values of the entity as found by measurement; (2) The expansion of u into $\sum c_i f_i$ furnishes a statistical ensemble of the α values by means of $c_i{}^2$. For example, consider the energy E. It can be seen readily that for a single particle, on which a force field $V(xyz)$ acts, the corresponding operator is given by

$$-\frac{\hbar^2}{2m} \nabla^2 + V(xyz) \qquad (66)$$

because the eigenfunctions of this operator satisfy the equation

$$\left[-\frac{\hbar^2}{2m} \nabla^2 + V(xyz) \right] f = \alpha f$$

This is the wave equation (27) which, as we have seen, can be solved only for a discrete set, $\alpha = E_0$, E_1, $\cdots$, by the functions ψ_0, ψ_1,

· · · · .   Therefore the α values are in truth the possible values furnished by a measurement, and the c_i terms of the expansion $u = \sum c_i \psi_i$, through $|c_i|^2$, determine the probabilities that the atom will assume one of the values E_i when a measurement of E is made.

Moreover, the theorem stated applies also when the state of the atom is represented in p space.   In this case, in order to arrive at equation (64′), we must correlate the operators $(\hbar/i)(\partial/\partial\xi)$, $(\hbar/i)(\partial/\partial\eta)$, $(\hbar/i)(\partial/\partial\zeta)$, together with the eigenfunctions $e^{(i/\hbar)\alpha\xi}$, $e^{(i/\hbar)\alpha\eta}$, $e^{(i/\hbar)\alpha\zeta}$, to the coordinates xyz.   This means that it is the expansion of $w(\xi\eta\zeta)$ in terms of the functions $e^{(i/\hbar)(x\xi+y\eta+z\zeta)}$ that provides the probability amplitudes for any position xyz.   Here the operator associated with the energy is given by

$$\frac{\xi^2 + \eta^2 + \zeta^2}{2m} + V\left(\frac{\hbar}{i}\frac{\partial}{\partial p}\right)$$

in which $V[(\hbar/i)(\partial/\partial p)]$ signifies the expression into which $V(xyz)$ is transformed by substituting $(\hbar/i)(\partial/\partial\xi)$, $(\hbar/i)(\partial/\partial\eta)$, $(\hbar/i)(\partial/\partial\zeta)$ for x, y, z, respectively.   The eigenfunctions of this operator are the functions $\chi_i(\xi\eta\zeta)$ defined by equation (60).

Thus, when we adopt a certain representation of the state, any observable of the system can be correlated to an operator. *This fact enables us to infer from the given statistics of certain observables the statistics of any other observable.*   More exactly, when the state is described by the probability function $u(xyz)$, it is determined statistically by this function with reference to all observables.   Expanding $u(xyz)$ in terms of certain eigenfunctions, we can anticipate the statistical results of measurements dealing with, for example, energy or momentum.   To the energy we must coordinate the operator (66) so that u is expanded into $u = \sum c_i \psi_i$.   When this equation is multiplied by $\psi_k^* \, dv$ and integrated over the whole space, we get, by virtue of equation (45), $c_k = \int u\psi_k^* \, dv$.   In this way we can evaluate from $u(xyz)$ the probability amplitudes of the energy.   On the other hand, the operator of a momentum component is $-(\hbar/i)(\partial/\partial q)$.   Accordingly in the case of momentum it is the expansion (64) that informs us about the probability amplitudes defined by equation (64′) as

$$w(\xi\eta\zeta) = \int u e^{(i/\hbar)(x\xi+y\eta+z\zeta)} \, dv$$

When, however, the state is described in terms of momentum statistics, that is, when the function $w(\xi\eta\zeta)$ is given, the operators belonging to energy and coordinates are

$$\frac{\xi^2 + \eta^2 + \zeta^2}{2m} + V\left(\frac{\hbar}{i}\frac{\partial}{\partial p}\right) \quad \text{and} \quad \frac{\hbar}{i}\frac{\partial}{\partial p}$$

and the corresponding amplitudes c_i and u can be evaluated by means of the equations

$$c_k = \int w\chi_k^* \, dp \quad \text{and} \quad u = \int we^{-(i/\hbar)(x\xi+y\eta+z\zeta)} \, dp$$

Finally let us consider the case in which the state is defined by the probability amplitudes c_i of the energy, that is, the description refers to the E space. Here the determination of the operators belonging to coordinates and momentum is not so easy. They are no longer differential operators since these could not be applied to something defined by a discrete set of numbers, c_0, c_1, $\cdots$, but are given by matrices with which we shall deal in the next chapter.

Thus quantum mechanics establishes certain transformation equations by which the statistical statements that can be made for a system in a given state are interrelated. However, in order to arrive at a valid mechanics, we must complete the plan by means of a law according to which the state of an unperturbed system changes with time—a law that can be formulated to agree with the time-dependence required by equations (47) and (63). This law can be stated as follows: *The probability amplitudes $c_i(t)$ of the energy of an unperturbed system, as far as time-dependence is concerned, are given by $c_i(t) = c_i e^{(i/\hbar)E_i t}$, where c_i represent the amplitudes for $t = 0$.* According to this law the probability $c_i(t)c_i^*(t)$ of finding the system in a certain energy state does not change in time, since $c_i(t)c_i^*(t) = c_i c_i^*$. Thus, if the system is in a definite stationary energy state E_k at $t = 0$ (that is, if $c_k = 1$, all other c_i being zero), it remains in this state as long as no disturbing forces act on the atom. This implies that in quantum mechanics there are also observables which, by their initial values, are uniquely determined for all the future. If we can infer from a measurement that at $t = 0$ the energy of the system is E_k, we may be sure that a measurement at any future time will furnish the same value.

The manner in which the probabilities uu^* and ww^* are affected by the time-dependence of c_i has been discussed in Section 13.

The transformation equations are not quite new to us. We used them unintentionally in Chapter 1 when we represented the amplitudes $u(xyzt)$ of a free particle by

$$u(xyzt) = \int a(\xi\eta\zeta)e^{(i/\hbar)Et}e^{-(i/\hbar)(x\xi+y\eta+z\zeta)} \, dp \qquad (12)$$

This expansion arose from the idea of correlating a wave packet with a particle so that we might be able to predict the probable results of future measurements. Now we can see that equation (12) can be looked upon as the connection that exists between the functions $u(xyzt)$ and $w(\xi\eta\zeta t)$ according to the transformation theory. For a particle on which no force is acting, $w(\xi\eta\zeta t)$ signifies the probability amplitude of a certain energy E, since here E depends only on ξ, η, ζ as given by $E = (\xi^2 + \eta^2 + \zeta^2)/2m$. Therefore $w(\xi\eta\zeta t)$ plays the part of $c_i(t)$ and depends on time by the factor $e^{(i/\hbar)Et}$. Thus the expansion coefficients $a(\xi\eta\zeta)$ in equation (12), which originally were considered amplitudes of de Broglie waves, now appear to have the significance of a statistical ensemble referring to the momentum components.

Let us make it clear also that equation (29) of Section 9

$$u(xyzt) = \int\int\int \gamma e^{i\delta}a(xyzE\alpha\beta)e^{(i/\hbar)[Et-S(xyzE\alpha\beta)]}\, dE\, d\alpha\, d\beta$$

which corresponds to the motion of a particle in a field of force, is in agreement with the transformation theory. The function u is here expanded in terms of the eigenfunctions ψ_i, that is, $u = \sum c_i \psi_i e^{(i/\hbar)E_i t}$. In the place of c_i in equation (29) we set $\gamma e^{i\delta}\, dE\, d\alpha\, d\beta$. The factor $\gamma e^{i\delta}$ is the one mentioned in Section 9; it remains arbitrary in the determination of ψ_i. The summation sign is replaced by an integral sign because Schroedinger's equation, within the approximations of geometric optics, is solved by a continuous sequence of functions. Accordingly ψ_i is replaced by the functions $a(xyzE\alpha\beta)e^{-(i/\hbar)S(xyzE\alpha\beta)}$ by means of which the wave equation can be integrated within the considered approximation; therefore they are to be used as eigenfunctions.

Finally let us consider the expectation values of Section 15. The formulas that have been evaluated there are, as can be easily seen, consistent with the following rule:

When a state is described by a function $u(xyz)$, the expectation value of any observable is found by multiplying u^* with the function into which u is changed by the operator belonging to the observable and then integrating this product over the whole configuration space.

This rule can be used inversely for determining the operator from the formula for expectation value. For example, for the expectation value p_x^2 we obtained the expression $\int u^*(\hbar/i)^2(\partial^2 u/\partial x^2)$ from which it follows that the operator of p_x^2 must be $(\hbar/i)^2(\partial^2/\partial x^2)$, that is, it is the reapplication of the operator $-(\hbar/i)(\partial/\partial x)$. The operator associated with the x component of the angular momentum is, according to equation (59'), given by $-(\hbar/i)[y(\partial/\partial z) - z(\partial/\partial y)]$. If repeated n times, this operator represents $d_x{}^n$. Moreover it follows from $\bar{x} = \int uu^*x \, dv$ that the operator belonging to the x coordinate consists in the *multiplication by* x.

The rule connecting expectation value and operator can be applied easily to a state described by the function $w(\xi\eta\zeta)$. Here we must multiply w by the function into which w is transformed by the operator and then integrate over the p space. Then we must correlate the coordinate x with the operator $(\hbar/i)(\partial/\partial\xi)$, whereas ξ is represented by multiplication by ξ. Accordingly we have

$$\bar{p}_x = \int ww^* \, \xi \, dp \qquad \bar{x} = \frac{\hbar}{i} \int w^* \frac{\partial w}{\partial \xi} \, dp \qquad (67)$$

17. The Linear Oscillator. At this point we wish to apply the methods of quantum mechanics to some examples. We shall consider first a simple linear oscillator, hence a system with but one degree of freedom. Let a particle of mass m move in the x direction subject to a force $V = ax^2/2$ centered at the origin of coordinates. The wave equation is given by

$$-\frac{\hbar^2}{2m} \nabla^2\psi + \frac{ax^2}{2} \psi = E\psi$$

or

$$\frac{\partial^2\psi}{\partial x^2} + \left(E - \frac{ax^2}{2}\right)\frac{2m}{\hbar^2}\psi = 0$$

On dividing through by $\sqrt{ma^2/\hbar^2}$ and introducing a new variable $x' = x\sqrt[4]{ma/\hbar^2}$, we obtain

$$\frac{\partial^2\psi}{\partial x'^2} + \left(E\sqrt{\frac{4m}{\hbar^2 a}} - x'^2\right)\psi = 0 \qquad (68)$$

It was shown in Section 11 that only for certain values, $E_0, E_1, \cdots$, of the parameter do regular solutions, $\psi_0, \psi_1, \cdots$, of equation (68) exist. It can be proved that these eigenvalues E_i are given by

$$E_i = \sqrt{\frac{\hbar^2 a}{4m}} \, (2i + 1) \qquad (69)$$

and correspond to the eigenfunctions

$$\psi_i = \alpha_i e^{-x'^2/2} H_i(x') \qquad (70)$$

the constants α_i being arbitrary and H_i representing certain polynomials, called Hermitean, which can be defined by

$$H_i(x') = (-1)^i e^{x'^2} \frac{d^i e^{-x'^2}}{dx'^i} \tag{71}$$

From this we see that

$$H_0 = 1$$

$$H_1 = -e^{x'^2} \frac{de^{-x'^2}}{dx'} = 2x'$$

$$H_2 = e^{x'^2} \frac{d^2 e^{-x'^2}}{dx'^2} = 4x'^2 - 2 \qquad \text{etc.}$$

Generally H_i is a polynomial of the ith order, beginning with $(2x')^i$:

$$H_i = (2x')^i - \frac{i(i-1)}{1!} (2x')^{i-2} + \frac{i(i-1)(i-2)(i-3)}{2!} (2x')^{i-4} \cdots$$

The proof that equation (68) is solved by (70) follows. From (71), for H_{i+1} we have

$$H_{i+1} = (-1)^{i+1} e^{x'^2} \frac{d}{dx'} \frac{d^i e^{-x'^2}}{dx'^i}$$

$$= -e^{x'^2} \frac{d}{dx'} (e^{-x'^2} H_i) = -\frac{dH_i}{dx'} + 2x' H_i \tag{72}$$

On the other hand, H_{i+1} can be written

$$H_{i+1} = (-1)^{i+1} e^{x'^2} \frac{d^i}{dx'^i} \frac{de^{-x'^2}}{dx'} = (-1)^i 2 e^{x'^2} \frac{d^i}{dx'^i} (x' e^{-x'^2}) \tag{73}$$

Now the ith derivative $(d^i/dx'^i)(x' e^{-x'^2})$ can be transformed step by step in the following way:

$$\frac{d^i}{dx'^i} (x' e^{-x'^2}) = \frac{d^{i-1}}{dx'^{i-1}} \left(e^{-x'^2} + x' \frac{de^{-x'^2}}{dx'} \right)$$

$$\frac{d^{i-1}}{dx'^{i-1}} \left(x' \frac{de^{-x'^2}}{dx'} \right) = \frac{d^{i-2}}{dx'^{i-2}} \left(\frac{de^{-x'^2}}{dx'} + x' \frac{d^2 e^{-x'^2}}{dx'^2} \right) \tag{74}$$

. . . .

By continuing this procedure i times and summing up all equations we get

$$\frac{d^i}{dx'^i} (x' e^{-x'^2}) = i \frac{d^{i-1} e^{-x'^2}}{dx'^{i-1}} + x' \frac{d^i e^{-x'^2}}{dx'^i}$$

When we introduce this expression into (73) we obtain

$$H_{i+1} = (-1)^i 2 e^{x'^2}\left(i\,\frac{d^{i-1}e^{-x'^2}}{dx'^{i-1}} + x'\,\frac{d^i e^{-x'^2}}{dx'^i} \right) = -2iH_{i-1} + 2x'H_i$$

From (72) and (74) it follows that

$$2iH_{i-1} = \frac{dH_i}{dx'} \qquad\qquad (75)$$

On differentiating (72) relative to x' and substituting $2(i+1)H_i$ for dH_{i+1}/dx' according to (75), we have

$$2(i+1)H_i = -\frac{d^2H_i}{dx'^2} + 2x'\,\frac{dH_i}{dx'} + 2H_i$$

or, since $H_i = (1/\alpha_i)\psi_i e^{x'^2/2}$,

$$2(i+1)\psi_i e^{x'^2/2} = -\left(\frac{d^2\psi_i}{dx'^2} + 2x'\,\frac{d\psi_i}{dx'} + x'^2\psi_i + \psi_i \right) e^{x'^2/2}$$

$$+ 2x'\left(\frac{d\psi_i}{dx'} + x'\psi_i \right) e^{x'^2/2} + 2\psi_i e^{x'^2/2}$$

Finally we obtain the equation

$$\frac{d^2\psi_i}{dx'^2} + (2i+1-x^2)\psi_i = 0$$

from which it is seen that (70) is truly a solution of (68) and that the corresponding eigenvalues are given by $E_i = (\hbar/2)\sqrt{a/m}\,(2i+1)$.

The solutions $e^{-x'^2/2}H_i$ of (68) form a system of orthogonal functions, that is, they satisfy the condition $\int e^{-x'^2}\,dx'H_iH_k = 0$ for $i \neq k$. This follows immediately from the orthogonality of the eigenfunctions, as proved in Section 13. In order to fulfill the normalization condition as well, the α_i terms are chosen in such a way that, for any i,

$$\int \psi_i^2\,dx' = \alpha_i^2 \int e^{-x'^2}H_i x'^2\,dx'$$

$$= \alpha_i^2\,\sqrt[4]{\frac{\hbar^2}{ma}} \int H_i(-1)^i\,\frac{d^i e^{-x'^2}}{dx'^i}\,dx' = 1$$

We can transform the integral by integrating by parts n times. This gives

$$\int e^{-x'^2}\,\frac{d^i}{dx'^i}\,H_i\,dx' = 2^i i! \int e^{-x'^2}\,dx' = 2^i i!\,\sqrt{\pi}$$

The solutions are normalized if for the α_i terms we choose the values

$$\alpha_i = \frac{1}{\sqrt{2^i i! \pi^{\frac{1}{2}}}} \sqrt[8]{\frac{ma}{h^2}}$$

We are especially interested in the energies E_i, which, according to (69), are given by

$$E_i = \frac{2i + 1}{2} h \sqrt{\frac{a}{m}}$$

As $\sqrt{a/m}/2\pi$ is identical with the classical characteristic frequency ν_0 of the oscillator, we may write $E_i = (2i + 1)(h\nu_0/2)$. It is remarkable that wave mechanics furnishes odd multiples of $h\nu_0/2$ for the energy levels of the oscillator, whereas, according to the original quantum theory E should be even multiples of $h\nu_0/2$. This difference is irrelevant for the evaluation of the spectra, since the frequencies of the lines depend only on the differences of the energy levels. It indicates, however, that the oscillator should have a zero-point energy of $h\nu_0/2$ in its lowest state. Indeed, there is some evidence that such a zero-point energy exists. The important point, however, is that the theory provides the correct distances of the energy levels and is able to achieve this without the help of any supplementary assumptions. In wave mechanics the selection of a discrete sequence of states is an effect of the regularity conditions imposed on the solutions of the wave equation. Thus the selection occurs just as naturally as in the case of a string which, because of boundary conditions, is capable of vibrations with an integral number of nodes only. In short, we do not have to resort to unintelligible postulates to attain the quantum states since the quantum conditions already are implied in the plan of the new mechanics.

According to equation (70), the eigenfunctions are given by $\psi_i = \alpha_i e^{-x'^2/2} H_i(x')$. If now we substitute for x' the value of x given in the equation

$$x' = x \sqrt[4]{\frac{4\pi^2 ma}{h^2}} = 2\pi x \sqrt[4]{\frac{am^2}{4\pi^2 h^2 m}} = 2\pi x \sqrt{\frac{m\nu_0}{h}}$$

we obtain

$$\psi_i = \alpha_i e^{-(2\pi^2 m\nu_0 x^2/h)} H_i\left(2\pi \sqrt{\frac{m\nu_0}{h}} x\right)$$

The first five eigenfunctions are plotted in Fig. 2. It will be observed that outside the considered domain, from $x = -3$ to $x = +3$, the functions tend asymptotically to zero very rapidly. It should be noticed that every eigenfunction shows several nodal points the number of which is the same as the i number of the eigenfunction. This follows at once from the fact that the polynomials are of the ith degree. Consequently, when the oscillator is in the ith stationary state, there are i places in which the electron is never found.

The functions ψ_i are partly negative, and, although this fact does not affect the probabilities $\psi_i\psi_i{}^*$, it is important for states represented by $u = \sum c_i\psi_i e^{(i/\hbar)E_i t}$.

The distinction between the description of the oscillation according to wave mechanics and that according to classical mechanics should be understood clearly. A stationary state no longer has the character of motion in the sense of kinematics. We can only specify the proba-

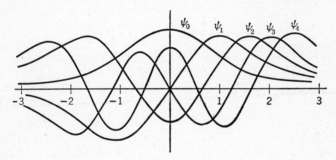

FIG. 2.

bility that a particle will be found at any point on the x axis when a measurement of position is made. However, a broad indication of the classical oscillation is present, because, according to classical mechanics, for every ψ_i there is a definite relation between the position of the maximum and the amplitude of the oscillation. For example, the maximum of ψ_1 lies at $x' = 1, 1$, and therefore $x = 1, 1\sqrt{h/4\pi^2 m\nu_0}$. In classical mechanics, however, the amplitude A, which is associated with the energy $3h\nu_0/2$, is assigned a value $aA^2/2 = 3h\nu_0/2$ and therefore $A = \sqrt{3}\sqrt{h/4\pi^2 m\nu_0}$. In general, it turns out that every eigenfunction gives a probability that differs from zero only within a domain that approximately covers the range of the classical oscillations.

Thus the stationary states of the oscillator contain only a few basic properties that may be taken as left-overs from the old pendulum oscillation. Nevertheless, according to Section 14, transition to this conception must be accomplished by considering states that unite a complex of eigenvibrations of high order, namely, those vibrations in which the terms of $\sum c_i\psi_i e^{(i/\hbar)E_i t}$ are associated with large values of i.

It must be possible to superpose the vibrations so that uu^* differs from zero only within a small domain. As we know, such a packet holds together for some time, moving through space like a point mass of classical mechanics. Schroedinger at one time worked this out in detail by a calculation which provides a good illustration of the transition from micro to macro mechanics.

18. The Hydrogen Atom. The theorem is subjected to its most important test in the application to the H atom. It is known that the energy terms of this atom could be determined correctly by the old quantum theory. The question here is whether wave mechanics leads to the same results. So that the cases of He^{++} and Li^{+++} may be included, let us assume that the charge on the nucleus is Ze. Disregarding the motion of the nucleus, we get for the wave equation

$$\frac{\hbar^2}{2m} \nabla^2 \psi + \left(E + \frac{Ze^2}{r} \right) \psi = 0 \tag{76}$$

On changing from rectangular to spherical coordinates wherein

$$x = r \sin \theta \cos \phi \qquad y = r \sin \theta \sin \phi \qquad z = r \cos \theta \tag{77}$$

we obtain

$$\frac{1}{r^2} \frac{\partial}{\partial r} \left(r^2 \frac{\partial \psi}{\partial r} \right) + \frac{1}{r^2 \sin \theta} \frac{\partial}{\partial \theta} \left(\sin \theta \frac{\partial \psi}{\partial \theta} \right) + \frac{1}{r^2 \sin^2 \theta} \frac{\partial^2 \psi}{\partial \phi^2}$$
$$+ \frac{2m}{\hbar^2} \left(E + \frac{Ze^2}{r} \right) \psi = 0 \tag{78}$$

To solve this equation we consider ψ the product of a function $R(r)$ and $Y(\theta\phi)$. Then equation (78) becomes

$$Y \frac{\partial}{\partial r} \left(r^2 \frac{\partial R}{\partial r} \right) + \frac{R}{\sin \theta} \frac{\partial}{\partial \theta} \left(\sin \theta \frac{\partial Y}{\partial \theta} \right) + \frac{R}{\sin^2 \theta} \frac{\partial^2 Y}{\partial \phi^2}$$
$$+ \frac{2m}{\hbar^2} (Er^2 + Ze^2 r) RY = 0$$

When this equation is divided by RY, the left-hand side consists of two parts one of which depends only on r and the other on θ and ϕ. The sum of these parts can be zero only if each part has a constant value. If we denote this constant by k, we have

$$\frac{\partial}{\partial r} \left(r^2 \frac{\partial R}{\partial r} \right) + \frac{2m}{\hbar^2} (Er^2 + Ze^2 r) R = kR \tag{79}$$

$$\frac{1}{\sin \theta} \frac{\partial}{\partial \theta} \left(\sin \theta \frac{\partial Y}{\partial \theta} \right) + \frac{1}{\sin^2 \theta} \frac{\partial^2 Y}{\partial \phi^2} = -kY \tag{80}$$

Each of the above equations is of the type that can be solved by regular functions for certain values of k only. Let us consider first the second of the two equations and show that its solutions are given by spherical harmonics. These functions can be defined in the following way: Assume that u is a homogeneous polynomial of the lth order in xyz which satisfies the equation $\nabla^2 u = 0$. When we replace the rectangular by spherical coordinates, u transforms into $r^l Y_l(\theta\phi)$, where Y_l is a function that depends only on θ and ϕ and therefore represents a function on the surface of a sphere of radius unity. These functions are called spherical harmonics of the lth order. When we set $u = r^l Y_l$, the equation $\nabla^2 u = 0$ becomes

$$Y_l l(l + 1) + \frac{1}{\sin\theta}\frac{\partial}{\partial\theta}\left(\sin\theta\frac{\partial Y_l}{\partial\theta}\right) + \frac{1}{\sin^2\theta}\frac{\partial^2 Y_l}{\partial\phi^2} = 0 \qquad (81)$$

as should be obvious if in $(78)r^l Y_l$ replaces ψ and the terms not due to the operator ∇^2 are eliminated. A comparison of (81) with (80) shows that (80) can be solved by the functions Y_l if for k we substitute the values $l(l + 1)$, where $l = 0, 1, 2, \cdots$. This means that we have determined the eigenvalues and eigenfunctions of (80). No stress is placed here on the proof that other solutions do not exist.

However, it is important to prove that there exist $2l + 1$ different harmonics of the lth order which are linearly independent. Linear independence means that, for a system of functions $f_1, f_2, \cdots$, the equation $c_1 f_1 + c_2 f_2 + \cdots = 0$ can be fulfilled only if $c_1 = c_2 = c_3 = \cdots = 0$. To prove the theorem recall the equation $\nabla^2 u = 0$ by which we have defined the functions Y_l. Let us take those of its solutions which are homogeneous in xyz and of the lth degree. In order to determine the solutions which, divided by r^l, will yield Y_l, it is convenient to introduce new variables ξ, η, ζ for xyz, defined by

$$\xi = x + iy \qquad \eta = x - iy \qquad \zeta = z \qquad (82)$$

so that

$$\frac{\partial}{\partial x} = \frac{\partial}{\partial\xi} + \frac{\partial}{\partial\eta} \qquad \frac{\partial^2}{\partial x^2} = \frac{\partial^2}{\partial\xi^2} + 2\frac{\partial^2}{\partial\xi\,\partial\eta} + \frac{\partial^2}{\partial\eta^2}$$

$$\frac{\partial}{\partial y} = i\frac{\partial}{\partial\xi} - i\frac{\partial}{\partial\eta} \qquad \frac{\partial^2}{\partial y^2} = -\frac{\partial^2}{\partial\xi^2} + 2\frac{\partial^2}{\partial\xi\,\partial\eta} - \frac{\partial^2}{\partial\eta^2}$$

and thus $\nabla^2 u$ can be transformed into

$$4\frac{\partial^2 u}{\partial\xi\,\partial\eta} + \frac{\partial^2 u}{\partial z^2} = 0 \qquad (83)$$

This equation can be solved if for u we choose the special form of the homogeneous polynomial of the lth order defined by

$$u = \xi^m z^n (1 + a_1 \xi \eta z^{-2} + a_2 \xi^2 \eta^2 z^{-4} + \cdots) \qquad (84)$$

In this equation the exponent of ξ exceeds that of η by m, where m is an arbitrary whole number between 0 and l. When we introduce (84) into (83) we obtain

$$4a_1(m + 1)\xi^m z^{n-2} + 4a_2(m + 2)2\xi^{m+1}\eta z^{n-4} + \cdots$$
$$+ n(n - 1)\xi^m z^{n-2} + a_1(n - 2)(n - 3)\xi^{m+1}\eta z^{n-4} + \cdots = 0$$

wherein again the exponents of ξ and η in the terms containing these differ by m, every term occurring twice. If, then, in order to satisfy the equation we set the factor of every product $\xi^i \eta^k z^l$ equal to zero, we obtain a recurrence formula by means of which the coefficients are determined uniquely. In this way we see that for the equation $\nabla^2 u = 0$ there exist $l + 1$ different homogeneous solutions which are linearly dependent and of such kind that in every term the exponent of ξ exceeds that of η by a whole number $m \geq 0$.

On the other hand, (83) can be solved as well by polynomials of the form

$$\eta^m z^n (1 + a_1 \xi \eta z^{-2} + a_2 \xi^2 \eta^2 z^{-4} + \cdots) \qquad (85)$$

wherein m is again a positive whole number $\leq l$ but zero is omitted this time because the corresponding solution has been considered already. Thus it is true, as we have maintained, that there are $2l + 1$ linearly independent solutions of the lth degree in $\xi \eta z$, and hence in xyz also. When divided by r^l they transform into as many spherical harmonics Y_l^m, the index m signifying the difference between the exponents of ξ and η; it can be any number in the sequence $-l, -l + 1, \cdots, 0, \cdots, l - 1, l$.

Reverting to spherical coordinates by means of the relations

$$\xi = x + iy = re^{i\phi} \sin \theta \qquad \eta = x - iy = re^{-i\phi} \sin \theta \qquad z = r \cos \theta$$

then according to (84) for values of $m \geq 0$ we obtain

$$Y_l^m = e^{im\phi} \sin^m \theta \cos^n \theta (1 + a_1 \sin^2 \theta \cos^{-2} \theta + \cdots) \qquad (86)$$

and for values of $m < 0$, according to (85), we get

$$Y_l^m = e^{im\phi} \sin^{-m} \theta \cos^n \theta (1 + a_1 \sin^2 \theta \cos^{-2} \theta + \cdots) \qquad (86')$$

The factors of $e^{im\phi} \sin^m \theta$ and $e^{im\phi} \sin^{-m} \theta$ sometimes are called the correlated spherical harmonics and may be designated by P_l^m.

Two spherical harmonics, Y_l and Y_k, of different orders are orthogonal. This means that the integral of $Y_l Y_k^*$ over the surface of a unit sphere vanishes. To prove this we apply Green's theorem

$$\int (u\nabla^2 v - v\nabla^2 u)\, dv = \int \left(u\frac{\partial v}{\partial n} - v\frac{\partial u}{\partial n} \right) df$$

to the unit sphere, wherein u and v represent the functions $Y_l r^l$ and $Y_k^* r^k$ respectively. The left-hand side vanishes because $Y_l r^l$ and $Y_k^* r^k$ are solutions of the equation $\nabla^2 u = 0$, but the right-hand side yields $\int Y_l Y_k^*(k - l)r^{k+l-1}\, df$. Thus $\int Y_l Y_k^*\, df = 0$ for $l \neq k$. The orthogonality also holds for two different harmonics Y_l^m and $Y_l^{m'}$ of the same order, since

$$\int Y_l^m Y_l^{m'*}\, df = \int_0^{2\pi} e^{i\phi(m-m')}\, d\phi \int d\theta \cdots = 0 \qquad \text{(for } m \neq m')$$

After this digression we return to the wave mechanics equations, (79) and (80), of the H atom. As we have seen, the second equation can be solved only if $k = l(l + 1)$ where $l = 0, 1, 2, \cdots$, and for every one of the eigenvalues we obtain not one but several eigenfunctions Y as defined by $Y_l^m (m = -l \cdots + l)$. Thus one part Y of $u = RY$ may be considered determined. The other part must be found by making use of equation (79) which, when $k = l(l + 1)$, becomes

$$\frac{1}{r^2}\frac{d}{dr}\left(r^2 \frac{dR}{dr} \right) + \frac{2m}{\hbar^2}\left[E + \frac{Ze^2}{r} - \frac{l(l+1)\hbar^2}{2mr^2} \right] R = 0 \qquad (87)$$

When we set

$$\frac{2m}{\hbar^2} E = A \qquad \frac{2m}{\hbar^2} Ze^2 = B \qquad l(l + 1) = C$$

and perform the operation

$$\frac{d}{dr}\left(r^2 \frac{dR}{dr} \right) = 2r\frac{dR}{dr} + r^2 \frac{d^2R}{dr^2} = r\frac{d^2}{dr^2}(rR)$$

(87) takes the form

$$\frac{d^2}{dr^2}(rR) + \left(A + \frac{B}{r} - \frac{C}{r^2} \right) rR = 0 \qquad (88)$$

When we introduce a new variable v by setting $rR = ve^{-\alpha r}$, the equation becomes

$$\frac{d^2 v}{dr^2} - 2\alpha \frac{dv}{dr} + \left(A + \alpha^2 + \frac{B}{r} - \frac{C}{r^2} \right) v = 0 \qquad (89)$$

If we choose $\alpha = \sqrt{-A}$, with the assumption that in the following E is negative so that α is real, then $A + \alpha^2$ in equation (89) vanishes. It can be shown that a differential equation of the form (89) can be solved for certain values by the polynomial

$$v = r^\gamma \sum_0^n a_i r^i \tag{90}$$

n being a finite number.   To determine γ and a_i we introduce (90) into (89) and obtain

$$\Sigma a_i(\gamma + i)(\gamma + i - 1)r^{\gamma+i-2} - 2\alpha\Sigma a_i(\gamma + i)r^{\gamma+i-1}$$
$$+ \Sigma a_i(Br^{\gamma+i-1} - Cr^{\gamma+i-2}) = 0$$

In order to satisfy this equation the factor of every power of r must be set equal to zero.   As the lowest power is $\gamma - 2$, the associated factor being $a_0\gamma(\gamma - 1) - Ca_0$ and as $C = l(l + 1)$, we obtain $\gamma = l + 1$ or $\gamma = -l$.   The second value is to be excluded because it would correspond to a function v that is not regular at the point $r = 0$.   By setting the other factors equal to zero we arrive at a recurrence formula for a_i wherein the first coefficient a_0 remains arbitrary.   In order to have the series a finite one the a_i terms must vanish from a certain $i = n$ upwards, that is, $a_{n+1} = a_{n+2} = \cdots = 0$.   To achieve this we determine the coefficient of $r^{\gamma+n-1}$ for which we have

$$a_{n+1}(\gamma + n + 1)(\gamma + n) - 2\alpha a_n(\gamma + n) + a_nB - a_{n+1}C$$

And, as a_{n+1} is to be zero, it is necessary that $2\alpha(\gamma + n) = B$.   Hence

$$\alpha = \sqrt{-A} = \frac{B}{2(l + 1 + n)} = \frac{mZe^2}{\hbar^2(n + l + 1)}$$

And, since $A = (2m/\hbar^2)E$,

$$E = - \frac{mZ^2e^4}{\hbar^2 2(n + l + 1)^2} \tag{91}$$

Thus, on the assumption of a negative E, the wave equation for R can be solved by a regular function only for those values of E that are identical with the terms of Balmer.   We do not consider here the proof that for $E < 0$ other solutions do not exist.

It is important to realize, however, that the preceding method has a meaning only for a negative E, because with a positive E the polynomial cannot be limited to a finite number of terms.   Then α becomes imaginary, so that the equality $2\alpha(n + \gamma) = B$ no longer applies because B by definition is real.   And so, when the energy is positive, the solution of (89) does not depend on certain values of E, there being a solution for any E. Thus the spectrum is no longer discrete but becomes continuous.

We shall, however, confine ourselves to the more important case of the discontinuous spectrum. Here the eigenfunctions and eigenvalues of the wave equation are given by

$$\psi = R_{nl}Y_l{}^m \qquad E_{nl} = -\frac{me^4Z^2}{2\hbar^2(n+l+1)^2} \qquad (92)$$

R_{nl} being defined by

$$R_{nl} = \frac{1}{r}\,e^{-\frac{mZe^2}{\hbar^2(n+l+1)}r}\,v_{nl} \qquad (93)$$

where v_{nl} designates the polynomials $\sum_0^n a_i r^{\gamma+i}$. We see that for the H atom a single number no longer suffices to characterize a given stationary state. We need three numbers, n, l, m. The energy of the atom depends only on the sum of n and l, being independent of m. And so there exist different stationary states of the same energy, a peculiarity which is called degeneracy. Every energy level possesses a certain degree of degeneracy, the degree being defined by the number of the states that belong to the level diminished by 1. For the level $n+l+1 = n'$, the degree of degeneracy is $n'^2 - 1$, since for l all whole numbers between 0 and $n'-1$ are admissible and for every one of these l's the number m can assume $2l+1$ different values. Accordingly the number of different states is $1+3+\cdots(2n'-1) = n'^2$, all of which have the same energy, $-mZ^2e^4/[2\hbar^2(n+l+1)^2]$. This means that the level with the principal quantum number n' is degenerated $n'^2 - 1$ times.

This concept of degeneration had been known in the old quantum theory. That theory was able to give to this concept a figurative interpretation, because in it the different states of the same energy could be distinguished by the elements of the rotational motion such as the eccentricity of the ellipses or the inclination of the orbit plane to the z axis. Wave mechanics cannot adopt this interpretation because the notion of a rotational motion no longer has a meaning. Therefore another criterion is required which will permit a distinction between states of the same energy and which can be found in the *expectation value of the angular momentum*.

By applying the principles of the transformation theory let us examine how a state described in q space by $\psi = R_{nl}Y_l{}^m$ and therefore specified by three integers n, l, m is to be specified relative to the z component of the angular momentum. According to Section 16, the operator of this component is $-(\hbar/i)[x(\partial/\partial y) - y(\partial/\partial x)]$, the meaning being that, if f_1, f_2, $\cdots$ are the eigenfunctions of the operator, that is, solutions of the equation

$$-\frac{\hbar}{i}\left(x\frac{\partial f}{\partial y} - y\frac{\partial f}{\partial x}\right) = \alpha f$$

and $\alpha_1\alpha_2 \cdots$ are the corresponding eigenvalues, a measurement of the component can furnish a value α_i only and we can obtain the probability of a certain α_i by expanding ψ in terms of f_i. The coefficient of the ith eigenfunction in that expansion is the amplitude for the result $d_z = \alpha_i$.

The equation for the f functions can be transformed by using the coordinates r, θ, ϕ instead of x, y, z; thus

$$\frac{\partial f}{\partial \phi} = \frac{\partial f}{\partial x}\frac{\partial x}{\partial \phi} + \frac{\partial f}{\partial y}\frac{\partial y}{\partial \phi} + \frac{\partial f}{\partial z}\frac{\partial z}{\partial \phi}$$

But

$$x = r\sin\theta\cos\phi \qquad y = r\sin\theta\sin\phi \qquad z = r\cos\theta$$

Therefore

$$\frac{\partial x}{\partial \phi} = -y \qquad \frac{\partial y}{\partial \phi} = x \qquad \frac{\partial z}{\partial \phi} = 0$$

and

$$\frac{\partial f}{\partial \phi} = -y\frac{\partial f}{\partial x} + x\frac{\partial f}{\partial y} \tag{94}$$

Therefore the equation for the f functions reduces to

$$-\frac{\hbar}{i}\frac{\partial f}{\partial \phi} = \alpha f$$

with the solutions $f = e^{-(i/\hbar)\alpha\phi}$, α being an arbitrary number. In order to find the probability that a measurement carried out on an atom in the state $\psi = R_{nl}Y_l^m$ gives the value α for the component d_z of angular momentum, we have to expand $R_{nl}Y_l^m$ in terms of $e^{-(i/\hbar)\alpha\phi}$. But by (86) the function $R_{nl}Y_l^m$ as it depends on ϕ has the form $e^{im\phi}f(r\theta)$. Therefore the expansion reduces to the single term with $\alpha = -\hbar m$. And so the measurement of d_z carried out on a state n, l, m leads with certainty to the result $d_z = -\hbar m$.

Let us examine further the square of the angular momentum $d^2 = d_x{}^2 + d_y{}^2 + d_z{}^2$. In Section 16 we saw that the operator of

$p_x{}^2$ consists of the repeated operation of $-(\hbar/i)(\partial/\partial x)$. Consequently we have to assume that the operator of d^2 is

$$-\hbar^2 \sum \left(y\frac{\partial}{\partial z} - z\frac{\partial}{\partial y} \right)\left(y\frac{\partial}{\partial z} - z\frac{\partial}{\partial y} \right)$$

Thus, if we wish to know how the atom is to be described with respect to d^2, we must find the eigenfunctions of this operator and carry out the corresponding expansion of ψ. Again it turns out that $\psi = R_{nl}Y_l{}^m$ is already an eigenfunction, as it is converted by the operator into a multiple of itself. In order to show this we differentiate ψ relative to θ, holding r and ϕ constant. Thus

$$\frac{\partial\psi}{\partial\theta} = \sum \frac{\partial\psi}{\partial x}\frac{\partial x}{\partial\theta} = \frac{\partial\psi}{\partial x} r\cos\theta\cos\phi + \frac{\partial\psi}{\partial y} r\cos\theta\sin\phi - \frac{\partial\psi}{\partial z} r\sin\theta$$

Multiplying the last term by $\sin^2\phi + \cos^2\phi$, we have

$$\frac{\partial\psi}{\partial\theta} = \left(z\frac{\partial\psi}{\partial x} - x\frac{\partial\psi}{\partial z} \right)\cos\phi - \left(y\frac{\partial\psi}{\partial z} - z\frac{\partial\psi}{\partial y} \right)\sin\phi$$

Defining the components of the vector product by

$$L_x = y\frac{\partial}{\partial z} - z\frac{\partial}{\partial y} \qquad L_y = z\frac{\partial}{\partial x} - x\frac{\partial}{\partial z} \qquad L_z = x\frac{\partial}{\partial y} - y\frac{\partial}{\partial x}$$

and considering these components operators rather than factors, we have [cf. (94)]

$$\frac{\partial}{\partial\theta} = \cos\phi\, L_y - \sin\phi\, L_x \qquad \frac{\partial}{\partial\phi} = L_z \qquad (95)$$

Furthermore it is readily seen that

$$xL_x + yL_y + zL_z = 0 \qquad (96)$$

It must be pointed out that, in all products containing L, the order of the factors is important. For example, $L\sin\phi$ is not the same as $\sin\phi L$. In the former, L also operates on $\sin\phi$, but in the latter it remains unchanged.

Because of (95), equation (96) may be written in the form

$$\cos\phi\, L_x + \sin\phi\, L_y = -\frac{\cos\theta}{\sin\theta}\frac{\partial}{\partial\phi} \qquad (97)$$

From (95) and (97) we obtain the values for L_x and L_y:

$$L_x = -\sin\phi\frac{\partial}{\partial\theta} - \cos\phi\frac{\cos\theta}{\sin\theta}\frac{\partial}{\partial\phi}$$

$$L_y = \cos\phi\frac{\partial}{\partial\theta} - \sin\phi\frac{\cos\theta}{\sin\theta}\frac{\partial}{\partial\phi}$$

A repeated operation of L_x gives the operator

$$L_x{}^2 = \left(\sin\phi\,\frac{\partial}{\partial\theta} + \cos\phi\,\cot\theta\,\frac{\partial}{\partial\phi}\right)\left(\sin\phi\,\frac{\partial}{\partial\theta} + \cos\phi\,\cot\theta\,\frac{\partial}{\partial\phi}\right)$$

$$= \sin^2\phi\,\frac{\partial^2}{\partial\theta^2} + \sin\phi\cos\phi\,\frac{\partial}{\partial\theta}\,\cot\theta\,\frac{\partial}{\partial\phi} + \sin\phi\cos\phi\,\cot\theta\,\frac{\partial^2}{\partial\theta\,\partial\phi}$$

$$+ \cos^2\phi\,\cot\theta\,\frac{\partial}{\partial\theta} + \cos\phi\sin\phi\,\cot\theta\,\frac{\partial^2}{\partial\phi\,\partial\theta}$$

$$- \sin\phi\cos\phi\,\cot^2\theta\,\frac{\partial}{\partial\theta} + \cos^2\phi\,\cot^2\theta\,\frac{\partial^2}{\partial\phi^2}$$

A corresponding expression holds for $L_y{}^2$, so that we obtain for D^2

$$-\hbar^2(L_x{}^2 + L_y{}^2 + L_z{}^2) = -\hbar^2\left(\frac{\partial^2}{\partial\theta^2} + \cot\theta\,\frac{\partial}{\partial\theta} + \cot^2\theta\,\frac{\partial^2}{\partial\phi^2} + \frac{\partial^2}{\partial\phi^2}\right)$$

$$= -\hbar^2\left[\frac{1}{\sin\theta}\,\frac{\partial}{\partial\theta}\left(\sin\theta\,\frac{\partial}{\partial\theta}\right) + \frac{1}{\sin^2\theta}\,\frac{\partial^2}{\partial\phi^2}\right]$$

When this operator acts upon the function $\psi = R_{nl}Y_l{}^m$, the result is $\hbar^2 l(l+1)\psi$, since $Y_l{}^m$ as a spherical harmonic satisfies the equation

$$\frac{1}{\sin\theta}\,\frac{\partial}{\partial\theta}\left(\sin\theta\,\frac{\partial Y}{\partial\theta}\right) + \frac{1}{\sin^2\theta}\,\frac{\partial^2 Y}{\partial\phi^2} = -l(l+1)Y$$

Thus ψ is an eigenfunction of d^2 with the eigenvalues $\hbar^2 l(l+1)$. Therefore, when a measurement of angular momentum is made on an atom in the state n, l, m, the measurement being possible at least mentally, we find with certainty that $d = \hbar\sqrt{l(l+1)}$.

19. Discussion of the Solution. Comparison with Bohr's Theory. As we have noticed already, the situation is more complicated for the H atom than for the oscillator. No longer do the eigenfunctions form a linear sequence to which the numbers 1, 2, 3, $\cdots$ can be coordinated. They correspond to a three-dimensional manifold of numbers n, l, and m. The reason for this evidently is that the system now has three degrees of freedom whereas the oscillator had but one. This means that a measurement of energy alone no longer suffices for the unique determination of state, for according to (91) the energy fixes the sum $n + l$ only; in addition we have to measure the amount of angular momentum d and the component d_z of the vector **d** in some direction. These measurements inform us about l and m, and so the state can be described by $\psi_{nlm} = R_{nl}Y_l{}^m$.

The old quantum theory characterized the states of the H atom by three whole numbers, n, k_1, k_2. The numbers originated in the postulate that the phase integrals $\int p \, dq$ which belong to the three degrees of freedom should be given for a stationary state by whole multiples of h. This idea led to the equation

$$E = -\frac{mZ^2 e^4}{2\hbar^2 (n + k_1 + k_2)} \tag{98}$$

for energy. Thus the former theory also considered the problem of degeneracy, since all states with the same sum, $n + k_1 + k_2$, agreed in energy. As regards the quantum numbers k_1 and k_2, they were related to the angular momentum in such a way that $k_1 + k_2 = k$ determined the amount of momentum $d = \hbar k$, whereas k_1 belonged to the component d_z, the value of which was $d_z = \hbar k_1$. As can be seen, there is a close correspondence between the former quantum numbers k, k_1 and the wave mechanics numbers l, m. At the same time we must not overlook the fact that the significance of the whole numbers which now appear as eigenvalues from a differential equation is quite different in wave mechanics from that of the former theory. We need only compare the denominators in the energy equations (98) and (92) to see this. In (98) the n' of a given energy $E = -mZ^2 e^4/2\hbar^2 n'^2$ is the sum $n + k$; thus $n' + 1$ different k values are allowed wherein $k = 0, 1, 2, \cdots, n'$. The former theory therefore was bound to assume the existence of $n' + 1$ terms of E, whereas experiment conforms only to n' terms. In order to have the theory agree with the facts, the value $k = 0$ was excluded on the ground that $k = 0$ would correspond to a motion in which the angular momentum is zero. The motion then would be a linear pendular oscillation, the consequence being a collision between nucleus and electron. At first this assumption seemed to be plausible, but it led to insurmountable difficulties later. It was here that wave mechanics immediately gave evidence of its advantages, for in this theory n' in the denominator of the energy equation represents the sum $n + l + 1$, and for a given n' the values of l range from $l = 0$ to $l = n' - 1$, this being in agreement with the experimental fact that the number of terms becomes n'. Accordingly wave mechanics, in substituting $l + 1$ for k, no longer needs to resort to doubtful assumptions. The assumption of a pendulum orbit at any rate would be of no use here, since in wave mechanics the concept of "orbit of an electron" is meaningless.

There is still another divergence between the two theories, one closely connected with the interpretation of the number n'. As we have remarked before, Bohr's circular and elliptic orbits appear in wave mechanics in the form of electronic clouds. The entirety of the possible positions of the electron no longer forms a distinct orbit but rather a statistical cloud in which the former orbit is recognizable only as an indistinct condensation. If the orbits were diffuse only, we might expect that the semiclassical and the wave-mechanical models of the atom would have some features in common, for example, angular momentum. Contrary to this expectation, the wave-mechanical states, irrespective of their diffuse nature, prove to be something quite different from the corresponding states of the Bohr theory. Let us consider the ground state. It was defined, by $n = 0$, as a circular motion of the electron. As such it was assumed to have a certain angular momentum d together with a corresponding magnetic moment μ, the relation between these two quantities being expressed by $\mu = ed/2m$. Since, for $k = 1$, $d = \hbar$, the magnetic moment should be just a magneton $\hbar e/2m$, so that the atoms in a magnetic field would be expected to orient themselves parallel or antiparallel to the direction of the field, the consequence being the deflection of the atoms from their rectilinear motion by a sufficiently inhomogeneous field. Indeed this conclusion seemed to be strikingly confirmed by the famous experiment of Stern and Gerlach.

Wave mechanics, however, takes a rather different view. In the ground state of the atom $l = 0$, and consequently $d = d_z = 0$. Hence, for the ground state and in general for any state with $l = 0$ (all S states), wave mechanics denies the existence of a magnetic moment due to the rotation of the electron. This viewpoint follows from the fact that all states for which $l = 0$ are spherically symmetric, since they are represented by $\psi = R_{no}Y_o$ or $\psi = R_{no}$, the spherical harmonic of the oth order being zero. Thus, according to wave mechanics, for an atom with $l = 0$ there is no plane that could be taken as an indication of a plane in which the motion of the electron takes place in such a way that the electron would be found there with prevalent probability; all planes through the nucleus are equivalent. This means that, apart from the spatial extension of the atom which we have yet to discuss, any similarity with the old atomic conception has vanished.

But now the question arises as to how the Stern-Gerlach experiment can lead to a positive result if there is no magnetic moment in an S state. This experiment leaves no doubt that an Ag atom in the ground state reacts like a magnet. To explain this we must resort to the hypothesis proposed by Uhlenbeck and Goudsmit according to which the electron possesses an angular momentum $d = \hbar/2$ of its own, this mechanical moment producing a magnetic moment $e\hbar/2m$. As is well known, this assumption of electron spin has proved to be of extraordinary usefulness. In Chapter 6 we shall see that the spin of an electron represents a relativity effect and is forthcoming from that theory as soon as the wave equation is formulated in a relativistically invariant way. But, as long as we confine ourselves to a non-relativistic treatment of quantum mechanics, we cannot cope with the spin in any other way than by postulating it on the basis of a hypothesis. The explanation of the Stern-Gerlach experiment then is that the electron belonging to an atom with $l = 0$ sets its magnetic axis parallel or antiparallel to the direction of the field acting on it, so that the moving atom must be deflected by an inhomogeneous field.

In contrast to the S states with $l = 0$, the P, D $\cdots$ states with $l = 1, 2, \cdots$ are axially symmetric with respect to the arbitrarily chosen z axis, for here the eigenfunctions are dependent on θ and ϕ through the factor $Y_l{}^m = e^{im\phi}f(\theta)$ but in such a way that in $\psi\psi^*$ the angle ϕ does not occur. And so the probability of finding the electron at a given position is a function of r and θ only. Because of its axial symmetry, the atom now has an angular momentum with $d = \hbar \sqrt{l(l + 1)}$ and $d_z = \hbar m$. The angle between the vector $\mathbf{d}$ and the z axis is θ, the cosine of which is given by $d_z/d = m/\sqrt{l(l + 1)}$. Since, for a given l, the magnetic quantum number may assume any of the $2l + 1$ integer values between $-l$ and $+l$, there exist $2l + 1$ different orientations of the vector $\mathbf{d}$. This fact was known in the older theory, but now we can state the theorem without using the concept of an electron orbit.

Another question still remains to be answered. The z axis having been chosen quite arbitrarily, how can it be explained that there are only certain "settings" of the vector $\mathbf{d}$ relative to this axis? Evidently this statement can have sense only if the z axis has some physical significance, since the atom itself cannot satisfy the required condition for any direction. The answer is that, without directly stating it, we have distinguished the z axis by assuming that component d_z was measured in that direction. We can carry out the measurement only by having a magnetic field act on the atom in the direction of the z axis and examining the effect produced by the field. Thus the measurement constitutes an interference owing to which the atom is forced to assume a certain orientation with respect to the direction in which the atom is acted upon, and the assertion of wave mechanics is that the settings then correspond to a component d_z equal to an integer multiple of $\hbar$. Therefore it is not illogical to state that the component d_z of the angular momentum is capable only of discrete values $m\hbar$ for any direction z. This does not mean, of course, that according to quantum mechanics there exists a vector the projection of which in any direction gives an integer multiple of $\hbar$ but that the measurement of d_z furnishes such a result.   The possibility of measuring simultaneously the components d_z and $d_{z'}$ corresponding to two directions z and z' is denied by quantum mechanics.   When we know the value of d_z we lose this knowledge by measuring $d_{z'}$, since the interference produced by the second measurement destroys the orientation effected by the first one.

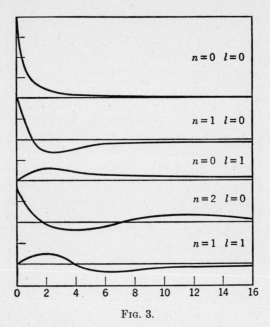

Fig. 3.

Let us consider further the radial part R of the eigenfunctions. According to (93) R_{nl} is given by the equation

$$R_{nl}r = e^{-me^2r/[\hbar^2(n+l+1)]}v_{nl}$$

where v_{nl} is a polynomial of the nth order in r.   In the old theory $\hbar^2/me^2$ is just the radius a_1 of the first electron orbit; consequently R_{nl} also may be written in the form

$$R_{nl}r = e^{-r/[a_1(n+l+1)]}v_{nl}$$

From the exponent of e it is to be expected that with increasing r the function R_{nl} will decrease toward zero, the more slowly the greater the value of $n + l$.   This is in agreement with the former assumption that the extension of the orbits increases with $n + k$.   In Fig. 3 the R_{nl} functions are plotted for different values of n and l.   Figure 4 shows $R_{nl}^2r^2$ as it depends on r, wherein the abscissas are measured in units of a_1.   The figure makes it clear that the domain within which $\psi\psi^*$ is noticeably different from zero has approximately the extension of the old quantum orbits.   For instance, for the ground state $n = l = 0$, the maximum of $R_{nl}{}^2 r^2$ lies at $x = a_1$; for the state $n = l = 1$ it lies at $r = 4a_1$, etc.   Thus the distances of the maxima from the nucleus are identical with the radii of the orbits in Bohr's theory.

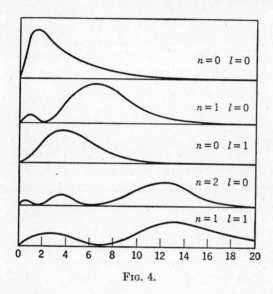

FIG. 4.

It is seen that the functions R_{nl}, except those with $n = 0$, vanish for certain values of r.   Accordingly there exist *nodal surfaces* on which it is certain that the electron is never to be found.   It can be shown that the number of such surfaces is given by the degree of the polynomial v_{nl}/r^γ.

It must be emphasized, however, that the given theory of the H atom is not yet quite exact.   It is based on a wave equation which is not invariant with respect to a Lorentz transformation and thus does not satisfy the requirements of relativity.   As a consequence we are not able to account for the *fine structure* of the spectrum.   In Chapter 6 we shall see how the theory can be made relativistic.   We only point out here that the improved wave equation furnishes energy terms in the expression of which the numbers n and l no longer appear in the sum $n + l$ but in such a way that any combination n, l of the same sum provides another term.   Thus *relativity cancels part of the degeneracy* and in this way causes a resolution of the spectral lines into a certain number of components.

20. Wave Mechanics and the Correspondence Principle. Transition Probabilities. We now return to the general investigation of systems consisting of a single particle. In two examples we have seen that wave mechanics leads to the correct energy terms; therefore Bohr's frequency condition, $h\nu = E_i - E_k$, enables us to evaluate the frequencies of the spectral lines emitted by an atom. But, besides frequency, a line possesses intensity as well, and the question arises whether the theory can inform us about this also. This problem of intensity was beyond the competence of the old theory. The intensity of a certain line, $\nu = (E_i - E_k)/h$ depends on the probability of the transition $i \rightarrow k$, that is, on the average number of atoms which undergo the transition in unit time. Bohr's theory was unable to determine this number, and in particular it could not explain why certain combinations are never observed in the spectra, thus signifying that the corresponding transition probabilities are zero. In order to contend with this situation of complete helplessness, Bohr proposed his famous correspondence principle, which gives a procedure for evaluating the intensities, and which, though unintelligible, was convincing by its success. By this principle one starts with the radiation that would be emitted by an electron moving in the ith orbit according to Maxwell's theory, its frequency and intensity being uniquely determined. From this one infers the radiation corresponding to transitions from the ith stationary state. This can be done in the following way. If ω denotes the classical frequency belonging to the motion in the ith orbit, the electron's motion can be represented, on making use of Fourier's theorem, by

$$x = \sum x_n \cos (2\pi n\omega t + \alpha_n) \qquad (99)$$

since x, as well as y and z, is a periodic function of time and any such function can be understood as a superposition of harmonic oscillations of frequencies ω, 2ω, $\cdots$ and of amplitudes x_n, which can be evaluated from the function by a well-known method. According to Maxwell's theory, every partial oscillator emits an electromagnetic wave of the same frequency and an energy, which, for unit time, is given by,

$$\frac{16\pi^4 e^2}{3c^3} \nu^4 (x_n^2 + y_n^2 + z_n^2) \qquad (100)$$

where x_n, y_n, z_n represent the amplitudes associated with $\nu = n\omega$ in the expansions of x, y, and z respectively. Bohr's correspondence principle sets down the following requirement: *In equation (100) one must substitute for ν the quantum-mechanical $\nu_{i,i-n}$ and take this*

*expression as an approximate measure of the intensity with which light is
emitted by the spontaneous transition from the ith into the $(i - n)$th
stationary state.* It is assumed further that the transition $i \rightarrow (i - n)$
does not occur at all if in the Fourier expansion the amplitudes x_n,
y_n, z_n of the corresponding partial oscillations are all zero.

Although this rule was only a makeshift one, it proved to be very
helpful. It is true that the evaluated intensities agreed only roughly
with the observed ones, but from the exclusion of certain lines an
exact selection rule could be derived which was of extreme value to
the former theory. Nevertheless, to be dependent on a rule that could
not be understood produced an uneasy feeling, and consequently it
became a matter of interest to see whether wave mechanics would be
able to uncover the exact law hidden behind the principle.

On the basis of the theory developed up to this point, a satisfactory
solution of the problem is not yet possible. All our considerations
have been concerned exclusively with systems that were supposed to
be closed and thus subject to the principle of the conservation of
energy. It is precisely this supposition which we have to drop when we
attempt to learn something about the transition probabilities, for
then we are dealing with processes in which the atom interacts with
the surrounding radiation field by exchanging energy with it. Accordingly we shall not be able to attack the problem of transition probabilities until we learn how to handle composed systems. Nevertheless we may, at this stage, try to discover a plausible method which
will aid us in making an exact formulation of the correspondence
principle.

We have seen that any state of an atom can be described by the form
$u = \sum c_i \psi_i e^{(i/\hbar)E_i t}$. If, in accordance with the procedure of the correspondence principle, we wish to represent the coordinate x as a
function of time, this can be done in quantum mechanics only by
considering the expectation value of x in its dependence on t, for of
itself the coordinate x for which the measurement may provide any
value has nothing to do with time. Now for $\bar{x}$ we have

$$\bar{x} = \int u u^* x \, dv = \int x \sum c_i \psi_i e^{(i/\hbar)E_i t} \sum c_k^* \psi_k^* e^{-(i/\hbar)E_k t} \, dv$$

$$= \int c_i c_k^* e^{(i/\hbar)(E_i - E_k)t} \int x \psi_i \psi_k^* \, dv$$

which may be written in the simpler form

$$\bar{x} = \sum c_i c_k^* x_{ki} e^{(i/\hbar)(E_i - E_k)t} \tag{101}$$

on letting

$$\int x\psi_i\psi_k^* \, dv = x_{ki} \tag{102}$$

The x_{ki} terms are quantities which depend on the nature of the system and which, because of their definition, satisfy the condition

$$x_{ik} = x_{ki}^* \tag{103}$$

Therefore, taking together the x_{ik} and x_{ki} terms, we obtain

$$\bar{x} = \sum_{ik} |c_ic_k^*|2|x_{ki}| \cos (2\pi\nu_{ik}t + \alpha_{ik}) \tag{104}$$

Thus according to wave mechanics the expectation value of x can be expanded, in terms of harmonic oscillations, into a series which, however, does not contain whole multiples of a fundamental frequency ω as did (99), but refers to the frequencies emitted by the atom according to Bohr's condition. Thus, as far as frequencies are concerned, we now meet with a strict agreement instead of a correspondence, and this makes it probable that there is an agreement in the amplitudes also, so that $|x_{ki}|$ may be assumed to represent the exact amplitudes and are to be substituted for x_n, y_n, z_n. As for the factors $|c_ic_k^*|$, they evidently must not be considered as having a meaning for the intensity law because, in contrast to the experimental facts, their effect would be that, for an atom for which every c_k except a certain c_i equals zero, that is, an atom in a certain stationary state, a spontaneous transition to other states would be impossible. Hence we come to the conclusion that the correspondence principle is to be formulated as follows: *When an atom is in the ith stationary state, the probability of a spontaneous transition into a state $k < i$ is given by*

$$\frac{64\pi^4e^2}{3c^3h} \nu_{ik}^3(|x_{ki}|^2 + |y_{ki}|^2 + |z_{ki}|^2) \tag{105}$$

As the transition is connected with the transition of energy ($h\nu_{ik} = E_i - E_k$), the intensity J of the radiation emitted by a great number N of atoms all in the same ith stationary must be

$$J = N \frac{64\pi^4e^2}{3c^3} \nu_{ik}^4(|x_{ki}|^2 + |y_{ki}|^2 + |z_{ki}|^2) \tag{106}$$

The x_{ki} terms in this equation must be evaluated, by making use of (102), from the normalized eigenfunctions, since otherwise they would not be single-valued. Indeed, we shall see in Chapter 8 that the law (106) can be given an exact quantum-mechanical foundation.

Of special interest is the case where the x_{ki} terms vanish for certain values of i and k. If x_{ki}, y_{ki}, and z_{ki} are also zero, then according to (105) a transition i to k cannot occur and a line of frequency ν_{ik} is not observed. But, if y_{ki} and z_{ki} equal zero with x_{ki} having a value different from zero, we may assume that there is emitted a radiation analogous to that in Maxwell's theory, where the radiation is due to an electron moving in the x direction. In other words, for this case we may expect the emission of light which is linearly polarized in the x direction. Finally, if only z_{ki} is zero, we can expect elliptically or circularly polarized light. Indeed the partial oscillations

$$|x_{ki}| \cos (2\pi \nu_{ik} t + \alpha) \qquad \text{and} \qquad |y_{ki}| \cos (2\pi \nu_{ik} t + \beta)$$

are then contained in $\bar{x}$ and $\bar{y}$, which together represent an elliptic or circular oscillation.

The application of these "selection and polarization rules" to the oscillator and the H atom leads to complete agreement with the facts. For the oscillator the theory requires that the only permissible transitions are those between two neighboring energy levels in which the light can be emitted or absorbed only in quanta $h\nu_0$. With

$$\psi_i = \alpha_i e^{-x'^2/2} H_i(x') \qquad x' = 2\pi x \sqrt{\frac{m\nu_0}{h}}$$

we have

$$x_{ki} = \alpha_i \alpha_k \frac{h}{4\pi^2 m \nu_0} \int_{-\infty}^{+\infty} e^{-x'^2} H_i(x') H_k(x') x' \, dx' \qquad (107)$$

When we integrate by parts, the integral becomes

$$-\left[\frac{e^{-x'^2}}{2} H_i H_k \right]_{-\infty}^{+\infty} + \frac{1}{2} \int_{-\infty}^{+\infty} e^{-x'^2} \left(\frac{dH_i}{dx'} H_k + \frac{dH_k}{dx'} H_i \right) dx'$$

We had for the function H_i

$$\frac{dH_i}{dx'} = 2i H_{i-1}$$

Thus (107) can be written

$$x_{ki} = \alpha_i \alpha_k \frac{h}{4\pi^2 m \nu_0} \int e^{-x'^2} (i H_{i-1} H_k + k H_{k-1} H_i) \, dx' \qquad (108)$$

Because the orthogonality condition holds for the functions $e^{-x'^2/2} H_i(x')$, the integral vanishes except for the values $k = i - 1$ and $i = k - 1$. Thus the selection rule permits only the transitions i to $i - 1$ and i to $i + 1$. For the first, (108) gives

$$x_{i-1,i} = \alpha_i \alpha_{i-1} \frac{hi}{4\pi^2 m\nu_0} \int e^{-x'^2} H_{i-1}{}^2 \, dx'$$

$$= \frac{1}{2\pi} \sqrt{\frac{hi}{2m\nu_0}} \int \alpha_{i-1}{}^2 e^{-x'^2} H_{i-1}{}^2 \, dx$$

wherein for α_i the value

$$\alpha_i = \frac{\text{constant}}{\sqrt{\pi^{\frac{1}{2}} 2^i i!}} = \frac{\alpha_{i-1}}{\sqrt{2i}}$$

is used. Because of the normalization factor the integral has the value unity. Therefore

$$x_{i-1,i} = \frac{1}{2\pi} \sqrt{\frac{hi}{2m\nu_0}} \tag{109}$$

In a corresponding manner we find that

$$x_{i+1,i} = \frac{1}{2\pi} \sqrt{\frac{h(i+1)}{2m\nu_0}} \tag{109$'$}$$

In order to apply the selection rule to the H atom we must prove first the theorem that any homogeneous polynomial of the lth order can be expressed in terms of spherical harmonics Y. To do this we shall determine the number of terms in the polynomial. There is one term with x^l, two with x^{l-1} since x^{l-1} can unite with either y or z, three terms with x^{l-2}, and so on, to $l + 1$ with x^0. Hence an arbitrary polynomial of the lth order contains $1 + 2 + 3 + \cdots + (l + 1)$ different products and as many constants. Now exactly the same number of constants is contained in the sum

$$r^l(Y_l + Y_{l-2} + \cdots) \tag{110}$$

which also represents a homogeneous polynomial of the lth order because, as we have seen, Y_l can be composed of $2l + 1$ spherical harmonics $Y_l{}^m$. Therefore the number of linearly independent harmonics in (110) is

$$(2l + 1) + [2(l - 2) + 1] + \cdots$$
$$= (l + 1 + l) + (l - 1 + l - 2) + \cdots$$
$$= (l + 1) + l + (l - 1) + (l - 2) + \cdots$$

By suitably choosing the factors of the Y, it must therefore be possible to make (110) agree with the given polynomial.

Using this theorem, we can show now that the H atom is capable only of transitions in which l is changed by $+1$ or -1. For this purpose consider the transition from a state nml to $n'm'l'$ wherein $l' < l$. Then x_{ik} is defined by

$$x_{nlm,n'l'm'} = \int x\psi_{nlm}{}^*\psi_{n'l'm'}\, dv$$

$$= \int r^2 R_{nl}R_{n'l'}\, dr \int x Y_l{}^{m*}Y_{l'}{}^{m'}\, d\omega \qquad (111)$$

where $d\omega$ signifies a surface element of the unit sphere. When we set $x Y_{l'}{}^{m'} = r^{-l'}x r^{l'}Y_{l'}{}^{m'}$, $x r^{l'}Y_{l'}{}^{m}$ is a homogeneous polynomial of the order $l' + 1$ and therefore it can be written in the form $r^{l'+1}(Y_{l'+1} + Y_{l'-1} + \cdots)$.
We have then

$$x_{nlm,n'l'm'} = \int r^3 R_{nl}R_{n'l'}\, dr \int Y_l{}^{m*}(Y_{l'+1} + Y_{l'-1} + \cdots)\, d\omega$$

According to Section 18 the integral of $Y_i{}^*Y_k$ differs from zero only for $i = k$. On the condition that $l' < l$, the integral (111) can, therefore, differ from zero only for $l = l' + 1$. If $l' > l$, we have to expand $x Y_l{}^{m*}$ and the condition turns out to be $l' = l + 1$. *Thus the only transitions possible are those in which l is changed by ± 1.*

This rule is of decisive importance for the interpretation of the spectral series, as it explains the fact that in the sequence of the S, P, D, $\cdots$ terms, which terms are defined by $l = 0, 1, 2, \cdots$, two nonconsecutive terms never combine.

As regards the magnetic quantum number m, we first evaluate

$$(x + iy)_{nlm,n'm'l'} = \int r^2 R_{nl}R_{n'l'}\, dr \int (x + iy) Y_l{}^{m*}Y_{l'}{}^{m'}\, d\omega$$

$$= \int R_{nl}R_{n'l'}r^3\, dr \int e^{i\phi(m'-m+1)}\, d\phi \int d\theta$$

The integral relative to ϕ differs from zero only if the power of e is zero, that is, if $m' = m - 1$. Similarly we find that $(x - iy)_{nlm,n'l'm'}$ differs from zero only if $m' = m + 1$. Finally $z_{nlm,n'l'm'}$ can be put into the form

$$z_{nlm,n'l'm'} = \int r^3 R_{nl}R_{n'l'}\, dr \int e^{i\phi(m'-m)}\, d\phi \int d\theta$$

from which we see that only for $m' = m$ does this quantity not vanish. Hence the following possibilities exist:

(i) $m \to m \pm 1$:

$$(x + iy)_{ki} = \begin{matrix} c \neq 0 \\ 0 \end{matrix} \qquad (x - iy)_{ki} = \begin{matrix} 0 \\ c \neq 0 \end{matrix} \qquad z_{ki} = 0$$

$$\therefore x_{ki} = \frac{c}{2} \qquad y_{ki} = \pm\frac{c}{2i} = x_{ki}e^{\mp\pi i/2} \qquad z_{ki} = 0$$

This means circular polarization of the emitted light.

(ii) $m \rightarrow m$: In this case $x_{ki} = y_{ki} = 0$ and z_{ki} is alone different from zero. The light is linearly polarized in a direction parallel to the z axis.

It is true that these rules cannot be put to the test on the spectrum of the unperturbed H atom, for according to Section 18 the terms then are independent of m and thus the spectrum gives us no information about the change of m. But the degeneracy in m is cancelled when a magnetic field in the z direction acts on the atom. Then the $2l + 1$ different m values give rise to as many different terms, and the selection rule comes into play. In fact, we can then see that an originally simple line when observed in the z direction is resolved into several circularly polarized lines which can be correlated to the transitions $m \rightarrow m - 1$ and $m \rightarrow m + 1$.

PROBLEMS

1. Find the Schroedinger equation for a rotator, that is, a rigid body rotating about a fixed axis. Show that the eigenvalues of the energy are given by $E_n = n^2(\hbar^2/2J)$, where n signifies successive whole numbers 1, 2, $\cdots$ and J is the moment of inertia, and that the eigenfunctions are given by $\psi_n = ae^{\pm in\phi}$. Discuss the spectrum emitted by the rotator.

2. Show that for a rotator the axis of which is not fixed in space the wave equation is given by

$$\frac{1}{\sin \theta} \frac{\partial}{\partial \theta}\left(\sin \theta \frac{\partial \psi}{\partial \theta}\right) + \frac{1}{\sin^2 \theta} \frac{\partial^2 \psi}{\partial \phi^2} + \frac{2J}{\hbar^2} E\psi = 0$$

Find the eigenfunctions and eigenvalues of this equation. Compare with the equation for the H atom.

3. How is it possible that the electron of an H atom in a stationary state can be found at any distance from the nucleus? Why is not this a contradiction of the equation $E = E_{kin} + E_{pot}$?

4. Show that $\overline{d\mathbf{p}}/dt = \overline{\mathbf{K}}$.

5. Show that $\overline{d\mathbf{d}}/\overline{\mathbf{M}}$.

6. If the motion of the nucleus is taken into account, how is the Kepler problem to be solved? ψ then depends both on the coordinates $x_1 y_1 z_1$ of the electron and on the coordinates $x_2 y_2 z_2$ of the nucleus. Accordingly the wave equation becomes

$$\frac{\hbar^2}{2m_1} \nabla_1^2 \psi + \frac{\hbar^2}{2m_2} \nabla_2^2 \psi + (E - V)\psi = 0$$

Instead of $x_2 y_2 z_2$ use the variables $\xi = x_1 - x_2$, $\eta = y_1 - y_2$, $\zeta = z_1 - z_2$, and put $\psi = \phi(x_1 y_1 z_1)\chi(\xi\eta\zeta)$. As V depends only on $\xi\eta\zeta$, the wave equation can be separated into two equations for $x_1 y_1 z_1$ and $\xi\eta\zeta$ respectively.

3

WAVE MECHANICS

IN MATRIX FORM

21. The Idea of Matrix Mechanics. Prior to Schroedinger, the new quantum mechanics had been developed by Heisenberg, along with Born and Jordan, in the form of the so-called matrix mechanics. It was Heisenberg's idea to replace Bohr's theory by a plan into which no entities are introduced except those physically observable. In consistently following out this idea he was led to a theory the form of which was entirely different from wave mechanics but the contents of which later proved to be identical with it.

In order to explain the nature of matrix mechanics let us recall the transformation theory developed in Section 16. We consider an arbitrary physical system under conditions that guarantee a *pure case*, that is, the following requirement must be fulfilled: when we take a great number of systems, all subject to the same conditions, and carry out measurements of any entity such as energy or angular momentum, the result will be a statistical array which, for the pure case, has to be the same for any sufficiently large part of the assemblage. Suppose now that we asserted that a measurement of energy with a probability $|c_0|^2$ furnishes a value E_0, and that with a probability $|c_1|^2$ furnishes a value E_1, and so on. We then can characterize the given state of the system by the numbers $c_0, c_1 \cdots$, disregarding for the present the fact that the numbers c_i are not uniquely determined by the probabilities. The transformation theory maintains that, for a system with one degree of freedom, *these numbers c_i define the state not only with respect to the energy but with respect to all other physical entities as well.* More accurately, it is assumed that from the c_i terms we can infer the probabilities that correspond to the measurements of any other entity. If we suppose that the other entities as well as energy have only discrete values, with the probabilities $|c_i'|^2$, $|c_i''|^2$, $\cdots$, it should be possible to evaluate the c_i', c_i'', $\cdots$ terms from the c_i.

It seems desirable to formulate this idea in the following way. In a space with an infinite number of dimensions let us correlate a vector

83

with the given state of the system and interpret the probability amplitudes c_0, c_1, c_2, $\cdots$ as the components of that vector referred to a certain coordinate system K. Similarly we interpret the numbers c', c'', $\cdots$ as the components of the same vector relative to other coordinate systems K', K'', $\cdots$. The problem of quantum mechanics is this: we have to determine the coordinate systems for all entities and fix their positions relative to an arbitrarily chosen reference system K_0. Then it is sufficient to know the components of the vector which represents the state relative to one of the systems in order to determine the probability amplitudes of any other entity by a transformation of coordinates. Thus by the c_i terms which refer to one of the systems, not necessarily energy, the state is uniquely defined in all entities; this statement holds not only for the instant considered but also for the future, provided that we know the law according to which the vector changes with time.

22. The Hilbert Space. Concept of Matrix. To carry out the plan described we begin with the representation of the mathematical means we shall need for our purpose. Our intention is to represent the given state of the system by a vector in a space with an infinite number of dimensions and to refer this vector to a coordinate system K. If the entity to which K belongs possesses an infinite set of discrete values as, for example, the energy of an atom, the axes of the coordinate system will scaffold a space the infinitely many dimensions of which are denumerable. At times, however, it will be necessary to use a concept of space with a continuum of dimensions. For example, we are faced with this necessity when we consider an entity the eigenvalues of which build a continuum. For the present, however, we shall confine our discussion to a discrete spectrum and postpone the discussion of a K system with a continuous infinity of axes until Section 30.

In order to arrive at a geometric interpretation of quantum mechanics we require a geometric scheme different from ordinary Euclidean geometry in so far as it admits vectors the components x_0, x_1, $\cdots$ of which are complex numbers. We express the magnitude of the vector $\mathbf{x}$ by the expression

$$|\mathbf{x}|^2 = x_0{}^* x_0 + x_1{}^* x_1 + \cdots = \sum_{n=0}^{\infty} x_n{}^* x_n \tag{112}$$

thus assuring a positive real number. A space in which this equation holds for the vector $\mathbf{x}$ (provided that it is referred to a suitable coordinate system K) is called a Hilbert space.

Equation (112) may be looked upon as the scalar product of $\mathbf{x}$

with itself.   Accordingly we define the scalar product of two vectors **x** and **y** by

$$\mathbf{x} \cdot \mathbf{y} = x_0{}^* y_0 + x_1{}^* y_1 + \cdots = \sum_{n=0}^{\infty} x_n{}^* y_n \tag{113}$$

It follows from this that the scalar multiplication of two Hilbert vectors is not commutative, for

$$\mathbf{x} \cdot \mathbf{y} = (\mathbf{y} \cdot \mathbf{x})^* \tag{114}$$

However, we see that the distributive law is satisfied:

$$(\mathbf{x} + \mathbf{y}) \cdot \mathbf{z} = \mathbf{x} \cdot \mathbf{z} + \mathbf{y} \cdot \mathbf{z} \tag{115}$$

When $\mathbf{x} \cdot \mathbf{y} = 0$, the vectors **x** and **y** are called orthogonal.   For any axis of the coordinate system a unit vector $\mathbf{e}_i$ is defined with the components given for $\mathbf{e}_0$ by

$$x_0 = 1 \qquad x_1 = x_2 = \cdots = 0$$

and for $\mathbf{e}_1$ by

$$x_0 = 0 \qquad x_1 = 1, \, x_2 = x_3 = \cdots = 0, \quad \text{etc.}$$

Consequently any vector can be represented by

$$\mathbf{x} = x_0 \mathbf{e}_0 + x_1 \mathbf{e}_1 + \cdots = \sum_{n=0}^{\infty} x_n \mathbf{e}_n \tag{116}$$

Among the unit vectors the following relations hold:

$$\mathbf{e}_i \cdot \mathbf{e}_i = 1 \qquad \mathbf{e}_i \cdot \mathbf{e}_k = 0 \qquad (i \neq k) \tag{117}$$

From the first of the relations above we see that each of the vectors $\mathbf{e}_i$ has a magnitude of unity.   From the second relation we observe that they are orthogonal.   Coordinate systems whose axes are orthogonal may be called *normal*.

Let us now consider two normal coordinate systems K and K'. The components of a vector **x** when referred to these are x_i and x_i'; therefore

$$\mathbf{x} = x_0 \mathbf{e}_0 + x_1 \mathbf{e}_1 + \cdots = x_0' \mathbf{e}_0' + x_1' \mathbf{e}_1' + \cdots$$

the primed unit vectors being associated with K'.   Then, exactly as in Euclidean geometry, the x_i and x_i' terms are related by linear equations of the form

$$x_i' = a_{i0} x_0 + a_{i1} x_1 + \cdots = \sum_{k=0}^{\infty} a_{ik} x_k \tag{118}$$

Thus the transformation from K to K' is effected by a system of linear equations with coefficients that can be set in the following arrangement:

$$\begin{bmatrix} a_{00} & a_{01} & a_{02} & \cdots \\ a_{10} & a_{11} & a_{12} & \cdots \\ a_{20} & a_{21} & a_{22} & \cdots \\ \cdot & \cdot & \cdot & \cdot \\ \cdot & \cdot & \cdot & \cdot \\ \cdot & \cdot & \cdot & \cdot \end{bmatrix}$$

This arrangement is called a *matrix;* it will be designated in what follows by A or $\|a_{ik}\|$. If the matrix is required to bring about the transformation from a normal system K to another normal system K', the coefficients must satisfy the condition that $\sum x_i^* x_i$, by the transformation, becomes $\sum x_i'^* x_i'$, since both sums represent the square of the magnitude $|\mathbf{x}|^2$ of the vector $\mathbf{x}$. When the a_{ik} terms satisfy this condition, the matrix is called unitary.

In many applications it is useful to interpret relation (118) not as a passage from K to K', wherein x_i and x_i' are the components of the same vector in relation to different coordinate systems, but rather as a linear coordination by which a vector $\mathbf{x}$ is transformed into a vector $\mathbf{x}'$ with components x_i'. In this case, $\mathbf{x}$ and $\mathbf{x}'$ are different vectors referred to the same coordinate system. This interpretation is closely connected with quantum mechanics, since according to Section 16 the concept of transformation plays an important part in transformation theory.

23. Addition and Multiplication of Matrices. In order to establish the rules for the addition and multiplication of matrices we choose to interpret a matrix as defining a linear transformation. It may be assumed that a first matrix $A = \|a_{ik}\|$ transforms a vector $\mathbf{x}$ with components x_i into a vector $\mathbf{x}'$ with components x_i', whereas a second matrix $B = \|b_{ik}\|$ transforms the same vector $\mathbf{x}$ into $\mathbf{x}''$ with components x_i''. Then we define the sum, $S = A + B$, as a matrix that transforms $\mathbf{x}$ into $\mathbf{x}' + \mathbf{x}''$. The elements s_{ik} of S must therefore satisfy the equations

$$\sum_k s_{ik} x_k = \sum_k a_{ik} x_k + \sum_k b_{ik} x_k$$

from which it follows that $s_{ik} = a_{ik} + b_{ik}$. Hence the rule for addition is: two matrices are added by adding their elements.

Now let us consider multiplication. If k is an ordinary number, we define the product kA as a matrix which transforms $\mathbf{x}$ into $k\mathbf{x}'$ with components kx_i', that is, $kA = \|ka_{ik}\|$.   Hence a matrix is multiplied by any ordinary number by multiplying every element by that number.

Let us imagine that two transformations A and B are performed successively.   First $\mathbf{x}$ may be transformed into $\mathbf{x}'$ by A, and then $\mathbf{x}'$ into $\mathbf{x}''$ by B.   Thus we have

$$x_i' = \sum_k a_{ik}x_k \qquad x_i'' = \sum_k b_{ik}x_k' \qquad\qquad (119)$$

We wish to know whether $\mathbf{x}$ can transform into $\mathbf{x}''$ by one transformation P, and, if so, how the elements of P are to be evaluated from those of A and B.   Considering the two equations (119), we can write

$$x_i'' = \sum_{kl} b_{ik}a_{kl}x_l$$

or

$$x_i'' = \sum_l p_{il}x_l \qquad p_{il} = \sum_k b_{ik}a_{kl} \qquad\qquad (120)$$

Thus the answer to the question is that the successive transformations A and B on a vector have the same effect as the matrix P with elements $p_{il} = \sum b_{ik}a_{kl}$. P is called the product of A and B and is written $P = BA$.   In this equation care must be taken with respect to the order of the factors. BA is to be read from the right to the left, meaning that first A operates on $\mathbf{x}$, and then B.   The inverse succession, $AB = P'$ with elements $p_{il}' = \sum a_{ik}b_{kl}$, gives a matrix that generally will be different from BA.   To obtain the element in the position il in the case of $BA = P$, we multiply the elements of the ith row of B with those of the lth column of A, whereas in the second case the lth column of B is combined with the ith row of A.

The beginner is advised to keep the multiplication rule well in mind. According to (120) we get the element p_{il} by writing down the letters a and b in the succession in which A and B occur in the product, attaching to them the indices $ikkl$ and summing up over all k.

It is easy to see how three or more matrices are to be multiplied. $D = CBA$ is the product of C and BA; therefore the elements of D are given by

$$d_{ik} = \sum_l c_{il}p_{lk} = \sum_{lm} c_{il}b_{lm}a_{mk}$$

The same matrix is obtained by multiplying CB by A.   Hence the associative law holds:

$$C(BA) = (CB)A$$

The validity of the distributive law is obvious:

$$C(A + B) = CA + CB$$

If in a matrix A only the coefficients a_{ik} with $i = k$ differ from zero, the matrix has the form

$$A = \begin{bmatrix} a_{00} & 0 & 0 & \cdots \\ 0 & a_{11} & 0 & \cdots \\ 0 & 0 & a_{22} & \cdots \\ \cdot & \cdot & \cdot & \cdot \cdot & \cdot \cdot & \cdot \cdot \\ \cdot & \cdot & \cdot & \cdot \cdot & \cdot \cdot & \cdot \cdot \\ \cdot & \cdot & \cdot & \cdot \cdot & \cdot \cdot & \cdot \cdot \end{bmatrix}$$

A is called a diagonal matrix. Of special importance is the diagonal matrix wherein all the diagonal elements equal unity. Then it is called a unit matrix and is designated by 1 or E. In this case $A = E$, and in equation (118) $x_i' = x_i$. Thus the E transformation is the idemfactor. The multiplication of an arbitrary matrix A by E gives, by (120),

$$AE = EA = A \qquad (121)$$

Let us now determine the matrix which effects a restitution of a vector $\mathbf{x}$ that is transformed by A into $\mathbf{x}'$. We denote this matrix by A^{-1} and call it the reciprocal of A. Because of its definition A must satisfy the condition

$$A^{-1}A = E \qquad (122)$$

This equation is not solved as easily as we might imagine. The matrices on the right and left must agree in all their elements so that we obtain the infinite number of equations

$$\sum_l a_{il}' a_{lk} = \delta_{ik} \qquad \delta_{ik} = \begin{array}{l} 0 \text{ for } i \neq k \\ 1 \text{ for } i = k \end{array} \qquad (123)$$

where the elements of A^{-1} are designated by a_{il}'. These can be solved only if the determinant of the a_{ik} elements differs from zero.

When we multiply (122) by A to the left we obtain $AA^{-1}A = A$. By interpreting the left-hand side as $(AA^{-1})A$, we see that AA^{-1} also equals E. The multiplication by the reciprocal is commutative just as in the case of multiplication by E.

Very often it is useful to give a vector the form of a matrix in which the first column contains the components x of a vector $\mathbf{x}$, the other elements being zero; thus

$$\mathbf{x} = \begin{bmatrix} x_0 & 0 & 0 & \cdots \\ x_1 & 0 & 0 & \cdots \\ x_2 & 0 & 0 & \cdots \\ \cdot & \cdot & \cdot & \cdot \cdot \cdot \cdot \\ \cdot & \cdot & \cdot & \cdot \cdot \cdot \cdot \\ \cdot & \cdot & \cdot & \cdot \cdot \cdot \cdot \end{bmatrix}$$

Equation (118) then can be written

$$\mathbf{x}' = A\mathbf{x} \tag{124}$$

if $A\mathbf{x}$ is understood to be the product of two matrices A and $\mathbf{x}$. If for the time being we denote the elements of $\mathbf{x}$ by x_{ik}, the x_{i0} alone differing from zero, the meaning of (124) is

$$x_{i0}' = x_i' = \sum_k a_{ik} x_{k0} = \sum a_{ik} x_k$$

which is in agreement with (118).

We make use of this formal possibility of expressing a vector as a matrix to solve the following problem. A transformation may be defined, with reference to a given coordinate system K, by a matrix $A = ||a_{ik}||$. The matrix transforms a vector $\mathbf{x}$ into another vector $\mathbf{y}$ which is related to $\mathbf{x}$ by

$$\mathbf{y} = A\mathbf{x}$$

When we introduce another coordinate system K', the components x_i and y_i of $\mathbf{x}$ and $\mathbf{y}$ are changed to

$$x_i' = \sum s_{ik} x_k \quad \text{and} \quad y_i' = \sum s_{ik} y_k$$

which we may write in the form

$$\mathbf{x}' = S\mathbf{x} \quad \text{and} \quad \mathbf{y}' = S\mathbf{y} \tag{125}$$

where S is the matrix formed by the s_{ik} coefficients. The problem is to find the linear relations between the x_i' and y_i' terms, that is, to determine the matrix A' which transforms $\mathbf{x}' = \mathbf{x}$ into $\mathbf{y}' = \mathbf{y}$ if $\mathbf{x}'$ and $\mathbf{y}'$ are referred to K'.

To answer the question we first solve equations (125) with respect to $\mathbf{x}$ and $\mathbf{y}$. Multiplying each by S^{-1}, keeping in mind that $S^{-1}S = E$, we obtain

$$\mathbf{x} = S^{-1}\mathbf{x}' \quad \text{and} \quad \mathbf{y} = S^{-1}\mathbf{y}'$$

When we introduce the expressions into $\mathbf{y} = A\mathbf{x}$, we obtain

$$S^{-1}\mathbf{y}' = AS^{-1}\mathbf{x}'$$

or

$$\mathbf{y}' = SAS^{-1}\mathbf{x}'$$

from which we can infer that $A' = SAS^{-1}$. Thus we can state the theorem: when the coordinate system is changed from K to K', the relation between these being given by $\mathbf{x}' = S\mathbf{x}$, a matrix A is changed into A' when

$$A' = SAS^{-1} \tag{126}$$

A and A' represent the same transformation but are referred to different coordinate systems.

24. Dual, Unitary, Hermitean Matrices. When in a matrix A the rows and columns are interchanged, that is, when element a_{ik} of the ith row and kth column is placed where the kth row intersects the ith column, the matrix A is changed into another matrix $\bar{A}$ which is called the *dual* of A. Thus the definition of $\bar{A}$ is $\bar{a}_{ik} = a_{ki}$. When the product $P = BA$ is subject to this operation, we get $\bar{P} = \overline{BA}$, with the elements

$$\bar{p}_{ik} = p_{ki} = \sum_l b_{kl}a_{li} = \sum_l \bar{a}_{il}\bar{b}_{lk}$$

Therefore

$$\overline{BA} = \bar{A}\bar{B} \tag{127}$$

The concept of the dual matrix makes it possible to represent the scalar product of two vectors $\mathbf{x}$ and $\mathbf{y}$ in the form of a matrix product. If we understand $\mathbf{x}^*$ to be the matrix

$$\mathbf{x}^* = \begin{bmatrix} x_0^* & 0 & 0 & \cdots \\ x_1^* & 0 & 0 & \cdots \\ x_2^* & 0 & 0 & \cdots \\ \cdot & \cdot & \cdot & \cdot & \cdot & \cdot & \cdot \\ \cdot & \cdot & \cdot & \cdot & \cdot & \cdot & \cdot \\ \cdot & \cdot & \cdot & \cdot & \cdot & \cdot & \cdot \end{bmatrix}$$

and hence

$$\overline{\mathbf{x}^*} = \begin{bmatrix} x_0^* & x_1^* & x_2^* & \cdots \\ 0 & 0 & 0 & \cdots \\ 0 & 0 & 0 & \cdots \\ \cdot & \cdot & \cdot & \cdot & \cdot & \cdot & \cdot \end{bmatrix}$$

then the product $\overline{\mathbf{x}^*}\mathbf{y}$ is a matrix in the upper left-hand corner of which is the element $\sum x_i^* y_i = \mathbf{x} \cdot \mathbf{y}$. All the other terms are zero. Thus there is a unique correspondence between the scalar product $\mathbf{x} \cdot \mathbf{y}$ and the matrix $\overline{\mathbf{x}^*}\mathbf{y}$. This affords a very simple way to derive the condition that must be fulfilled by a matrix S which is required to effect the transition from a normal coordinate system K to another normal system K'. We know that this transition leaves the magnitude of the vector $\mathbf{x}$ invariant so that $\sum x_i^* x_i = \sum x_i'^* x_i'$. This condition can be expressed by

$$\overline{\mathbf{x}^* \mathbf{x}} = \overline{\mathbf{x}'^* \mathbf{x}'} \tag{128}$$

Now $\mathbf{x}' = S\mathbf{x}$, and thus $\mathbf{x}'^* = S^* \mathbf{x}^*$ if S^* represents the matrix whose elements are the conjugates complex to those of S. According to (127) the dual matrix of $\mathbf{x}'^* = S^* \mathbf{x}^*$ is $\overline{\mathbf{x}^* S^*}$. Hence (128) can be written

$$\overline{\mathbf{x}^* \mathbf{x}} = \overline{\mathbf{x}^* S^*} S \mathbf{x}$$

from which we see that a unitary transformation S must satisfy the condition

$$\overline{S^*} S = E \tag{129}$$

When we multiply the last equation on the left by S, we get $S \overline{S^*} S = S$ and therefore $S \overline{S^*} = E$. If we multiply on the right by S^{-1} we find that $\overline{S^*} = S^{-1}$.

Of special importance in quantum mechanics are the so-called Hermitean matrices which are defined by $A = \overline{A^*}$ or $a_{ik} = a_{ki}^*$. Throughout this text we shall use the notation $\tilde{A}$ for $\overline{A^*}$; and thus a Hermitean matrix will be given by $A = \tilde{A}$. If A is Hermitean, the scalar product of $\mathbf{x}$ and $\mathbf{y} = A\mathbf{x}$ is

$$\mathbf{x} \cdot \mathbf{y} = \sum_n x_n^* y_n = \sum_{nk} x_n^* a_{nk} x_k$$

This expression is called the Hermitean form of $\mathbf{x}$ and assumes only positive values, for, since $a_{ik} = a_{ki}^*$, two terms $a_{nk} x_n^* x_k$ and $a_{kn} x_k^* x_n$ are conjugate complex and hence their sum is real.

It is readily seen that $\mathbf{x} \cdot A\mathbf{x} = A\mathbf{x} \cdot \mathbf{x}$, since (113) gives for the latter product

$$\sum y_k^* x_k = \sum a_{kn}^* x_n^* x_n = \sum x_n^* a_{nk} x_k$$

25. Transformation to Principal Axes. In order to get some idea about how to continue the mathematical procedure, let us recall the quantum-mechanical principle of correlating a transformation to any physical entity or, as we shall write from here on, to any observable. When the transformation is applied to the vector $\mathbf{x}$, we obtain another vector $A\mathbf{x}$ which in general differs from $\mathbf{x}$ in both magnitude and direction. However, certain vectors do exist, called the eigenvectors of the transformation, which are changed by the transformation into a multiple α of themselves, so that $\mathbf{x}$ and $A\mathbf{x}$ differ only in magnitude. Hence to each of the vectors we can assign a certain eigenvalue and a certain direction called a principal axis of the transformation. The fundamental idea of quantum mechanics then is this: when on a given system we carry out a measurement of an observable belonging to the operator A, the result must always be an eigenvalue α of A. Just which particular α will be observed depends on the direction of the vector representing the state. When $\mathbf{x}$ happens to coincide in direction with a principal axis, that α which is the eigenvalue for that direction will be the certain result of the measurement. For all other cases there is for any α only a certain probability which can be calculated from the direction of the representing vector. Thus quantum mechanics is interested primarily in the eigenvalues of the transformation, and as a consequence our most important task will be to work out a method which enables us to determine the eigenvalues and the directions of the principal axes for a given transformation A.

This problem is solved on the supposition that the matrix A is Hermitean, this type being of special interest in quantum mechanics, and also on the supposition that the vector space has a *finite* number of dimensions. Although it is true that in reality we are concerned with spaces having an infinite number of dimensions, it seems probable that the method to be developed will hold for that case as well.

In $(n + 1)$-dimensional space we lay out a normal coordinate system. Relative to K, the components of $\mathbf{x}$ may be given by x_0, x_1, x_2, $\cdots$, and the Hermitean A may be defined by

$$A = \begin{bmatrix} a_{00} & a_{01} & a_{02} & \cdots & a_{0n} \\ a_{10} & a_{11} & a_{12} & \cdots & a_{1n} \\ \cdot & \cdot & \cdot & & \\ \cdot & \cdot & \cdot & & \\ \cdot & \cdot & \cdot & & \\ a_{n0} & a_{n1} & a_{n2} & \cdots & a_{nn} \end{bmatrix}$$

The problem is to find another coordinate system K' such that in the transition $K \to K'$ the matrix A is converted to the diagonal matrix

$$A = \begin{bmatrix} \alpha_0 & 0 & 0 & \cdots & 0 \\ 0 & \alpha_1 & 0 & \cdots & 0 \\ 0 & 0 & \alpha_2 & \cdots & 0 \\ \cdot & \cdot & \cdot & & \cdot \\ \cdot & \cdot & \cdot & & \cdot \\ \cdot & \cdot & \cdot & & \cdot \\ 0 & \cdots & \cdots & \cdots & \alpha_n \end{bmatrix} \tag{130}$$

If we succeed in finding such a system we have solved the problem and can consider the α terms the eigenvalues, and the axes of K' the principal axes of A, for the equation $\mathbf{y} = A\mathbf{x}$ when referred to K' changes into $\mathbf{y}' = A'\mathbf{x}'$; that is,

$$y_0' = \alpha_0 x_0' \qquad y_1' = \alpha_1 x_1' \cdots \qquad y_n' = \alpha_n x_n'$$

Thus a vector $\mathbf{x}'$ with the components $x_0' = a$, $x_1' = x_2' = \cdots = x_n' = 0$ is transformed into $\mathbf{y}$ with components $y_0' = \alpha_0 a$, $y_1' = y_2' = \cdots = y_n' = 0$, a vector having the direction of the first axis of K', and changed only in magnitude. Hence $\mathbf{x}'$ is an eigenvector of A belonging to the eigenvalue α_0, and the same is true for every vector having the direction of any axis of K'.

If eigenvalues exist for A at all, there must exist also a system K', but of course there is no a priori certainty that K' is normal, so that, in the transition $K \to K'$, $|\mathbf{x}|^2$ is transformed into $|\mathbf{x}'|^2$. However, it can be shown that this is the case when A is Hermitean, so that $A = \tilde{A}$. Here we can achieve the diagonal form (130) by performing a unitary transformation. To prove this first let us consider the normal coordinate system K and determine a vector $\mathbf{x}(x_0, x_1, \cdots, x_n)$ which differs from the vector $\mathbf{y} = A\mathbf{x}$ in magnitude only, that is, $A\mathbf{x} = \alpha\mathbf{x}$, or, since the components of $A\mathbf{x}$ are given by $y_i = \sum a_{ik}x_k$,

$$y_i = \sum a_{ik}x_k = \alpha x_i \qquad (i = 0, 1, 2, \cdots)$$

This means that we must solve the homogeneous equations

$$(a_{00} - \alpha)x_0 + a_{01}x_1 + \cdots + a_{0n}x_n = 0$$
$$a_{10}x_0 + (a_{11} - \alpha)x_1 + \cdots + a_{1n}x_n = 0$$

$$\tag{131}$$

$$a_{n0}x_0 + a_{n1}x_1 + \cdots + (a_{nn} - \alpha)x_n = 0$$

in which α, x_1, x_2, $\cdots$, x_n are considered to be unknown but the a_{ik} terms are given. These equations can be solved only if the determinant equation below is satisfied.

$$\begin{vmatrix} a_{00} - \alpha & a_{01} & \cdots & a_{0n} \\ a_{10} & (a_{11} - \alpha) & \cdots & a_{1n} \\ \vdots & & & \\ a_{n0} & \cdots & \cdots & (a_{nn} - \alpha) \end{vmatrix} = 0$$

This is an equation of the $(n + 1)$th degree in α, and accordingly there are n solutions. Let one of these be α_0. Introducing this value in (131), we can solve these equations for a vector $\mathbf{x}_0$ with components x_0, $x_1, \cdots , x_n$ and we can construct a coordinate system K_0 so that one of the axes has the direction of $\mathbf{x}_0$. When the transformation A is referred to this system, A is changed into the matrix $A' = \|a_{ik}'\|$, which transforms a vector $x_0' = a$, $x_1' = x_2' = \cdots = x_n' = 0$ into $y_0' = \alpha a$, $y_1' = y_2' = \cdots = y_n' = 0$. Thus the following relations must be satisfied.

$$y_0' = \sum a_{0k}'x_k' = a_{00}'a = \alpha_0 a \qquad y_1' = a_{10}'a = 0 \qquad y_n' = a_{n0}'a = 0$$

From this it follows that $a_{00}' = \alpha_0$, $a_{10}' = \cdots = a_{n0}' = 0$. It is easy to prove that the a_{0i}' terms must vanish with the a_{i0}' ones, for, if S is the unitary matrix which effects the transition $K \rightarrow K_0$ by $\mathbf{x}' = S\mathbf{x}$, then, according to (126), $A' = SAS^{-1}$ and $\tilde{A}' = \tilde{S}^{-1}\tilde{A}\tilde{S}$. Now A is Hermitean and S is unitary, so that $\tilde{A} = A$, $\tilde{S} = S^{-1}$, and $\tilde{S}^{-1} = S$. Consequently we obtain $\tilde{A}' = SAS^{-1} = A'$, and thus A' is also Hermitean. This means that $a_{0i}' = a_{i0}'^* = 0$ for $i \neq k$.

Thus the transformation A when associated with the system K_0 is of the form

$$A' = \begin{bmatrix} \alpha & 0 & 0 & \cdots & 0 \\ 0 & a_{11}' & a_{12}' & \cdots & a_{1n}' \\ 0 & a_{21}' & a_{22}' & \cdots & a_{2n}' \\ \cdot & \cdot & \cdot & & \\ \cdot & \cdot & \cdot & & \\ \cdot & \cdot & \cdot & & \\ 0 & a_{n1}' & a_{n2}' & \cdots & a_{nn}' \end{bmatrix}$$

We refer now to the system K_0 and seek a vector $\mathbf{x}_1(x_0'x_1' \cdots x_n')$ which must satisfy two conditions:

(i) It must be perpendicular to $\mathbf{x}_0$.
(ii) It must represent an eigenvector of A.

The first condition requires that $x_0' = 0$, for the scalar product $(\mathbf{x}_0\mathbf{x}_1)$ equals zero only if this is so. The second condition gives us the n equations:

$$(a_{11}' - \alpha)x_1' + a_{12}'x_2' + \cdots + a_{1n}'x_n' \qquad = 0$$

$$\begin{matrix} \cdot & & \cdot & & \cdot \\ \cdot & & \cdot & & \cdot \\ \cdot & & \cdot & & \cdot \end{matrix} \qquad (132)$$

$$a_{n1}'x_1' \qquad + a_{n2}'x_2' + \cdots + (a_{nn}' - \alpha)x_n' = 0$$

Using these equations, we repeat the procedure to determine α_1, for which the determinant equation is

$$
\begin{vmatrix}
a_{11}' - \alpha & a_{12}' & \cdots & a_{1n}' \\
a_{21}' & a_{22}' - \alpha & \cdots & a_{2n}' \\
\cdot & \cdot & & \cdot \\
\cdot & \cdot & & \cdot \\
\cdot & \cdot & & \cdot \\
a_{n1}' & a_{n2}' & \cdots & a_{nn}' - \alpha
\end{vmatrix} = 0
$$

and with $\alpha = \alpha_1$ we obtain a solution $\mathbf{x}_1$ from (132). We then rotate the K_0 system about the fixed $\mathbf{x}_0$ axis until a second axis coincides with the direction of $\mathbf{x}_1$, this being possible since $\mathbf{x}_0$ and $\mathbf{x}_1$ are perpendicular. In this way a coordinate system K_1 is established relative to which the transformation A is represented by a matrix:

$$
A'' = \begin{bmatrix}
\alpha_0 & 0 & 0 & \cdots & 0 \\
0 & \alpha_1 & 0 & \cdots & 0 \\
0 & 0 & a_{22}' & \cdots & a_{2n}' \\
\cdot & & & & \\
\cdot & & & & \\
\cdot & & & & \\
0 & 0 & a_{n2}' & \cdots & a_{nn}'
\end{bmatrix}
$$

It is obvious that a continuation of this procedure ultimately will furnish a normal coordinate system for which A has the form of a diagonal matrix. Thus it can be asserted that in the case of a Hermitean transformation A there exists always a coordinate system the axes of which coincide with the principal axes of A.

If the eigenvalues all differ from each other, no other system besides K exists relative to which the transformation can be effected by a diagonal matrix.† If, however, two or more of the α terms agree, the

---

† Speaking more precisely, there is no system that differs from K in the directions of the axes. A certain arbitrariness, however, is left in the choice of the unit vectors, $\mathbf{e}_0 \mathbf{e}_1 \cdots \mathbf{e}_n$ which are required for the complete specification of the coordinate system. A given vector $\mathbf{x}$ is related to the $\mathbf{e}_i$ vectors by $\mathbf{x} = x_0 \mathbf{e}_0 + \cdots + x_n \mathbf{e}_n$, from which we see that the components x_i of $\mathbf{x}$ are determined by the $\mathbf{e}_i$ vectors. The unit vectors $\mathbf{e}_i$ must satisfy the condition $|\mathbf{e}_i|^2 = 1$; but this condition remains fulfilled when we multiply $\mathbf{e}_i$ by a factor of the form $e^{i\gamma_i}$. From K we then get another system K' relative to which the vector has other components x_i', which are related to the x_i components by the equation

$$
\mathbf{x} = x_0 \mathbf{e}_0 + \cdots + x_n \mathbf{e}_n = x_0' \mathbf{e}_0' + \cdots + x_n' \mathbf{e}_n'
$$

With $\mathbf{e}_i' = e e^{i\gamma_i}$, we get from this equation $x_i' = x_i e^{-i\gamma_i}$. This corresponds to a

K system is not uniquely determined because that part of the system which has the same value for the α terms is capable of a rotation within the space associated with a common α without A losing its diagonal form. For example, let us assume $\alpha_0 = \alpha_1 = \alpha_2 = \alpha$. Then the transformation $\mathbf{y} = A\mathbf{x}$ in the principal system K is described by the equations $y_0 = \alpha x_0$, $y_1 = \alpha x_1$, $y_2 = \alpha x_2$, $\cdots$. Now we replace K by another system K' by exchanging the first three axes of K for three others, keeping the remainder, the condition being fulfilled that the three new axes are not only perpendicular to one another but to all the rest as well. The transition $K \to K'$ is described by the equations

$$x_0' = s_{00}x_0 + s_{01}x_1 + s_{02}x_2$$
$$x_1' = s_{10}x_0 + s_{11}x_1 + s_{12}x_2 \qquad (133)$$
$$x_2' = s_{20}x_0 + s_{21}x_1 + s_{22}x_2$$

with the components from x_3 upward being unchanged. The components x_0, x_1, and x_2 are changed by the operator A in the ratio α. Because of (133), this means that x_0', x_1', x_2' are changed in the same ratio, so that the matrix A is diagonal whether referred to K or K'.

If the α eigenvalues are not all different one from the other, the system is degenerated. Hence a degenerated A does not define the principal coordinate system uniquely but permits a unitary rotation of the system within the space of degeneracy.†

---

transformation of the form

$$S = \begin{bmatrix} e^{-i\gamma_1} & 0 & \cdots & 0 \\ 0 & e^{-i\gamma_2} & \cdots & 0 \\ \cdots & \cdots & \cdots & \cdots \\ 0 & \cdots & \cdots & e^{-i\gamma_n} \end{bmatrix}$$

Thus, in the case of a different α, all coordinate systems relative to which A appears as a diagonal matrix coincide in the directions of the axes but differ by a unitary matrix of the kind represented above.

† In order to determine the matrix S corresponding to such a rotation we assume that the eigenvalues α_0, α_1, $\cdots$ occur r_0, r_1, r_2, $\cdots$ times respectively. By S^{r_0}, S^{r_1}, S^{r_2}, $\cdots$ we denote unitary matrices consisting of r_0, r_1, r_2, $\cdots$ rows and as many columns. Then we may maintain: If all these matrices are amalgamated into one matrix in such a way that S^{r_0}, S^{r_1}, S^{r_2} are arranged along the diagonal, as

$$S = \begin{bmatrix} S^{r_0} & 0 & 0 & \cdots \\ 0 & S^{r_1} & 0 & \cdots \\ 0 & 0 & S^{r_2} & \cdots \\ \cdots & \cdots & \cdots & \cdots \end{bmatrix}$$

the matrix A retains its diagonal form when the principal coordinate system K is changed, with the help of the above, into another system K'. The reader will have no difficulty in verifying this statement by applying (126).

The theorem concerning the transformation to principal axes can be formulated in yet another way which brings in the Hermitean form, $A\mathbf{x} \cdot \mathbf{x}$ defined in Section 24. As we know, a unitary operator which changes $\mathbf{x}$ and $\mathbf{y}$ into $\mathbf{x}'$ and $\mathbf{y}'$ respectively leaves the scalar product $\mathbf{x} \cdot \mathbf{y} = \sum x_n{}^* y_n$ invariant, that is, $\mathbf{x} \cdot \mathbf{y} = \sum x_n{}^* y_n = \mathbf{x}' \cdot \mathbf{y}' = \sum x_n{}'^* y_n{}'$. Therefore the transition to the principal system will change $A\mathbf{x} \cdot \mathbf{x}$ into $A'\mathbf{x}' \cdot \mathbf{x}'$ or $\sum a_{ik} x_i{}^* x_k$ into $\alpha_0 x_0{}'^* x_0{}' + \alpha_1 x_1{}'^* x_1{}' + \cdots$, giving us the theorem: *Any Hermitean form $\sum a_{ik} x_i{}^* x_k$ can be changed into $\alpha_0 x_0{}'^* x_0{}' + \alpha_1 x_1{}'^* x_1{}' + \cdots$ by a transformation to the principal axes of A.*

A question of importance in quantum mechanics is that which seeks to learn under what conditions two Hermitean operators, A and B, can be made diagonal simultaneously, that is, by the same transformation. It is easy to show that this is possible only for two matrices which are commutative, so that $AB = BA$. Let us assume that K' is a coordinate system in which both operators are of the required form.

$$
A' = \begin{bmatrix} \alpha_0 & & & \\ & \alpha_1 & & \\ & & 2 & \\ & & & \ddots \\ & & & & \ddots \end{bmatrix}
\qquad
B' = \begin{bmatrix} \beta_0 & & & \\ & \beta_1 & & \\ & & \beta_2 & \\ & & & \ddots \\ & & & & \ddots \end{bmatrix}
$$

The $A'B'$ is a matrix with the elements

$$
p_{ik} = \sum_l a_{il} b_{lk} = \begin{cases} \alpha_i \beta_i & \text{for } i = k \\ 0 & \text{for } i \neq k \end{cases}
$$

Thus $A'B'$ is diagonal with $p_{ii} = \alpha_i \beta_i$, and exactly the same holds for $B'A'$ since in that case we simply interchange α_i and β_i. Therefore $A'B' = B'A'$. If, now, S is a matrix corresponding to the transition $K \to K'$, then, according to (126), $A' = SAS^{-1}$ and $B' = SBS^{-1}$, so that the equality $A'B' = B'A'$ can be written

$$
SAS^{-1}SBS^{-1} = SBS^{-1}SAS^{-1}
$$

and, since $S^{-1}S = E$ and $AEB = AB$, we have

$$
AB = BA
$$

And so, to have a simultaneous transformation to principal axes, A

and B must be commutative. Although it is not difficult to prove that this condition is sufficient as well, we shall accept it without proof.

26. Functions of Matrices. When a group of matrices, $A_1 A_2$ $\cdots A_n$, are given, new matrices can be formed from these by addition and multiplication. By so doing, we get functions of the A_i matrices. The simplest examples are the sum, $S = A_i + A_k$, and the product, $P = A_i A_k$. Functions of a general type are obtained when the A_i matrices are multiplied with one another in an arbitrary succession, and these products, when provided with coefficients, are united as polynomials. In such a manner we obtain the function

$$F(A_1 \cdots A_n) = \sum c_{i_1 i_2 \ldots i_m} A_{i_1} A_{i_2} \cdots A_{i_m}$$

where i_1, i_2, $\cdots$, i_m signify equal or different numbers of the sequence 1, 2, 3, $\cdots$, n. When in all terms of F the succession of factors is inverted and the conjugate complex values c^* are substituted for the coefficient c, we obtain

$$G(A_1 \cdots A_n) = \sum c_{i_1 i_2 \ldots i_m}{}^* A_{i_m} A_{i_{m-1}} \cdots A_{i_1}$$

which is called the *adjunct* function of F. If G and F are identical, F is said to be adjunct to itself. For example, $F = A_1{}^2 + A_2{}^2 + \cdots A_n{}^2$ is such. We shall note here a theorem which will be used later: if $A_1 A_2 \cdots A_n$ are Hermitean and F is self-adjunct, F is Hermitean also. Indeed we can write

$$\tilde{F} = \sum c_{i_1 i_2 \ldots i_m}{}^* \tilde{A}_{i_m} \cdots \tilde{A}_{i_1} = \sum c_{i_1 i_2 \ldots i_m}{}^* A_{i_m} \cdots A_{i_1} = G = F$$

When we transform from a system K to which the matrices are referred to another system K', carrying out a unitary transformation, the matrices are changed into

$$A_1{}' = SA_1 S^{-1} \qquad A_2{}' = SA_2 S^{-1}$$

and so on. From this it follows that the product $A_{i_1} A_{i_2} \cdots A_{i_m}$ becomes

$$A_{i_1}{}' A_{i_2}{}' \cdots A_{i_m}{}' = SA_{i_1} S^{-1} SA_{i_2} S^{-1} \cdots = SA_{i_1} A_{i_2} \cdots A_{i_m} S^{-1}$$

Thus an arbitrary function of matrices F is transformed by S just as a single matrix into

$$F' = SFS^{-1} \qquad\qquad (134)$$

Operations having the nature of differentiation can be performed on functions of matrices, and these processes can be defined in different ways. For the purposes of quantum mechanics it is convenient to define the derivative of a function as follows: If F is a function of the matrices $X, Y, Z, \cdots$, the derivative of F with respect to X is

$$\frac{\partial}{\partial X} F(XYZ \cdots) = \lim_{a=0} \frac{F(X + aE, YZ \cdots) - F(XYZ \cdots)}{a}$$

where aE is the unit matrix multiplied by a. The ordinary derivative is given by

$$\frac{\partial f}{\partial x} (xyz \cdots) = \lim \frac{f(x + a, yz \cdots) - f(xyz \cdots)}{a}$$

from which we see that the only difference between the derivative of $F(XYZ)$ and the ordinary one is that X is increased by aE and not simply by a, which would be meaningless since a matrix cannot be added to an ordinary number. Accordingly, if $F = X$,

$$\frac{\partial F}{\partial X} = \lim \frac{X + aE - X}{a} = E$$

If $F = XX = X^2$,

$$\frac{\partial F}{\partial X} = \lim \frac{(X + aE)^2 - X^2}{a} = 2X$$

If $F = XYZ$,

$$\frac{\partial F}{\partial X} = \lim \frac{(X + aE)YZ - XYZ}{a} = YZ$$

If F_1 and F_2 are two different functions of XYZ, it is clear that

$$\frac{\partial}{\partial X} (F_1 + F_2) = \frac{\partial F_1}{\partial X} + \frac{\partial F_2}{\partial X}$$

Furthermore

$$\frac{\partial}{\partial X} (F_1 F_2) = \lim \frac{F_1(X + aE)F_2(X + aE) - F_1(X)F_2(X)}{a}$$

The numerator can be put into the form

$$F_1(X + aE)[F_2(X + aE) - F_2(X)] + [F_1(X + aE) - F_1(X)]F_2(X)$$

Therefore

$$\frac{\partial(F_1 F_2)}{\partial X} = \frac{\partial F_1}{\partial X} F_2 + F_1 \frac{\partial F_2}{\partial X} \qquad (135)$$

A matrix, then, can be a function of other matrices. It can also just as well be a function of an ordinary variable such as time. This case arises if the elements of A are functions of time; $a_{ik} = a_{ik}(t)$. The derivative dA/dt is defined by the matrix $\|da_{ik}/dt\|$. For example, if we consider the vector $\mathbf{x}$ to be a matrix which contains the elements of $\mathbf{x}$ in the first column, all the other elements being zero, then $d\mathbf{x}/dt$ is the matrix

$$\frac{d\mathbf{x}}{dt} = \begin{bmatrix} \dfrac{dx_0}{dt} & 0 & 0 & \cdots \\[2ex] \dfrac{dx_1}{dt} & 0 & 0 & \cdots \\[1ex] \cdot & & & \\ \cdot & & & \\ \cdot & & \cdots \cdots \cdots \end{bmatrix}$$

The preceding matrix calculus is not sufficient for all applications to quantum mechanics. However, it is desirable to defer the remaining requirements until the occasion for their use arises later. At this point we wish to return to the field of physics in order to carry out the plan mentioned in Section 21.

27. The Quantum-Mechanical Interpretation of Matrices. In contrast to classical theory, it has been made clear that quantum mechanics holds it to be impossible to determine with any desired accuracy the state of a system as far as all observables are concerned. If p and q are two canonically conjugate observables, a measurement of q cancels the result of an antecedent measurement of p and vice versa, thus making it impossible to arrive at an exact knowledge of both p and q. Hence, according to quantum mechanics, it is meaningless to imagine a system to be described by specifying the values of all observables. No experiment could justify such a description. The only way in which we can proceed is as follows. We consider a state which is subject to certain physical conditions. What are we able to find out about the state of the system? As we know, there is the difficulty that one measurement is sufficient to destroy the state and thus all further measurements will be useless. Thus, as long as our investigation has to do with one system only, the results will consist of a single datum. However, the state we are investigating can be realized for a great number of systems which are exposed to exactly the same conditions. Then we can make as many measurements as there are systems and work out a statistical ensemble that will inform us about the probability of finding a given value of an

observable.   We assume that the same statistical array holds for any
sufficiently large partial assemblage.   Thus the conditions are such
that they guarantee any system to be in the same state.   The state
is then called "well-defined in the quantum-mechanical sense," and
we consider it as completely described by the statistical array which
contains everything that experimental possibilities permit to be
known about the state.

Thus the new mechanics is satisfied with a definition of the state
that is far short of the requirements of classical physics.   It is possible
that the value of not even one observable is known with certainty,
and yet the state possesses a maximum of definition.   Of course,
there are states too for which the values of one or more observables,
such as energy and angular momentum, have certainty.   But it is
impossible that this apply to all observables, for in the case of two
canonically conjugate observables such as coordinates and momenta
a simultaneous exact measurement is impossible.

It is the purpose of quantum mechanics to represent any state of a
given system by a unit vector in a Hilbert space with an infinite
number of dimensions and to interpret as probability amplitudes the
components of $\mathbf{x}$ along the axes of certain coordinate systems, the
probabilities being set equal to the squares of the lengths.   As for the
coordinate systems, it is assumed *that any observable is representable
by a matrix operator and that the coordinate system associated with an
observable is defined by the principal axes of the operator.*   At first this
may seem a rather strange procedure, but it is easy to realize that the
method is exactly adequate to the possibilities of observation.

Let us consider a system the energy of which can only assume values
$E_0, E_1, \cdot \cdot \cdot$, and which is supposed to be not degenerated as far as
the energy is concerned, so that there are not two different states of
the same energy.   The conditions to which the system is subject may
be such that the energy value E_k may be expected with the probability
$|x_k|^2$, $\left(\sum |x_k|^2 = 1 \right)$.   In the Hilbert space we then can scaffold a
normal coordinate system K, the axes of which can be correlated to
the different E_k, and construct a vector the components of which
relative to K are given by $x_k = |x_k| e^{i\delta_k}$, the δ terms being constants
which may be left undetermined for the present.

We now correlate a linear operator with any observable of the
system, that is, with any coordinate in general such as the coordinates
and momentum components of the electron belonging to an atom.
When referred to K, the operator shall be described by a Hermitean
matrix.   We shall see later that only Hermitean matrices enter into

this question.   We demand that the *eigenvalues be given by the possible values of the observable under consideration.*   At the moment we are not interested in how these operators or matrices can be determined. We are concerned only with the method and assume that we already know the operator for any observable.   For example, in the case of a linear oscillator the operators associated with coordinate, momentum, and such of the oscillating particle may be the matrices Q, P, $\cdots$ respectively.   Then every one of these defines a normal coordinate system K', K'', $\cdots$ by the directions of its eigenvectors.   The postulate of quantum mechanics then is: *The vector* x, *which, when referred to the energy system* K, *has the components* x_k, *will have, when referred to the systems* K', K'', $\cdots$, *the components* x_k', x_k'', $\cdots$ *which by the values* $|x_k'|^2$, $|x_k''|^2$, $\cdots$ *determine the probabilities which a measurement of observables under consideration provides for the eigenvalue belonging to the kth axis of the corresponding coordinate system.*

We shall use the theorem first to fix the phase constant δ_k which we left undetermined.   From the statistics of the energy values we can infer only the $|x_k|^2$ values, so that measurements of the energy alone are insufficient to determine the vector x uniquely.   To understand this we must recall the possibilities for the simultaneous measurement of two conjugate quantities according to the uncertainty relations. If the measurement of one of them is inexact, this lack of exactness is compensated by the possibility of measuring the other within certain limits of accuracy.   Thus a state of which the energy is not exactly known can be considered as well-defined only if, together with the energy, the conjugate coordinate (the time t as the phase of the motion) also is measured with the maximum of accuracy which accords with the uncertainty relations.   This is why the terms $|x_k|^2$ do not suffice for the unique determination of the vector x.   Besides the energy we must take into account the phase (or another observable that commutes with the phase) in order to define the state uniquely.   This means that the values are to be chosen in such a way that the components of x in the coordinate system associated with phase provide the correct probability amplitudes of the phase.   Only then is the vector x fixed uniquely and, if quantum mechanics is correct, must now furnish automatically the correct probability amplitudes for all other observables of the system.

The phase becomes meaningless only if the direction of x coincides with an axis of K, that is, if for a certain k, $|x_k|^2 = 1$, all other x_i being zero.   Then the state corresponds to a certain energy $E = E_k$, and the components of x in the phase coordinate system are all equal since the phase can assume any value with the same probability.   In this case **x** is determined uniquely by $|x_k|^2 = 1$ except for a factor $e^{i\delta}$ which has no physical meaning.

28. The Commutation Relations. We have seen that in quantum mechanics there is correlated to any observable of a system a linear operator which transforms a vector **x** into a vector **y**. The relation between the observable and the operator is this: when the vector **x** with components x_k in the arbitrarily chosen reference system K has the components x_k' in the direction of the kth principal axis of the operator, the probability that a measurement of the observable will furnish the eigenvalue α_k belonging to the corresponding axis is given by $x_k'^* x_k'$. The values α_k represent the possible results of the measurement, and if **x** should have the direction of the axis we may expect α_k with certainty. From this interpretation of the formalism we can infer at once an important relationship between the matrices associated with two canonically conjugate observables. If we designate two such matrices by P and Q, associated, for example, with the coordinate and momentum of a linear oscillator, and by K' and K'' the corresponding principal systems, we can maintain that the axes of K' cannot coincide with those of K''. If this were so, a vector lying in the common direction of two principal axes would correspond to a state which is sharply defined relative to both of the observables simultaneously. This would be a contradiction to the fundamental postulate of quantum mechanics. Accordingly we can infer that two matrices P and Q belonging to canonically conjugate observables cannot be transformed to principal axes simultaneously. According to Section 26 this conclusion can be expressed by $QP - PQ \neq 0$. This statement implies that the two intervals of accuracy, Δq and Δp, within which the values of q and p are found by measurement, can, by no measuring arrangement, be confined simultaneously to zero. According to the uncertainty relations under no circumstances can the product $\Delta q \, \Delta p$ be made less than h. In quantum mechanics this fundamental postulate is expressed by the so-called commutation relations,

$$QP - PQ = \frac{\hbar}{i} E \qquad (136)$$

To prove this we shall consider the two matrices Q and P as representing coordinate x and momentum ξ respectively of a particle moving in the x direction. Since both these quantities may assume any value between $-\infty$ and $+\infty$, each of the operators possesses a continuous set of eigenvalues and as a result there is a continuous infinity of principal axes forming the systems K' and K''. Therefore the components of the vector **x** can have values relative to K' and K'' only in the form of functions $u(x)$ and $\omega(\xi)$. We have used these functions previously wherein u^*u and $\omega^*\omega$ were defined as probabilities of the values x and ξ. This is in accord with the present interpretation of u and ω as components of $\mathbf{x}$.

Now let us consider the transition from the principal energy system K to the x system K'. This transformation is effected by a transformation matrix $S = \|s_{ik}\|$. If the components of $\mathbf{x}$ in K and K' are represented by x_k and x_k' [x_k' is identical with $u(x)$], then $\mathbf{x}' = S\mathbf{x}$ or $x_k' = \sum s_{ki}x_i$. In the transformation Q and P become

$$Q' = SQS^{-1} \quad \text{and} \quad P' = SPS^{-1}$$

These new matrices have a peculiar nature in that they refer to coordinate systems with continuous sets of axes and thus themselves have continuous structure. When they act as operators on $\mathbf{x}$, which has components $u(x)$ in K', the vector is transformed to $Q'\mathbf{x}$ and $P'\mathbf{x}$ respectively. Now, according to Section 26, we obtain $Q'\mathbf{x}$ and $P'\mathbf{x}$ by making use of the multipliers x and $-(\hbar/i)(\partial/\partial x)$ respectively. Hence $Q'\mathbf{x}$ is a vector with components $xu(x)$, and $P'\mathbf{x}$ is one with components $-(\hbar/i)(\partial u/\partial x)$. Furthermore $Q'P'\mathbf{x}$ is the vector obtained when P' and Q' operate on $\mathbf{x}$ in that order. In this case the components of $Q'P'\mathbf{x}$ are $-x(\hbar/i)(\partial u/\partial x)$, whereas the components of $P'Q'\mathbf{x}$ are $-(\hbar/i)(\partial/\partial x)xu$. Hence $(Q'P' - P'Q')\mathbf{x}$ is

$$\frac{\hbar}{i}u = \frac{\hbar}{i}\mathbf{x} = \frac{\hbar}{i}E\mathbf{x}$$

or

$$Q'P' - P'Q' = \frac{\hbar}{i}E$$

Now

$$Q' = SQS^{-s} \quad \text{and} \quad P' = SPS^{-1}$$

Therefore

$$S(QP - PQ)S^{-1} = \frac{\hbar}{i}E = \frac{\hbar}{i}SES^{-1}$$

and

$$QP - PQ = \frac{\hbar}{i}E$$

We see that this proof eventually reverts to the uncertainty relations, for the assumption that x and ξ are represented by the operators x and $-(\hbar/i)(\partial/\partial x)$ is based on the relation

$$u(x) = \int c(\xi)e^{-(i/\hbar)x\xi}\,d\xi$$

However, we were led to this relation by the desire to represent the state of a particle by a wave packet, as only in this way can we give a description that satisfies the uncertainty relations.

Thus the commutation relation (136) is nothing but the translation of the uncertainty relations into matrix notation, and consequently we may be certain that it holds for any pair of canonically conjugate observables.

On the other hand, let us consider two observables which can be measured simultaneously with any desired accuracy. In this case it must be possible to transform the corresponding matrices simultaneously to principal axes, for there exist states the vector of which coincides simultaneously with a principal axis of A and one of B. This means that the matrices A and B are commutative so that $AB - BA = 0$. The coordinates x, y, z, are examples of observables which can be measured simultaneously. The same is true of the momentum components $\xi \eta \zeta$. If we denote the corresponding matrices by Q_x, Q_y, Q_z and P_x, P_y, P_z, then

$$Q_i Q_k - Q_k Q_i = 0 \qquad \text{and} \qquad P_i P_k - P_k P_i = 0 \qquad (i, k = x, y, z)$$

Moreover we can write

$$Q_i P_k - P_k Q_i = 0 \qquad (i \neq k)$$

because, for example, x and η can be measured independently.

The general meaning of the commutation relations can be expressed as follows: According to quantum mechanics the relation between two observables depends essentially on whether the possibility of a simultaneous measurement is given. If given, the corresponding matrices must be capable of a simultaneous transformation to principal axes, that is, they are commutative. If not given, $QP \neq PQ$. For the special case of canonically conjugate observables, $QP - PQ = (\hbar/i)E$.

If two hermitean matrices Q and P satisfy (136), we shall call them canonical, implying by this that the matrices are correlated to each other in the same sense as two canonical entities of classical mechanics.

It is readily seen that canonical matrices have to be infinite, since for finite matrices the sum of the diagonal elements, the so-called "spur" of $QP - PQ$, would be $\sum (q_{ik}p_{ki} - p_{ik}q_{ki}) = 0$, whereas according to (136) the sum should be $n(\hbar/i)$, where n is the order of the matrices. Thus (136) can be satisfied only by matrices for which $\sum (q_{ik}p_{ki} - p_{ik}q_{ki}) \neq 0$. This is possible only for infinite matrices, for then there is a difference depending on whether the summation $\sum q_{ik}p_{ki}$ is carried out first over i or over k.

29. Hermitean Forms and Expectation Values. When we represent the state of a system by a vector $\mathbf{x}$ of components x_k relative to the coordinate system K of the energy, the result of an energy measurement is expected to be E_k with the probability $x_k^* x_k$. Thus the state $\mathbf{x}(x_0, x_1, \cdots)$, as far as energy is concerned, corresponds to the expectation value

$$\bar{E} = \sum x_k^* x_k E_k \tag{137}$$

according to which, if $\mathbf{x}$ has the direction of the kth axis of K,

$$\bar{E} = E_k$$

Let us further consider an arbitrary observable a corresponding to the Hermitean matrix A. Let us denote the eigenvalues of A by $\alpha_0, \alpha_1, \alpha_2, \cdots$ and let the normal coordinate system scaffolded by the principal axes of A be K'. Then the α_i terms represent the possible results of a measurement and are found with the probabilities $x_i'^* x_i'$. The x_i' terms can be evaluated from the x_i terms by a transformation matrix S which performs the transition $K \rightarrow K'$ according to $\mathbf{x}' = S\mathbf{x}$ or $x_i' = \sum s_{ik} x_k$. Thus the probability $x_i'^* x_i'$ can be written

$$x_i'^* x_i' = \sum_{km} s_{ik}^* x_k^* s_{im} x_m$$

If the vector $\mathbf{x}$ signifies an energy state, $E = E_k$, that is, if all the x_i vanish with the exception of $|x_k|^2 = 1$, we have

$$x_i'^* x_i' = s_{ik}^* s_{ik} = |s_{ik}|^2$$

Therefore the matrix S can be given the following definition: The elements of the kth column, s_{ik}, give, by $|s_{ik}|^2$, the probabilities that a will have the value α_i for a state of energy E_k.

There is yet another important theorem. Again consider an arbitrary state $\mathbf{x}(x_0, x_1, \cdots)$ and determine the expectation value of a quantity a. This can be expressed by

$$\bar{a} = \sum x_k'^* x_k' \alpha_k$$

According to (113) this can be interpreted as the scalar product of two vectors the components of which, relative to K', are x_k' and $x_k'\alpha$ respectively. The first vector is simply $\mathbf{x}$, and the other is identical with $A\mathbf{x}$, for the operator A has the effect of changing the x_k' terms into $\alpha_k x_k'$ because the axes of K' are the eigenvectors of A. Thus

$$\bar{a} = (\mathbf{x}, A\mathbf{x}) = \sum x_i^* a_{ik} x_k \tag{138}$$

This equation shows why a Hermitean matrix must be correlated to any observable. Let us assume first that $\mathbf{x}$ has the direction of an energy axis. The sum reduces to $a_{ii}x_i{}^*x_i$, and the diagonal elements of A must be real since, by its very nature, the expectation value of a is always real. Furthermore, if $\mathbf{x}$ has only two components x_i and x_k which are different from zero, we have

$$\bar{a} = a_{ik}x_i{}^*x_k + a_{ki}x_k{}^*x_i + a_{ii}x_i{}^*x_i + a_{kk}x_k{}^*x_k$$

and this sum is real only if $a_{ik} = a_{ki}{}^*$ or $A = \tilde{A}$. Therefore a physical entity can be connected only with a Hermitean matrix and we can state the following theorem: If A is the matrix belonging to the observable a, the expectation value of a for the state represented by the vector $\mathbf{x}$ is given by $\sum a_{ik}x_i{}^*x_k$. In this theorem, also, the expectation value $\bar{E}$ of (137) is implied, since, relative to the system K which consists of the principal energy axes, the operator of the energy is defined by the diagonal matrix,

$$\begin{bmatrix} E_0 & 0 & 0 & \cdots \\ 0 & E_1 & 0 & \cdots \\ 0 & 0 & E_2 & \cdots \\ \cdots & \cdots & \cdots & \cdots \end{bmatrix}$$

so that $\sum a_{ik}x_i{}^*x_k = \sum E_i x_i{}^*x_i$.

Up to this point the energy has been distinguished by defining the vector $\mathbf{x}$ in terms of components relative to the principal system K of the energy. It goes without saying that this preference for a certain observable is quite arbitrary and appears justified only because of the special importance of the energy. We could, as well, define the vector by its components $x_k{}'$ relative to the system K' of any other observable. Then the matrices have to be changed into

$$A' = SAS^{-1}$$

S being the unitary transformation matrix corresponding to the transition $K \to K'$. The energy operator H then loses its character of a diagonal matrix and transforms into $H' = SHS^{-1}$, with the elements

$$h_{ik}{}' = \sum_{mn} s_{im}h_{mn}s_{nk}{}^{-1} = \sum_m s_{im}E_m s_{mk}{}^{-1}$$

The formulas for the expectation values are not changed by the transition to another coordinate system, since $\bar{a}$ is given by the scalar product $\mathbf{x} \cdot A\mathbf{x}$, which remains invariant and is expressed in the K'

system by

$$\mathbf{x} \cdot A\mathbf{x} = \mathbf{x}' \cdot A'\mathbf{x} = \sum a_{ik}' x_i'^* x_k'$$

Thus the same physical entity is represented by different matrices which depend on the coordinate system to which the representation is referred and which are connected with each other by unitary transformations. A unitary transformation does not destroy the Hermitean character of the matrices. Together with A, $A' = SAS^{-1}$ is also Hermitean, for, since

$$\tilde{S} = S^{-1} \quad \text{and} \quad \tilde{S}^{-1} = S$$

$$\tilde{A}' = \tilde{S}^{-1} \tilde{A} \tilde{S} = SAS^{-1} = A'$$

30. Coordinate Systems with a Continuous Infinity of Axes. The Passage from Matrix to Wave Mechanics. We are confronted with a peculiar situation when the representing vector $\mathbf{x}$ is referred to a system K which is the principal system of an observable with a continuous infinity of eigenvalues. Examples of such are the coordinate x and the momentum ξ of a particle, for the measurement of these may furnish any value between $-\infty$ and $+\infty$. *When the representation is referred to such a coordinate system, matrix mechanics takes on the form of wave mechanics.*

In what follows, x signifies an observable which can assume any value between $-\infty$ and $+\infty$. Then K consists of a continuity of axes, all of them belonging to a certain value of x. If the vector $\mathbf{x}$ has the direction of any of these axes, a measurement of x furnishes the value belonging to the axis, and we can say that the vector has the "direction x." For every axis let us define a vector $\mathbf{e}_x$, the subscript denoting its correlation to the eigenvalue. (We can denumerate the axes no longer.) As the axes of K are orthogonal to one another, the scalar product of two vectors $\mathbf{e}_x$ and $\mathbf{e}_{x'}$ must vanish, that is, $\mathbf{e}_x \cdot \mathbf{e}_{x'} = 0$. This corresponds to the second equation of (117) in Section 22. The first equation, $|\mathbf{e}_x|^2 = 1$, no longer holds, for if it did we could not possibly arrive at an appropriate formalism. To arrive at a simple theory the vectors $\mathbf{e}_x$ must be chosen in such a way that the integral of $\mathbf{e}_x \cdot \mathbf{e}_{x'}$ over a domain surrounding x, however small this domain be chosen, has the value unity. Thus

$$\int (\mathbf{e}_x \cdot \mathbf{e}_{x'}) \, dx' = 1 \tag{139}$$

As $\mathbf{e}_x \cdot \mathbf{e}_{x'} = 0$ for $x' \neq x$, the integral may be extended from $-\infty$ to $+\infty$. The usual notation for the equation is

$$\mathbf{e}_x \cdot \mathbf{e}_{x'} = \delta(x - x') \tag{140}$$

$\delta(x - x')$ being defined as an improper function of x which vanishes when x' is not equal to x. When x equals x', however, it becomes infinite in such a way that the integral has the value unity. The transition from matrix to wave mechanics is carried out in such a way that, in the case of a system K with a continuous infinity of axes, equation (140) replaces (117).

In order to develop the new formalism let us consider the vector $\mathbf{x}$. Designate its components relative to K by $\psi(x)$. This new function $\psi(x)$ is used now instead of $x_0 x_1 \cdots$, since the components are no longer denumerable. Accordingly the vector $\mathbf{x}$ will be represented by the equation

$$\mathbf{x} = \int \mathbf{e}_x \psi(x) \, dx \qquad (141)$$

which takes the place of the equation $\mathbf{x} = \sum x_i \mathbf{e}_i$. Because of (140) this gives us, for $|\mathbf{x}|^2$,

$$|\mathbf{x}|^2 = \mathbf{x} \cdot \mathbf{x} = \int \psi^*(x) \, dx \int \psi(x') \, dx' \; \mathbf{e}_x \cdot \mathbf{e}_{x'}$$
$$= \int \psi^*(x) \, dx \int \psi(x') \, \delta(x - x') \, dx' = \int \psi^* \psi \, dx$$

This means that we can interpret $\psi^* \psi \, dx$ as the probability of x having a value between x and $x + dx$ so that we can normalize $\mathbf{x}$ by the requirement $\int \psi^* \psi \, dx = 1$.

Now in addition to K we introduce another system K' associated with an observable ξ which also has a continuous character. We shall denote the unit vectors of K' by $\mathbf{e}_\xi$ and the components of $\mathbf{x}$ relative to K' by χ_ξ. Then we have

$$\mathbf{x} = \int \mathbf{e}_x \psi(x) \, dx = \int \mathbf{e}_\xi \chi(\xi) \, d\xi$$

By forming the scalar product $\mathbf{e}_x \cdot \mathbf{x}$ we get

$$\mathbf{e}_x \cdot \mathbf{x} = \int (\mathbf{e}_x \cdot \mathbf{e}_{x'}) \psi(x') \, dx' = \int (\mathbf{e}_x \cdot \mathbf{e}_\xi) \chi(\xi) \, d\xi$$

from which it follows that

$$\psi(x) = \int (\mathbf{e}_x \cdot \mathbf{e}_\xi) \chi(\xi) \, d\xi \qquad (142)$$

The scalar products occurring in the integral will depend, of course, on the nature of the observables x and ξ. Therefore we shall evaluate the case in which x and ξ signify the coordinate and momentum component of a particle. According to Section 28 the operator of ξ in the K system is $-(\hbar/i)(\partial/\partial x)$ and has the eigenfunctions $\alpha e^{-(i/\hbar)x\xi}$, where α is still an undetermined constant. These eigenfunctions represent the resolution relative to the K axes of a vector $\mathbf{e}_\xi$. The constant α can be determined with the aid of the condition expressed by (140). Setting $\mathbf{e}_\xi = \int \mathbf{e}_x \alpha e^{-(i/\hbar)x\xi}\, dx$, we obtain

$$\int (\mathbf{e}_\xi \cdot \mathbf{e}_{\xi'})\, d\xi' = \alpha^2 \int d\xi' \int e^{(i/\hbar)x\xi}\, dx \int (\mathbf{e}_x \cdot \mathbf{e}_{x'}) e^{-(i/\hbar)x'\xi'}\, dx'$$

$$= \alpha^2 \int d\xi' \int e^{-(i/\hbar)x(\xi'-\xi)}\, dx$$

$$= \lim_{g \doteq \infty} \alpha^2 \int \frac{2\hbar \sin g(\xi' - \xi)}{\xi' - \xi}\, d\xi'$$

Hence, by (139),

$$\lim_{g \doteq \infty} \alpha^2 \int g\, \frac{2\hbar \sin g(\xi' - \xi)}{g(\xi' - \xi)}\, d(\xi' - \xi) = \alpha^2 \hbar 2\pi = 1$$

$$\therefore\ \alpha = h^{-\frac{1}{2}}$$

Because $\mathbf{e}_\xi = h^{-\frac{1}{2}} \int \mathbf{e}_{x'} e^{-(i/\hbar)x'\xi}\, dx'$ and because of (140), we now obtain for $\mathbf{e}_x \cdot \mathbf{e}_\xi$

$$\mathbf{e}_x \cdot \mathbf{e}_\xi = h^{-\frac{1}{2}} \int (\mathbf{e}_x \cdot \mathbf{e}_{x'}) e^{-(i/\hbar)x'\xi}\, dx' = h^{-\frac{1}{2}} e^{-(i/\hbar)x\xi} \qquad (143)$$

Accordingly equation (142) changes over into the relation

$$\psi(x) = h^{-\frac{1}{2}} \int \chi(\xi) e^{-(i/\hbar)x\xi}\, d\xi$$

which, when applied to xyz, leads to the wave mechanics equation (60').

In a coordinate system with a continuity of axes, the matrix is replaced by a linear operator D by means of which a vector $\mathbf{x}$, described by a function $\psi(x)$, is transformed into $\mathbf{x}'$ corresponding to a function $D\psi(x)$. The linearity of D is expressed by the conditions

$$D(\phi + \psi) = D\phi + D\psi \qquad \text{and} \qquad D(k\psi) = kD\psi$$

where k is an ordinary number. The operator $-(\hbar/i)(\partial/\partial x)$ evidently satisfies these conditions, whereas the operator which consists in taking the square of the function does not. Of course, a matrix is also a linear operator, and hence the notation linear operator may be applied to matrices as well. We have seen that the expectation value of an observable represented by a matrix A is given by $\bar{a} = \mathbf{x} \cdot A\mathbf{x}$. In the case of an operator D working on a vector $\mathbf{x} = \psi(x)$, we have to express

$\bar{a}$ by

$$\bar{a} = \mathbf{x} \cdot D\mathbf{x} = \int \psi^*(x)\, dx \int D\psi(x')(\mathbf{e}_x \cdot \mathbf{e}_{x'})\, dx' = \int \psi^* D\psi\, dx \quad (144)$$

For a Hermitean matrix we have $\bar{a} = \bar{a}^*$. Thus a linear operator will be Hermitean if

$$\int \psi^* D\psi\, dx = \int (D\psi)^*\psi\, dx \quad (145)$$

The relation (144) can be used for the transformation of an operator into a matrix. We assume K and K' are systems belonging to observables with a continuous and a discrete spectrum of eigenvalues respectively. For instance, in K the coordinate x may be diagonal and in K' the energy E may be diagonal. In K the operator representing x is given by multiplication by x, and in K' by a matrix $Q = \|q_{ik}\|$, so that the expectation value $\bar{x}$ for a state $\mathbf{x}$ represented in K by the function $\psi(x)$ and in K' by $x_0 x_1 \cdots$ is given by

$$\bar{x} = \mathbf{x} \cdot Q\mathbf{x} = \sum q_{ik} x_i^* x_k = \int x\psi^*\psi\, dx$$

When $\sum x_i\psi_i$ is substituted for $\psi(x)$ on the right-hand side, ψ_i being the eigenfunctions of the energy operator, we get

$$\sum q_{ik} x_i^* x_k = \sum x_i^* x_k \int \psi_i^* x\psi_k\, dx$$

and, since the equation must hold for any vector $\mathbf{x}(x_0 x_1 \cdots)$,

$$q_{ik} = \int \psi_i^* x\psi_k \quad (146)$$

Similarly the elements p_{ik} of the momentum matrix P are found to be

$$p_{ik} = -\frac{\hbar}{i} \int \psi_i^* \frac{\partial \psi_k}{\partial x}\, dx \quad (147)$$

We have already evaluated the integral $\int \psi_i^* x\psi_k\, dx$ in the case of the oscillator in Section 20. As we shall see in the following section, the values for $x_{i,i-1}$ and $x_{i,i+1}$ of (109) agree exactly with those that can be deduced from the matrix mechanical formalism.

31. The Fundamental Problem of Matrix Mechanics. We have seen that the essential idea of quantum mechanics is to correlate a certain operator to any observable of the system considered. When the operators are known, we need only to construct the corresponding principal systems K in a Hilbert space and to project onto the axes of K the vector which, on the basis of statistical investigations, is found to represent the state of the system. If we but know how the operators are to be ascertained for a given system, this prccedure leads to a complete description of the state. It is true that we cannot say then how the state will change in time, and so there remains the problem of finding the law pertaining to dx/dt. If we wish to develop matrix mechanics as a self-contained discipline, we must not demand the assistance of wave mechanics but must find a method which, together with the commutation relations, can furnish the operator for any observable. It is a matter of course that this problem can be solved only if certain physical information about the nature of the system is given. The situation is the same as in classical mechanics where a description of the system is provided by the Hamiltonean function which expresses the energy of the system in terms of coordinates and momenta. We shall follow the same method, keeping in mind, however, that we must not seek a relationship connecting the value of the energy with those of coordinates and momenta. The expression of such a connection would be meaningless in quantum mechanics wherein coordinate and momentum cannot be measured simultaneously. What we can connect are matrices only, or more generally, the operators of the observables mentioned above. Therefore we shall adopt the following theorem:

There is for any physical system a certain relationship between the matrix H of the energy and the matrices Q and P of coordinate and momentum.

The function $H = H(QP)$, which describes this relationship, is called the Hamiltonian, and we assume that it is defined by the nature of the system. How this function is to be found for a given system cannot be determined by matrix mechanics, just as classical mechanics is unable to explain, for example, that for an oscillator the Hamiltonian is given by $p^2/2m + aq^2/2$. There is no other instruction for determining H than to find the function that gives a correct description of the system. It seems probable, however, that there is a far-reaching correspondence between the matrix-mechanical and the classical H so that, for example, the Hamiltonian of an oscillator may be supposed to be

$$H(QP) = \frac{P^2}{2m} + \frac{aQ^2}{2}$$

This suggestion that the classical expression for H be simply translated into a matrix function is, however, not unique, for in classical mechanics the multiplication of two quantities is commutative, whereas in matrix mechanics it makes a difference whether we write, for example,

Q^2P or PQ^2 or QPQ.   However, in such ambiguous cases we are helped by the postulate that the matrix must be Hermitean; it is only then that we are sure that the expectation value $\mathbf{x} \cdot H\mathbf{x}$ of the energy is real.   According to Section 26 a function H of Hermitean matrices Q and P is Hermitean only if it is self-adjunct, that is, if it remains identical when read in the inverse order.   In the example above, only the product QPQ has this property.   But this does not exclude Q^2P and PQ^2 altogether because the expression $\frac{1}{2}(Q^2P + PQ^2)$ is also Hermitean and could be used for H.   And so, too, the requirement that H has to be Hermitean does not help us toward a definite decision, and in the end there is no other way to judge whether a possible H is correct or not than to put H to the test.

But let us suppose that for a given system we know the Hamiltonian $H = H(QP)$, the matrices H, Q, and P (all of which are considered unknown at first) being referred to the normal coordinate system K belonging to the energy.   Then the method for determining H, Q, P is the following: We must find two matrices Q and P which

(i) satisfy the commutation relation

$$QP - PQ = \frac{\hbar}{i} E \tag{148}$$

(ii) gives the function $H(QP)$ the form of a diagonal matrix.

The second condition must be imposed upon Q and P because K is supposed to be the principal system of the energy.   Should it turn out that the problem has only one solution, Q and P represent the operators corresponding to the coordinate and momentum, and $H(QP)$, by its diagonal elements, provides the energy values E_k of the system in its different stationary states.

To illustrate the procedure we consider a linear harmonic oscillator the Hamiltonian of which may be assumed to be

$$H = \frac{P^2}{2m} + \frac{aQ^2}{2}$$

We then must solve the equation

$$\frac{P^2}{2m} + \frac{aQ^2}{2} = \begin{bmatrix} E_0 & 0 & 0 & \cdots \\ 0 & E_1 & 0 & \cdots \\ 0 & 0 & E_2 & \cdots \\ \cdot & \cdot & \cdot & \cdots \\ \cdot & \cdot & \cdot & \cdots \\ \cdot & \cdot & \cdot & \cdots \end{bmatrix} \tag{149}$$

by matrices Q and P which fulfill condition (148), Q and P as well as E_0, E_1, $\cdots$ being unknown. When we multiply (149) on the left and the right by Q, upon subtraction we get

$$\frac{1}{2m}(QP^2 - P^2Q) = QH - HQ \tag{150}$$

On the other hand, (148), when multiplied by P, gives

$$QP^2 - PQP = \frac{\hbar}{i}P$$

so that the left-hand side of (150) may be written

$$\frac{1}{2m}\left(\frac{\hbar}{i}P + PQP - P^2Q\right) = \frac{1}{2m}\left[\frac{\hbar}{i}P + P(QP - PQ)\right]$$

$$= \frac{1}{2m}\left(\frac{\hbar}{i}P + \frac{\hbar}{i}P\right) = \frac{\hbar}{im}P$$

Equation (150) then becomes

$$\frac{\hbar}{im}P = QH - HQ$$

and for the elements p_{ik} of P we obtain

$$p_{ik} = \frac{mi}{\hbar}\sum(q_{il}h_{lk} - h_{il}q_{lk}) = \frac{mi}{\hbar}q_{ik}(E_k - E_i) \tag{151}$$

A corresponding equation for the q_{ik} terms can be derived. We multiply (149) on the left and right by P, and upon subtraction we obtain

$$\frac{a}{2}(PQ^2 - Q^2P) = PH - HP \tag{152}$$

Furthermore from (148) we find

$$Q^2P - QPQ = \frac{\hbar}{i}Q$$

Accordingly the left-hand side of (152) can be transformed into

$$\frac{a}{2}\left(PQ^2 - \frac{\hbar}{i}Q - QPQ\right) = \frac{a}{2}\left[(PQ - QP)Q - \frac{\hbar}{i}Q\right] = -\frac{a\hbar}{i}Q$$

Thus we obtain

$$-a\frac{\hbar}{i}q_{ik} = \sum(p_{il}h_{lk} - h_{il}p_{lk}) = p_{ik}(E_k - E_i)$$

or, on substituting the expression (151) for p_{ik},

$$q_{ik} \left[1 - \frac{m}{a\hbar^2} (E_k - E_i)^2 \right] = 0 \tag{153}$$

It follows that the q_{ik} terms are not equal to zero only for those values of i,k for which

$$1 - \frac{m}{a\hbar^2} (E_k - E_i)^2 = 0$$

and thus, since $1/2\pi \sqrt{a/m} = \nu_0$, where ν_0 is the characteristic frequency of the oscillator,

$$E_k - E_i = \pm h\nu_0 \tag{154}$$

This result suggests the idea of arranging the diagonal elements of the matrix H in an arithmetic series beginning with an unknown term ϵ and increasing by $h\nu_0$ so that $E_k = \epsilon + kh\nu_0$. Then every q_{ik} and p_{ik} term vanishes except those for which $k = i \pm 1$, and we obtain for the first diagonal element of H

$$H_{00} = E_0 = \epsilon = \frac{1}{2m} \sum p_{0l}p_{l0} + \frac{a}{2} \sum q_{0l}q_{l0} = \frac{1}{2m} p_{01}p_{10} + \frac{a}{2} q_{01}q_{10}$$

Now, because of (151), we have

$$p_{01} = \frac{mi}{\hbar} q_{01}h\nu_0 \qquad p_{10} = -\frac{mi}{\hbar} q_{10}h\nu_0$$

and furthermore, because of the Hermitean nature of Q, $q_{ik} = q_{ki}{}^*$. Therefore $q_{01}q_{10} = |q_{01}|^2$; hence the expression for ϵ becomes

$$E_0 = \epsilon = |q_{01}|^2 \left(\frac{4\pi^2 m^2 \nu_0^2}{2m} + \frac{a}{2} \right)$$

Now, from the commutation relation it follows that

$$q_{01}p_{10} - p_{01}q_{10} = \frac{\hbar}{i}$$

or

$$-|q_{01}|^2 4\pi mi\nu_0 = \frac{\hbar}{i} \qquad |q_{01}|^2 = \frac{\hbar}{4\pi m\nu_0}$$

Thus we obtain

$$E_0 = \epsilon = \frac{h}{8\pi^2 m\nu_0} \left(\frac{4\pi^2 m\nu_0^2}{2} + \frac{a}{2} \right) = \frac{h\nu_0}{2}$$

The diagonal elements of H are now found to be $E_k = [(2k + 1)/2]h\nu_0$, and we can evaluate the q_{ik} terms as follows. If we take the kth diagonal element on both sides, the commutation relation gives

$$q_{k,k-1}p_{k-1,k} + q_{k,k+1}p_{k+1,k} - p_{k,k-1}q_{k-1,k} - p_{k,k+1}q_{k+1,k} = \frac{\hbar}{i}$$

and thus, because of (151),

$$\left|q_{k+1,k}\right|^2 - \left|q_{k-1,k}\right|^2 = \frac{\hbar}{4\pi m\nu_0}$$

Thus the $\left|q_{ik}\right|^2$ terms also form an arithmetic series with the initial term $\hbar/4\pi m\nu_0$ and the differences $\hbar/4\pi m\nu_0$. Therefore

$$\left|q_{k+1,k}\right|^2 = \frac{(k + 1)\hbar}{4\pi m\nu_0}$$

The q_{ik} terms are now determined to be

$$q_{k+1,k} = q_{k,k+1}^* = q_{k,k+1} = \frac{1}{2\pi}\sqrt{\frac{(k + 1)\hbar}{2m\nu_0}}$$

$$q_{k,k-1} = q_{k-1,k} = \frac{1}{2\pi}\sqrt{\frac{kh}{2m\nu_0}}$$

(155)

For the p_{ik} terms we obtain

$$p_{k+1,k} = p_{k,k+1} = -i\sqrt{\frac{(k + 1)hm\nu_0}{2}}$$

$$p_{k,k-1} = p_{k-1,k} = -i\sqrt{\frac{kmh\nu_0}{2}}$$

(156)

It can be confirmed easily that the matrices Q and P, by the relation $p^2/2m + aQ^2/2$, define a diagonal matrix with the elements $[(2k + 1)/2]h\nu_0$ as required.

32. Unique Nature of the Solution. We have yet to prove that there is no other solution of the problem or, at least, none that would be different physically from the one we have just found. This can be shown by the following argument, which holds for any non-degenerated problem. We shall first formulate the problem in another way by referring not to the principal system K of the energy, but to a quite arbitrary normal coordinate system K_0 which need not be the principal system for any observable. Now we take two Hermitean matrices Q_0 and P_0 which need only satisfy the commutation relation. When we introduce these matrices into $H(QP)$ we obtain a matrix H_0, and the question is to what coordinate system K must H_0 be referred in order for it to become a diagonal matrix. If we are able to answer this, the quantum-mechanical problem is solved. For the transition $K_0 \rightarrow K$ transforms Q_0 and P_0 into $Q = SQ_0S^{-1}$ and $P = SP_0S^{-1}$, which also are Hermitean and satisfy the commutation relation. Furthermore $H = SH_0S^{-1}$ is a diagonal matrix, and thus both postulates of the preceding section are fulfilled. The problem then is simply to determine, for a given operator, the system of the corresponding principal axes. This can be done, as we saw in Section 25, essentially in one way only. That which remains arbitrary, in the case of a non-degenerated problem, is the choice of the unit vectors e_k of K which may be multiplied by $e^{i\gamma_k}$ so that there are different principal systems which can be transformed into one another by a unitary matrix of the form

$$
S = \begin{bmatrix}
e^{i\gamma_1} & 0 & 0 & 0 & \cdots \\
0 & e^{i\gamma_2} & 0 & 0 & \cdots \\
0 & 0 & e^{i\gamma_3} & 0 & \cdots \\
\cdot & \cdot & \cdot & \cdot & \cdot & \cdot & \cdot & \cdot & \cdot \\
\cdot & \cdot & \cdot & \cdot & \cdot & \cdot & \cdot & \cdot & \cdot \\
\cdot & \cdot & \cdot & \cdot & \cdot & \cdot & \cdot & \cdot & \cdot
\end{bmatrix}
$$

It is true that this means there are different K systems, but in all of them we get the same diagonal matrix for the energy since H is changed by S into $H' = SHS^{-1} = H$. The matrices Q and P are transformed by S into other matrices, but this is due only to a change of the unit vectors and has just as little physical significance here as do the units in which the coordinates xyz are measured in classical mechanics.

Our argument does not prove yet that the quantum-mechanical problem is unique, since it could just as well be that we do not obtain the same solution with *any* pair of Hermitean matrices which are referred to *any* coordinate system K_0. However, we shall accept without proof that this is not so.

When studying quantum mechanics the beginner is likely to lose sight of the physical meaning, fixing his whole attention on the strange formalism. Therefore, using the example of the oscillator, let us make it clear once more how quantum-mechanical statements must be understood. Let us start with the result that the elements of the diagonal energy matrix are $E_k = [(2k + 1)/2]h\nu_0$. The meaning of this is: When an energy measurement is made on an oscillator of mass m and elastic force ax, the result is always one of the values E_0, E_1, $\cdots$. With respect to the matrices Q and P we imagine that the oscillator is given in the state $\mathbf{x}$ which, relative to the energy, is defined by the coordinates x_k. Then a great number of measurements of position and momentum, carried out on a correspondingly great number of oscillators all in the same state, on the average, furnish the mean values $\bar{x} = \sum q_{ik} x_i^* x_k$ and $\bar{p} = \sum p_{ik} x_i^* x_k$. If we wish to know the probability of a measurement of x or p giving a certain value α, we have to construct the principal systems K' and K'' which correspond to Q and P and project the vector $\mathbf{x}$ onto the axis which belongs to the eigenvalue α.

33. The Dynamical Law of Quantum Mechanics. The Principle of Causality. We now have to answer the following question. If the state of a closed system is given for time $t = 0$, that is, if we know the vector $\mathbf{x}$ that represents it at that instant, what can be said about the state of the system at a later time t? Evidently the answer to this question depends on the sense in which the concept of causality is understood. In Section 4 we saw that there also must exist some sort of causality in quantum mechanics. If we were to maintain that the initial state has no bearing on the future, we would bring into question the possibility of physics at all. On the other hand, however, there can be no doubt that the significance of causality in quantum mechanics must be quite different from its significance in classical physics. The classical position was that, if we know the state of a closed system for $t = 0$, this state being defined by exact values of certain observables, we know the exact values of the observables for all future time. Quantum mechanics must deny this principle on the ground that it has no physical meaning. We cannot measure simultaneously the exact values of all observables, and hence we are bound, in speaking of "states of a system," to use the concept of state in a sense that conforms with the experimental possibilities. According to these possibilities we can describe a given state by a vector $\mathbf{x}$, and the only question is whether it is possible from the vector $\mathbf{x}_0$, which describes the initial state, to conclude the vector $\mathbf{x}$ defining the state at a future time. We make the assumption that there is a law with the help of which $\mathbf{x}$ can be evaluated from $\mathbf{x}_0$ and accept *the existence of such a law for the quantum-mechanical idea of causality.* Thus the theorem that, *if we know the initial state of a closed system, we also know the state for any future time* holds both in quantum mechanics and in classical physics, the only difference being that the concept "state" is now given another interpretation which is in accordance with the possibilities of observation.

The situation then is this: Quantum mechanics agrees with the viewpoint that there must be a way to conclude the future from the present, but the conclusion must not be more exact than the premise. From one probability we can infer only another probability. The only thing we know about the present is that the measurement of an observable will furnish a given value with a certain probability, and we cannot draw conclusions about the future from this knowledge which would give us more exact knowledge. Such knowledge would be of no use to us anyway, since it would be impossible to subject it to experimental test.

On the basis of these preliminary remarks we are now going to formulate a law by means of which the sequence of future states can be foreseen. As a matter of fact we are already familiar with the law, for it is contained in the postulate that the probability amplitudes x_k of the energy, as far as time-dependence is concerned, are given by

$$x_k = x_k{}^0 e^{(i/\hbar)E_k t} \tag{157}$$

This equation implies time-dependence not only for the energy but for all other observables as well. In the case of energy, we have already emphasized in Section 16, that the probabilities $x_k{}^* x_k$ of the different energy values do not vary with time; consequently the energy is sure of retaining the value E_k if its value at $t = 0$ is sure of being E_k. This is the way in which quantum mechanics expresses the conservation of energy. The other observables, however, with the exception of those which commute with energy, are not subject to the conservation law. For example, consider some observable a. The probability of a value α_i being found for a at $t = 0$, where α_i is an eigenvalue of a, is given by

$$\left| \sum s_{ik} x_k{}^0 \right|^2 \tag{158}$$

where $\|s_{ik}\|$ is the transformation matrix that effects the transition from the principal energy system K to the system K' of a. (For the sake of simplicity we assume a discrete eigenspectrum for a.) On the other hand, the probability for time t is given by

$$\left| \sum s_{ik} x_k{}^0 e^{(i/\hbar)E_k t} \right|^2 \tag{159}$$

which agrees with (158) only when a definite energy state is involved. Differentiating (157) relative to t, we obtain

$$\frac{dx_k}{dt} = \frac{i}{\hbar} E_k x_k{}^0 e^{(i/\quad)E_k t} = \frac{i}{\hbar} E_k x_k \tag{160}$$

which can be put in the form of a matrix equation:

$$\frac{d\mathbf{x}}{dt} = \frac{i}{\hbar} H \mathbf{x} \tag{161}$$

In the product, $\mathbf{x}$ is considered a matrix the first column of which contains the x_k terms, all the other elements being zero. H is the matrix of the energy, that is, a diagonal matrix with the elements E_k. From the multiplication rule it is readily seen that $H\mathbf{x}$ is a matrix with the elements $E_k x_k$ in the first column, all the others being zero. Equation (161) is considered a fundamental law which for quantum mechanics means the same as Newton's second law for classical mechanics.

When the vector $\mathbf{x}$ changes with time, the change, of course, has nothing to do with the principal systems belonging to the different observables. The change concerns the components of $\mathbf{x}$ only, whereas the axes of the systems remain fixed in space. In other words, this means that the operators Q and P are independent of time. But, as only the position of $\mathbf{x}$ relative to the coordinate systems is of significance, we can describe the time-dependence of the system just as well on the supposition that $\mathbf{x}$ remains fixed in space, and the operators Q, P, and so on are changed. Then we must proceed in the following way. We consider a matrix A belonging to some observable of the system and assume S to be the transformation matrix corresponding to the transition of the principal energy system K to the system K' of A. For the components of $\mathbf{x}$ belonging to the ith axis of K' we obtain

$$x_i' = \sum s_{ik} x_k$$

Therefore

$$\frac{dx_i'}{dt} = \sum s_{ik} \frac{dx_k}{dt}$$

In this equation S is considered constant and $\mathbf{x}$ is considered as the variable. If, however, $\mathbf{x}$ is considered to be constant, then in order to obtain the same dx_i'/dt we must substitute such functions of t for the s_{ik} terms that

$$\sum s_{ik} \frac{dx_k}{dt} = \sum \frac{ds_{ik}}{dt} x_k$$

or, written in the form of a matrix equation,

$$S \frac{d\mathbf{x}}{dt} = \frac{dS}{dt} \mathbf{x}$$

When we use (161), this becomes

$$\frac{i}{\hbar} SH\mathbf{x} = \frac{dS}{dt}\mathbf{x}$$

Therefore

$$\frac{dS}{dt} = \frac{i}{\hbar} SH$$

We evaluate dA/dt from dS/dt. To accomplish this, we first transform A with the help of S to the principal system K' of A, obtaining $A' = SAS^{-1}$, or

$$A'S = SA \tag{162}$$

Because of the significance of K', A' is a diagonal matrix independent of time, because its elements are the eigenvalues of A' and these are independent of time. Upon differentiating (162) relative to time, we obtain

$$A'\frac{dS}{dt} = \frac{dS}{dt}A + S\frac{dA}{dt}$$

or

$$\frac{i}{\hbar}(A'SH - SHA) = S\frac{dA}{dt}$$

and, because of (162),

$$\frac{dA}{dt} = \frac{i}{\hbar}(AH - HA) \tag{163}$$

Accordingly the time-dependence of a system can be represented not only by the dynamical law, (161), but also in such a way that *the vector* **x** *is kept constant while the matrix of any observable is considered a function of time satisfying (163)*.

From (163) we see again that the systems remain unchanged only relative to observables that can be measured simultaneously with the energy and are therefore represented by matrices that commute with H. Only then does $dA/dt = 0$, that is, the corresponding principal system remains fixed in space so that the probability of any eigenvalue does not change with time.

When we refer all the matrices to the principal energy system K, which system is considered fixed in space, H consists only of its diagonal elements E_k and therefore the decomposition of (163) furnishes the relations

$$\frac{da_{ik}}{dt} = \frac{i}{\hbar} a_{ik}(E_k - E_i) \qquad a_{ik} = a_{ik}{}^0 e^{(i/\hbar)(E_k-E_i)t} \tag{164}$$

It is remarkable that equations (163) for $A = Q$ and $A = P$ can be given a form in which they correspond exactly to the canonical equations of classical mechanics:

$$\frac{dq}{dt} = \frac{\partial H}{\partial p} \qquad \frac{dp}{dt} = -\frac{\partial H}{\partial q}$$

To verify this we make use of the theorem that, if $F(QP)$ is an arbitrary polynomial of the canonical matrices Q and P,

$$\frac{\hbar}{i}\frac{\partial F}{\partial P} = QF - FQ \tag{165}$$

The equation certainly holds for $F = P$, for it then becomes

$$\frac{\hbar}{i}E = QP - PQ$$

which is the commutation relation that is assumed to be satisfied by Q and P. For the same reason it holds for $F = Q$. If, however, equation (165) holds for two special functions F_1 and F_2, it must hold for the sum $F_1 + F_2$ and the product F_1F_2, for we have

$$\frac{\hbar}{i}\frac{\partial F_1 F_2}{\partial P} = \frac{\hbar}{i}\left(\frac{\partial F_1}{\partial P}F_2 + F_1\frac{\partial F_2}{\partial P}\right) = QF_1F_2 - F_1QF_2 + F_1QF_2 - F_1F_2Q$$

$$= QF_1F_2 - F_1F_2Q$$

Accordingly (165) may be applied to any polynomial formed from Q and P and to any sum of such polynomials. Hence the theorem stated is true. Similarly it can be shown that, for any $F(QP)$,

$$\frac{\hbar}{i}\frac{\partial F}{\partial Q} = FP - PF$$

Thus (163) for $A = Q$ and $A = P$ may be written in the form

$$\frac{dQ}{dt} = \frac{i}{\hbar}(QH - HQ) = \frac{\partial H}{\partial P} \qquad \frac{dP}{dt} = \frac{i}{\hbar}(PH - HP) = -\frac{\partial H}{\partial Q} \tag{166}$$

In these equations for the matrices Q, $\partial H/\partial P$, and so on, the Hermitean form $\mathbf{x} \cdot Q\mathbf{x}$, $\mathbf{x} \cdot (\partial H/\partial P)\mathbf{x}$, and so on, representing the expectation values of Q, $\partial H/\partial P$, $\cdots$, may be substituted and $\mathbf{x}$ must be considered constant. Thus we return to the relations mentioned at the end of Section 15. The internal connection between quantum mechanics and classical theory is especially clear here and can be characterized by this statement: *The laws of classical mechanics also hold in quantum mechanics provided that they are considered relations between statistical mean values.*

34. Systems with Many Degrees of Freedom.

Up to this point, for the sake of simplicity, we have considered systems with only one degree of freedom. If there are n degrees of freedom, where $n > 1$, as when a particle can have motion in all directions, we must correlate a matrix Q_k to each of the n coordinates q_k by which the spatial configuration of the system is described. A canonically conjugate momentum P_k must be coordinated to every Q_k, any pair $Q_k P_k$ satisfying the commutation relation

$$Q_k P_k - P_k Q_k = \frac{\hbar}{i} E \qquad (167)$$

whereas, if $i \neq k$,

$$Q_k P_i - P_i Q_k = 0 \qquad (168)$$

because two entities that can be characterized by different indices can be observed simultaneously and thus the corresponding matrices can be transformed to the same system K of principal axes. In addition there are the relations

$$Q_k Q_i - Q_i Q_k = 0 \qquad P_k P_i - P_i P_k = 0$$

From these we observe that all the principal systems belonging to $Q_1, Q_2, \cdots$ form a system K of the following kind. With any axis of K we can correlate an eigenvalue $\alpha_m{}^{(1)}$ of Q_1, an eigenvalue $\alpha_n{}^{(2)}$ of Q_2, and so on, so that we can speak of the axis $\alpha_m{}^{(1)}, \alpha_n{}^{(2)}, \cdots$. When the vector $\mathbf{x}$ which describes the state has the direction of this axis, a simultaneous measurement of the coordinates $q_1, q_2, \cdots$ will, with certainty, furnish the results $\alpha_m{}^{(1)}, \alpha_n{}^{(2)}, \cdots$. Evidently the eigenvalues $\alpha_m{}^{(1)}, \alpha_n{}^{(2)}, \cdots$ of $Q_1, Q_2, \cdots$ may be associated in any combination so that there is an axis of K for any set of these. Thus the principal system of any Q_k is degenerated, that is, there exists for any eigenvalue $\alpha_m{}^{(k)}$ of Q_k an $(n - 1)$-times infinite manifold of different axes every one of which is correlated to another combination of $\alpha_m{}^{(k)}$ with the eigenvalues of the other Q. The same holds for the P_k operators. They too are degenerated, and we can correlate an axis to any combination of eigenvalues $\beta_m{}^{(1)}, \beta_n{}^{(2)}, \cdots$.

It is easy to answer the question of the manner in which the state of a system, subjected to given physical conditions, is to be investigated and the question of requirements the state has to satisfy in order to be "well-defined" in the sense of Section 27. We consider a great number of systems and form a statistical ensemble for the group by measuring the values of the coordinates q_1, q_2, $\cdots$ for any one of them. In this way we find a certain probability $\left| x_{\alpha_m{}^{(1)}\alpha_n{}^{(2)}} \cdots \right|^2$ for any set of eigenvalues $\alpha_m{}^{(1)}$, $\alpha_n{}^{(2)}$, $\cdots$, and similarly the probabilities $\left| x'_{\beta_m{}^{(1)}\beta_n{}^{(2)}} \cdots \right|^2$ of finding $\beta_m{}^{(1)}\beta_n{}^{(2)} \cdots$ for the momenta can be ascertained. If the probabilities for any large assemblage are identical, we call the state "well-defined" and represent it by a vector the squares of magnitudes of the components of which, relative to the principal systems of coordinates and momenta, give the observed probabilities.

Of course, such a representation is possible only after the principal systems of Q_k and P_k have been ascertained. For this purpose we adopt the same method as for a system with one degree of freedom. We first consider an arbitrarily chosen normal coordinate system K_0 and determine a pair of matrices $Q_k{}^0$, $P_k{}^0$ that satisfy (167) and (168). With the determination of these pairs the problem is solved, since then we know the systems K' and K'' which are formed by the principal axes of $Q_k{}^0$ and $P_k{}^0$ respectively. In order to find the principal energy system K, a unitary transition $K_0 \to K$ has to be performed by means of which the given Hamiltonian $H(Q_1, Q_2, \cdots, P_1, P_2, \cdots)$ of the system is transformed into a diagonal matrix. In the case of a non-degenerated H, that is, if there is only one state x of a given energy, the principal system K is uniquely determined by H. Then there exists only one unitary matrix S which effects the transition $K_0 \to K$ and transforms the matrices $Q_k{}^0$ and $P_k{}^0$ into $Q_k = SQ_k{}^0S^{-1}$ and $P_k = SP_k{}^0S^{-1}$.

In general, however, H is degenerated. Then there exist r_k different axes of K, all belonging to the same eigenvalue E_k, or, in other words, there are r_k different well-defined states of the same energy E_k. For example, let us assume that the eigenvalue E_1 is twice degenerated, so that the first three axes of K (which may be designated by 1, 2, 3) correspond to the same energy E_1. These three axes then will scaffold a three-dimensional space containing all the vectors x for which only the components x_1, x_2, and x_3 differ from zero. Any of these vectors is transformed by H into a multiple E_1 of itself, for since H is of the form

$$
H = \begin{bmatrix}
E_1 & 0 & 0 & \cdots \\
0 & E_1 & 0 & \cdots \\
0 & 0 & E_1 & \cdots \\
\cdot & \cdot & \cdot & \cdots \\
\cdot & \cdot & \cdot & \cdots \\
\cdot & \cdot & \cdot & \cdots
\end{bmatrix}
$$

the equation $\mathbf{y} = H\mathbf{x}$ gives

$$y_1 = E_1x_1 \qquad y_2 = E_1x_2 \qquad y_3 = E_1x_3 \qquad y_4 = y_5 = \cdots = 0$$

Thus any vector $\mathbf{x}$ belonging to the space scaffold of the axes 1, 2, 3 represents an eigenvector of H, the corresponding eigenvalue being E_1, so that $\mathbf{x}$ indicates a state of sharply measured E_1. This means, however, that, *instead of the 1, 2, 3 directions, we may choose as well three other normal directions of the space E_1 for the first three axes of K*. Because of this arbitrariness, the transformation to principal axes in the case of a degenerated H is not unique but permits different solutions. Together with K, K_1 is also a solution which can be obtained from K with the aid of a unitary matrix of the kind

$$S = \begin{bmatrix} S^{(r_0)} & 0 & 0 & \cdots \\ 0 & S^{(r_1)} & 0 & \cdots \\ 0 & 0 & S^{(r_2)} & \cdots \\ \cdot & \cdot & \cdot & \cdots \\ \cdot & \cdot & \cdot & \cdots \\ \cdot & \cdot & \cdot & \cdots \end{bmatrix} \tag{169}$$

where $S^{(r_k)}$ is a unitary matrix of the order r_k.

In the case of a degenerated H, the following point should be brought out: Let us assume that a given state of a system is represented by $\mathbf{x}$, its components relative to K being x_k. How are we to determine the probability that an energy measurement will give the value E_k if this value occurs r_k times? If H were non-degenerated, this probability would be given by the square of the component of $\mathbf{x}$ in that direction. If there are more than one E_k directions, this rule is meaningless and we must modify it as follows: *The probability in question equals the sum* $\sum x_k{}^*x_k$ *extended over all the x_k components that belong to the axes of the same E_k*. This postulate is consistent with the whole plan, since the assumed probability is indifferent to a possible change of the principal system K, for, if K is transformed by the matrix (169) into K_1, the components x_k of the space E_k are altered in such a way that

$$\sum x_k{}^*x_k = \sum x_k'{}^*x_k'$$

We again obtain for the expectation value $\bar{E}$ the expression $\sum x_k{}^*x_kE_k$ in which all the components of $\mathbf{x}$ are to be considered so that every E_k contributes as many terms as the postulate about the probability of E_k demands.

PROBLEMS

1. Prove that the commutability of two matrices is not only a necessary but also a sufficient condition that the matrices can be diagonalized.

2. Given three matrices which satisfy the relations

$$AB - BA = 2iC$$

$$BC - CB = 2iA \quad \text{and} \quad A^2 = B^2 = C^2 = 1$$

$$CA - AC = 2iB$$

show that the following equations must hold:

$$AB = -BA \qquad BC = -CB \qquad CA = -AC \quad \text{and} \quad ABC = i$$

3. Given the same matrices as in Problem 2. If A, B, and C are considered the components of a vector $\mathbf{S}$, the components of $\mathbf{S}$ referred to a new set of axes are given by

$$A' = \alpha_1 A + \beta_1 B + \gamma_1 C, \text{ etc.}$$

Show that A', B', and C' satisfy the same equations as A, B, C.

4. From $C^2 = 1$ in Problem 2, it can be inferred that the eigenvalues of C must be $+1$ and -1. Thus, for example, C in its diagonal form will be given by

$$C = \begin{bmatrix} 1 & 0 \\ 0 & -1 \end{bmatrix}$$

Show that A and B are then given by

$$A = \begin{bmatrix} 0 & 1 \\ 1 & 0 \end{bmatrix} \qquad B = \begin{bmatrix} 0 & -i \\ i & 0 \end{bmatrix}$$

5. Find the eigenvalues of the matrix

$$\begin{bmatrix} 0 & 0 & 0 & 1 \\ 0 & 0 & -1 & 0 \\ 0 & 1 & 0 & 0 \\ -1 & 0 & 0 & 0 \end{bmatrix}$$

6. Show that for Dirac's function $\delta(x)$ the following equations hold:

$$x\,\delta(x) = 0 \qquad\qquad \delta(ax) = a^{-1}\,\delta(x)$$

$$x\,\delta'(x) = 0 \qquad f(x)\,\delta(x - a) = f(a)\,\delta(x - a)$$

7. The components of angular momentum are $m_x = yp_z - zp_y$, etc., with $p_x = (\hbar/i)(\partial/\partial x)$. Prove that the following relations hold. (The notation $[ab]$ is an abbreviation for $ab - ba$.)

$$[m_z x] = y \qquad\qquad [m_z y] = -x \qquad\qquad [m_z z] = 0$$

$$[m_z p_x] = p_y \qquad\qquad [m_z p_y] = -p_x \qquad\qquad [m_z p_z] = 0$$

$$[m_y m_z] = m_x \qquad\qquad [m_z m_x] = m_y \qquad\qquad [m_x m_y] = m_z$$

8. Prove that, if $\theta = m_x{}^2 + m_y{}^2 + m_z{}^2$, $[m_x\theta] = [m_y\theta] = [m_z\theta] = 0$.

9. Discuss the transformation $A' \to SAS^{-1}$ if the unitary matrix S differs from unity by a small matrix C the square of which may be neglected.

10. Describe the connection between the commutation relation and the uncertainty relation.

4

PERTURBATION THEORY

35. Perturbation of Non-degenerated Systems. Thus far we have assumed always that the systems were closed, and on this assumption was developed a theory which cannot be applied to many important problems. The theory fails when some external force, for example an electric or magnetic field or the field of a light wave, acts on the system. We know from experience that certain characteristic effects are observed in this case, effects that can be explained by quantum mechanics only by using a theory that applies to open systems as well. It is quite true that we could subscribe to the view that there is no need for an elaborate perturbation theory because a perturbed system can always be formed into a closed one by uniting it with the perturbing system. In most cases, however, this is not practical because it leads to equations that cannot be solved with the ordinary means of mathematical analysis; therefore we must resort to other methods. In what follows we present a method which is useful provided that the perturbation is sufficiently weak.

Let us assume that the energy of the unperturbed system is non-degenerated. When there is no perturbation, the solution of the problem can be known and is given by the canonical matrices Q_0 and P_0 with which the function $H_0(QP)$ becomes diagonal.

$$H_0 = H_0(Q_0 P_0) = \begin{bmatrix} E_1 & 0 & 0 & \cdots \\ 0 & E_2 & 0 & \cdots \\ 0 & 0 & E_3 & \cdots \\ \cdot & \cdot & \cdot & \cdots \\ \cdot & \cdot & \cdot & \cdots \\ \cdot & \cdot & \cdot & \cdots \end{bmatrix}$$

Let the coordinate system associated with $Q_0 P_0$ and H_0 be denoted by K_0. Now assume that the perturbation is taking place. The relation between energy, coordinates, and momenta changes from $H_0(QP)$ to $H(QP)$. If the perturbation is sufficiently weak, H_0 and H differ but slightly and we may write

$$H(QP) = H_0(QP) + H'(QP) \tag{170}$$

127

where $H'(QP)$ is a small matrix function of (QP) which depends on the nature of the perturbation and is assumed to be self-adjunct so that H as well as H_0 is Hermitean. We find an approximate solution for the perturbed system in the following way. As the unperturbed system is supposed to be non-degenerated, all its eigenvalues $E_k{}^0$ will differ from each other. If we denote the corresponding eigenvectors by $x_k{}^0$, then $H_0 x_k{}^0 = E_k{}^0 x_k{}^0$. The perturbation will change the eigenvalues and eigenvectors to E_k and x_k respectively. Because of the smallness of the perturbation, the differences $E_k - E_k{}^0$ and $x_k - x_k{}^0$ will be small and we may write, for E_k and x_k,

$$E_k = E_k{}^0 + E_k{}^1 + E_k{}^2 + \cdots$$
$$x_k = x_k{}^0 + x_k{}^1 + x_k{}^2 + \cdots \tag{171}$$

in which $x_k{}^1$ and $E_k{}^1$ are terms of the same degree of smallness as the perturbation itself, $x_k{}^2$ and $E_k{}^2$ are small to the second degree, and so on. Then $H x_k = E_k x_k$ becomes

$$(H_0 + H')(x_k{}^0 + x_k{}^1 + x_k{}^2 + \cdots)$$
$$= (E_k{}^0 + E_k{}^1 + E_k{}^2 + \cdots)(x_k{}^0 + x_k{}^1 + x_k{}^2 + \cdots)$$

By separating terms of different orders of magnitudes, we obtain

$$H_0 x_k{}^0 = E_k{}^0 x_k{}^0 \tag{172}$$

$$H_0 x_k{}^1 + H' x_k{}^0 = E_k{}^0 x_k{}^1 + E_k{}^1 x_k{}^0 \tag{173}$$

$$H_0 x_k{}^2 + H' x_k{}^1 = E_k{}^0 x_k{}^2 + E_k{}^1 x_k{}^1 + E_k{}^2 x_k{}^0 \tag{174}$$

Equation (172) shows again that $E_k{}^0$ and $x_k{}^0$ represent a state of the unperturbed system. From (173) we can evaluate the first-order corrections, $x_k{}^1$ and $E_k{}^1$. To do this we take from all the vectors of (173) the components referring to the nth axis of the principal system K_0, which belongs to the energy of the unperturbed system. If we denote the components of $x_k{}^1$ in K_0 by $x_n{}'$, then $H_0 x_k{}^1$ is a vector with the components $E_n{}^0 x_n{}'$, because H_0 is diagonal in K_0 and thus transforms a vector $x_0{}', x_1{}', \cdots$ into $E_0{}^0 x_0{}', E_1{}^0 x_1{}', \cdots$. Furthermore $H' x_k{}^0$ is a vector with components $\sum_l H_{nl}{}' x_l = H_{nk}{}'$, since of

the components of $x_k{}^0$ only x_k is unity, all the rest being zero. Finally, the components of the vectors on the right-hand side are $E_k{}^0 x_n{}'$ and $E_k{}^1 \delta_{nk}$ wherein, for $n = k$, $\delta_{nk} = 1$, and, for $n \neq k$, $\delta_{nk} = 0$. Thus (173) gives

$$E_n{}^0 x_n{}' + H_{nk}{}' = E_k{}^0 x_n{}' + E_k{}^1 \delta_{nk}$$

and, when $n = k$, we obtain

$$E_k{}^1 = H_{kk}'$$ (175)

Therefore the correction term $E_k{}^1$ of the first order for the kth eigenstate is given by the diagonal element H_{kk}' of the perturbation matrix. On the other hand, when $n \neq k$, we have

$$x_n{}' = \frac{H_{nk}'}{E_k{}^0 - E_n{}^0}$$ (176)

The $x_n{}'$ terms are the components of the correction vector $\mathbf{x}_k{}^1$. Thus, by (176), we can evaluate the $\mathbf{x}_k{}^1$ vectors with the exception of the kth component, which remains arbitrary.

In a corresponding way the correction terms of the second order can be found from (174). Again we take from all the vectors the components in the direction of the nth axis of K_0, which we shall designate by $x_n{}''$. We obtain

$$E_n{}^0 x_n{}'' + \sum_l H_{nl}' x_l{}' = E_k{}^0 x_n{}'' + E_k{}^1 x_n{}' + E_k{}^2 \delta_{nk}$$

which, for $n = k$, gives

$$E_k{}^2 = \sum_l H_{kl}' x_l{}' - E_k{}^1 x_k{}^1 = \sum H_{kl}' x_l{}' - H_{kk}' x_k{}'$$

and, because of (176),

$$E_k{}^2 = \sum_{l \neq k} \frac{H_{kl}' H_{lk}'}{E_k{}^0 - E_l{}^0}$$ (177)

For the case $n \neq k$ we obtain an equation from which the $x_n{}''$ components of the vector $\mathbf{x}_k{}^2$ can be evaluated. It is not necessary to explain how this process is continued in order to get the correction terms of higher order.

The formulas derived can be translated without difficulty into the notation of wave mechanics. Instead of H_0 we then have an operator L which acts on a function $\psi(xyz)$, determining the eigenfunctions $\psi_k{}^0$ and the eigenvalues $E_k{}^0$ of the unperturbed system by the equation $L\psi = E\psi$. The perturbation changes L into $L + L'$ with the eigenquantities ψ_k and E_k. The correction terms $E_k{}'$ and $\psi_k{}'$ can then be evaluated from (175) and (176). Making use of the rules of Section 30, we obtain

$$E_k{}^1 = \int \psi_k{}^{0*} L' \psi_k{}^0 \, dv$$

$$x_n{}' = \frac{\int \psi_n{}^{0*} L' \psi_k{}^0 \, dv}{E_k{}^0 - E_n{}^0} \qquad \text{(for } n \neq k\text{)}$$ (178)

and, from x_n', we find

$$\psi_k{}^1 = \sum_{n \neq k} x_n'\psi_n{}^0$$

36. Perturbation of Degenerated Systems.

Now we consider the case of a system, such as the H atom, which is degenerated if no perturbation acts on it, so that there are different states having the same energy E_k. It may turn out that the degeneracy is cancelled by the perturbation, with the result that an originally single spectral line is resolved into a group of lines. If in the unperturbed atom the energy E_i is degenerated $r_i - 1$ times and E_k is degenerated $r_k - 1$ times, the line $\nu_{ik} = (E_i - E_k)/h$ represents a complexity of $r_i r_k$ lines of different origins which coincide in the line ν_{ik} and decompose if the respective E_i and E_k values are influenced in a different way by the perturbation.

Thus we assume now an energy matrix H_0 of the unperturbed system which, when referred to the corresponding principal system K_0, is diagonal and contains the E_0 term r_0 times, the E_1 terms r_1 times, and so on. Accordingly there exist for any of the values E_k, r_k different eigenvectors which can be designated by $\mathbf{x}_{k_1}{}^0$, $\mathbf{x}_{k_2}{}^0$, $\cdots$ and which scaffold an orthogonal coordinate system in the E_k space. The $\mathbf{x}_{k_i}{}^0$ vectors are not uniquely determined, since we can exchange the coordinate system for any other orthogonal one without changing the matrix H_0. Then we obtain other eigenvectors which are also transformed by H_0 into a multiple E_k of themselves. This implies a certain complication in the theory. If we write the eigenvectors $\mathbf{x}_{k_1}$, $\mathbf{x}_{k_2}$, $\cdots$ of the perturbed system in the form

$$\mathbf{x}_{k_i} = \mathbf{x}_{k_i}{}^0 + \mathbf{x}_{k_i}{}^1 + \mathbf{x}_{k_i}{}^2 + \cdots \qquad (179)$$

the terms after the first on the right are small only if $\mathbf{x}_{k_i}{}^0$ is as near as possible to $\mathbf{x}_{k_i}$. It is assumed that we know the $\mathbf{x}_{k_i}{}^0$ vectors which satisfy this condition although, a priori, we cannot say how these are to be found. However, this will be learned from the equations to which the assumption leads us. As in Section 35, these equations are

$$H_0\mathbf{x}_{k_i}{}^0 = E_k{}^0\mathbf{x}_{k_i}{}^0$$

$$H_0\mathbf{x}_{k_i}{}^1 + H'\mathbf{x}_{k_i}{}^0 = E_k{}^0\mathbf{x}_{k_i}{}^1 + E_{k_i}{}^1\mathbf{x}_{k_i}{}^0 \qquad (180)$$

Now we choose one of the principal axes n of H_0. This need not belong to the E_k space. If, as we did in Section 35, we take all the components of the vectors in (180) which have the direction of n, we obtain

$$\sum_i H_{ni}{}^0 x_i' + \sum_i H_{ni}' x_i = E_k{}^0 x_n' + E_{ki}{}^1 x_n$$

the components of $\mathbf{x}_{ki}{}^0$ and $\mathbf{x}_{ki}{}^1$ being x_i and x_i' respectively.

We apply this equation first for the case in which the direction of n lies within the E_k space. Then, since H_0 is diagonal, $H_{ni}{}^0$ differs from zero only for $i = n$ and equals $E_k{}^0$. The equation reduces to

$$\sum H_{ni}' x_i = E_{ki}{}^1 x_n \qquad (181)$$

As the x_i terms in (181) signify the components of the vector $\mathbf{x}_{ki}{}^0$, they differ from zero only within the E_k space, and hence the summation above is to be extended over that space only, that is, the sum in (181) applies only to that part of the matrix H_{ik}' which corresponds to the E_k space. Therefore, in this case, (181) becomes an eigenvector problem, for we have to find those vectors $\mathbf{x}_{ki}{}^0$ the components x_i of which are transformed by H' into multiples of themselves. To solve this problem that part of H' which refers to the E_k space must be made diagonal. The coordinate system in which H' is diagonal fixes the orthogonal directions of $\mathbf{x}_{k_1}{}^0$, $\mathbf{x}_{k_2}{}^0$, $\cdots$ which were used in (179) as satisfying the condition that $\mathbf{x}_{k_i}{}^1, \mathbf{x}_{k_i}{}^2, \cdots$ become small in this case. From (181) we see that the correction terms $E_{k_1}{}^1$, $E_{k_2}{}^1$, $\cdots$ of the energy E_k are given by the elements of that part of H' which corresponds to the E_k space and is diagonal.

Unless this part of H' is degenerated again, the degeneracy is cancelled and the consequent procedure is the same as in the preceding section.

37. Perturbation as Causing Transitions. The purpose of the method described in the two preceding sections was to evaluate the terms with which we must correct the energy levels and the eigenfunctions of the unperturbed system in order to obtain the characteristic quantities of the perturbed system. Very frequently, however, we are interested in another problem: Let us assume that the perturbation has been effective for some time. Before action starts, the system may have been in one of the eigenstates of the matrix H_0. Now let H' begin to operate, and then after a time t let its action cease. The system, again being unperturbed, is now investigated and is found to be in some other eigenstate of H_0 rather than in the original one. That which we wish to determine is the probability of finding the system at time t in an arbitrarily given final state.

For the solution of this problem we assume that the system is in the state x_k, satisfying the equation $H_0 x_k = E_k x_k$, once the perturbation has started. Because of the perturbation, the state changes according to the equation

$$\frac{\hbar}{i}\frac{d\mathbf{x}}{dt} = (H_0 + H')\mathbf{x}$$

Resolving the vectors into components relative to the principal system K_0 of H_0, we obtain

$$\frac{\hbar}{i}\frac{dx_n}{dt} = E_n x_n + \sum_m H_{nm}' x_m \tag{182}$$

For $H' = 0$, the solution of this equation would be

$$x_n = x_n^0 e^{(i/\hbar)E_n t}$$

where $x_n^0 = \delta_{nk}$. In other words, the system would remain in the state E_k. The perturbation makes this impossible, thus causing the state to change with time. To describe this process it is convenient to give the solution of (182) in the form

$$x_n = \xi_n(t)e^{(i/\hbar)E_n t}$$

where $\xi(t)$, which replaces x_n^0, is a function of t which is to be determined. Then, for (182), we obtain

$$\frac{\hbar}{i}\frac{d\xi_n}{dt} = \sum H_{nm}' \xi_m e^{(i/\hbar)(E_m - E_n)t} \tag{183}$$

If we assume a small H', this equation, which is still exact, can be solved to a first approximation if we substitute for the $\xi_m(t)$ terms their values at $t = 0$; and thus $\xi_m = \delta_{mk}$. Then we obtain

$$\frac{\hbar}{i}\frac{d\xi_n}{dt} = H_{nk}' e^{(i/\hbar)(E_k - E_n)t}$$

Therefore

$$\xi_n(t) = H_{nk}' \frac{e^{-(i/\hbar)(E_k - E_n)t} - 1}{E_k - E_n} \tag{184}$$

and

$$|\xi_n(t)|^2 = |H_{nk}'|^2 \frac{4}{(E_k - E_n)^2} \sin^2 \frac{(E_k - E_n)t}{2\hbar} \tag{184'}$$

$|\xi_n|^2$ is the probability with which a measurement of the energy, carried out on the system at time t, at which time the perturbation has ceased, gives the value E_n. Thus the effect of the perturbation is that the system does not maintain its original state but in time t changes into another state, the probability of the transition being given by (184'), which, we note, is proportional to $|H_{nk}'|^2$.

It may happen that H_{nk}' vanishes for certain values of n and k. Then, to a first approximation, the probability of a transition $k \to n$ is zero. However, the transition can be effected through the intervention of one or more intermediate states, the system first going from k to m and then from m to n. The necessary condition for this process is that both H_{km}' and H_{mn}' be not zero. On proceeding from the first to the second approximation, we must carry out the calculation as follows: According to (184) we have

$$\xi_m(t) = H_{mk}' \frac{e^{(i/\hbar)(E_k - E_m)t} - 1}{E_k - E_m}$$

Introducing this into (183), we obtain

$$\frac{\hbar}{i} \frac{d\xi_n}{dt} = \sum_m H_{nm}' H_{mk}' \frac{e^{(i/\hbar)(E_k - E_n)t} - e^{(i/\hbar)(E_m - E_n)t}}{E_k - E_m}$$

Hence

$$\xi_n(t) = \sum_m \frac{H_{nm}' H_{mk}'}{E_k - E_m} \left(\frac{e^{(i/\hbar)(E_k - E_n)t} - 1}{E_k - E_n} - \frac{e^{(i/\hbar)(E_m - E_n)t} - 1}{E_m - E_n} \right) \quad (185)$$

As we shall see, the second term of this expression is generally negligible; therefore we can write

$$|\xi_n(t)|^2 = |H'|^2 \frac{4}{(E_k - E_n)^2} \sin^2 \frac{(E_k - E_n)t}{2\hbar} \quad (186)$$

where

$$H' = \sum_m \frac{H_{nm}' H_{mk}'}{E_k - E_m}$$

which now replaces H_{nk}'. As the product $H_{mk}' H_{nm}'$ now occurs in ξ_n, the probability of finding the system in the state n is now small in the fourth order rather than in the second order. Where there are no intermediate states for which H_{nm}' and H_{mk}' are not zero, we can, of course, continue the procedure by considering transitions that are effected by the intervention of two or more intermediate states.

In the application of perturbation theory we are frequently confronted with the case wherein there exist a great number of states the energies of which nearly agree with that of the considered final state. For example, let us consider the case of an atom interacting with the surrounding radiation. The emission of light is caused by a transition

of the system (which consists of atom and radiation) by which the
state of the atom is changed from a into b, and simultaneously the
quantum number of a radiation oscillator is increased by 1. (The
significance of a radiation oscillator will be explained in Chapter 7.)
Now the frequencies of the oscillators of a cavity radiation form a very
dense line spectrum, and it is therefore of no importance to know the
probability that a certain oscillator will be changed by the process.
It is sufficient to ascertain the probability that, by the transition
$a \rightarrow b$ of the atom, some oscillator or other of a small spectral interval
is induced to change its quantum number. This probability can be
calculated in the following way. We denote the number of the final
states which have an energy between E and $E + dE$ by $\rho(E)\, dE$.
(In the example considered, $\rho(E)\, dE$ is the number of oscillators which,
when their quantum number is increased by 1 and the state of the
atom simultaneously is changed into b, correspond to the total energy
of the system between E and $E + dE$.) The probability of a transition into one of these states is found then by multiplying (184′) by
$\rho(E)\, dE$. We obtain

$$w(E)\, dE = |\xi|^2 \rho(E)\, dE$$
$$= |\overline{H'}|^2 \frac{4}{(E_0 - E)^2} \sin^2 \frac{(E_0 - E)t}{2\hbar} \rho(E)\, dE \qquad (187)$$

$|\overline{H'}|^2$ is to be taken as the mean value of $|H_{nk'}|^2$ for the considered
final states. The initial energy and the final energy of the system are
denoted by E_0 and E. The factor $w(E)$, as a function of E, has a
maximum of the amount $|\overline{H'}|^2(t^2/\hbar^2)\rho(E_0)$ at $E = E_0$, that is, for a
final state the energy of which equals that of the initial state provided
that t is sufficiently great. Hence the probability is noticeably different from zero only for those transitions which satisfy the principle of
energy conservation. We find the total probability of such a transition which takes place within time t (in our example, the transition
$a \rightarrow b$ of the atom together with the emission of a corresponding light
quantum) by integrating (187) over a small interval ΔE surrounding
the final state $E = E_0$. Since $w(E)$ is very small outside ΔE, we may
just as well integrate over ΔE from $-\infty$ to $+\infty$, and, since

$$\int_{-\infty}^{+\infty} \frac{\sin^2 x}{x^2}\, dx = \pi$$

we obtain

$$W = \int w(E)\, dE = |\overline{H'}|^2 4\rho(E_0) \int_{-\infty}^{+\infty} \frac{\sin^2 x}{x^2} \frac{t}{2\hbar}\, dx = |H'|^2 \frac{2\pi t}{\hbar} \rho(E_0)$$
$$(188)$$

An expression of this form holds also if the transition $0 \to n$ is only possible by the intervention of intermediate states, the only difference being that $\left| \sum_m \dfrac{H_{nm}' H_{m0}'}{E_0 - E_m} \right|^2$ must be substituted for $|H'|^2$. Then the second term with the denominator $E_m - E_n$, occurring in (185), can be omitted (except for $E_n = E_m$), since it is, when compared with the first term, very small and thus its contribution to W is negligible. Furthermore transitions are possible only when energy is conserved. It should be noticed, however, that the transitions into the intermediate states are not restricted by this condition. The latter may contradict the conservation law, the intermediate states being permitted to differ in energy from the initial state by any amount. This does not mean that the conservation principle loses its validity because the intermediate states as such cannot be measured. The conservation of energy enters the question only when we investigate the probability of a transition to a final state with energy E which differs from E_0. According to (187), this probability turns out to be negligibly small.

PROBLEMS

1. Compute the first-order perturbation of a system with the help of a unitary transformation $S = 1 + C$ which makes $H + H'$ diagonal, if only terms of the first order in C are considered.

2. Consider an oscillator on which an extra potential ax^3 is acting. What is the effect of this potential on the energy levels?

3. The energy caused by the action of an electric field on an atom is given by

$$er \cdot \mathbf{E} = er \cdot \mathbf{E}_0 \cos 2\pi\nu t = \tfrac{1}{2} er \cdot \mathbf{E}_0 (e^{i2\pi\nu t} + e^{-i2\pi\nu t})$$

where $\mathbf{r}$ is the vector of the electron. If $\mathbf{E}$ has the direction of the x axis, the energy may be represented by $\tfrac{1}{2} eQE$. Find how the vector representing the state of the atom changes with time.

4. Calculate the third-order terms of a perturbation.

5

SYSTEMS OF MANY PARTICLES

38. Schroedinger's Equation for the Many-Body Problem.
The systems considered so far have been assumed to consist exclusively of one movable particle, and thus the theory we have at our disposal suffices only for systems of the simplest kind such as the oscillator and the H atom with fixed nucleus. Therefore it is insufficient for cases such as the He atom or the H_2 molecule. It is to be expected that we should encounter a more complex situation when we attempt to extend the theory to systems containing many movable particles. First of all, the greater number of particles will complicate the calculations. In addition, there is another point which has been of no consequence in the classical theory for the many-body problem but which is of decisive importance for the epistemologically prejudiced quantum mechanics. The situation is this: On principle, there is no possibility of distinguishing particles of the same kind, such as electrons, from one another. Let us imagine that the n electrons of an atom are numbered 1, 2, 3, $\cdots$, n. Now, if a measurement carried out on the atom shows that at a given instant of time the electrons are in the positions $P_1, P_2, \cdots, P_n$, then on principle we cannot state which position is occupied by the electron with the number i. Thus, if P_1 and P_2 for two particles are found by measurement, the interpretation could be either that P_1 belongs to electron 1 and P_2 to electron 2 or that electron 1 is at P_2 and electron 2 at P_1. This inability to distinguish the particles leads to very peculiar consequences which are quite unknown in classical mechanics.

To take a simple case, let $n = 2$ and denote the coordinates of the two particles by $x_1y_1z_1$ and $x_2y_2z_2$ respectively. At first consider the particles to be distinguishable. Then the state of the system can be described in wave mechanics by a function $u(x_1y_1z_1x_2y_2z_2t)$ which has the following significance: the function u when multiplied by the volume element $dx_1dy_1dz_1dx_2dy_2dz_2$ of the six-dimensional configuration space gives the probability that a measurement, carried out at time t, will find particle 1 within $dx_1dy_1dz_1$ and particle 2 within $dx_2dy_2dz_2$. In wave mechanics it will be possible to treat the many-body problem by essentially the same method as a single particle,

136

the only difference being that the probability waves $u(x_1 y_1 z_1 x_2 y_2 z_2 t)$ are propagated in six-dimensional space rather than in three-dimensional. This involves no difficulty in the statistical theory, according to which the waves have a purely symbolic meaning.

The first thing to do is to set up Schroedinger's equation, and for this purpose we begin, according to Section 31, with the classical equation for the Hamiltonian H of the system, which is given by

$$\frac{\xi_1{}^2 + \eta_1{}^2 + \zeta_1{}^2}{2m_1} + \frac{\xi_2{}^2 + \eta_2{}^2 + \zeta_2{}^2}{2m_2} + V(x_1 y_1 z_1 x_2 y_2 z_2) \quad (189)$$

where $V(x_1 y_1 z_1 x_2 y_2 z_2)$ is the potential energy of the system, the particles being at $x_1 y_1 z$ and $x_2 y_2 z_2$ respectively. On substituting $-(\hbar/i)(\partial/\partial x_1), \cdots, -(\hbar/i)(\partial/\partial z_2)$ for $\xi_1 \cdots \zeta_2$ and denoting by $\psi(x_1 \cdots z_2)$ an eigenfunction of the energy, with the eigenvalue E,

$$-\frac{\hbar^2}{2m_1}\left(\frac{\partial^2\psi}{\partial x_1{}^2} + \frac{\partial^2\psi}{\partial y_1{}^2} + \frac{\partial^2\psi}{\partial z_1{}^2}\right) - \frac{\hbar^2}{2m_2}\left(\frac{\partial^2\psi}{\partial x_2{}^2} + \frac{\partial^2\psi}{\partial y_2{}^2} + \frac{\partial^2\psi}{\partial z_2{}^2}\right)$$
$$+ V(x_1 \cdots z_2) = E\psi \quad (190)$$

Now suppose that the particles are indistinguishable. Then the potential energy $V(x_1 \cdots z_2)$ is bound to be symmetric in the indices 1 and 2, that is, V must remain identical when 1 and 2 are interchanged because this interchange means only that the particles exchange positions, and this cannot influence the energy because the particles are exactly the same kind. Let us assume further that the particles are bound by forces of some kind or other to a nucleus which has a fixed position. Then the energy V can be resolved into two parts, the first being due to the attraction of the nucleus and of the form $V'(x_1 y_1 z_1) + V'(x_2 y_2 z_2)$ and the second part $V''(x_1 y_1 z_1 x_2 y_2 z_2)$ corresponding to the forces with which the particles act on one another. Equation (190) can then be put into the form

$$-\frac{\hbar^2}{2m}(\nabla_1{}^2\psi + \nabla_2{}^2\psi)$$
$$+ [V'(x_1 y_1 z_1) + V'(x_2 y_2 z_2) + V''(x_1 \cdots z_2)]\psi = E\psi$$

We attempt a solution of this equation by assuming that the term V'' is small compared to the two V' terms. Then we can apply the methods of the perturbation theory. First neglect V'' and solve the equation

$$-\frac{\hbar^2}{2m}(\nabla_1{}^2 + \nabla_2{}^2)\psi + [V'(x_1 y_1 z_1) + V'(x_2 y_2 z_2)]\psi = E\psi \quad (191)$$

From this approximation of order zero we try to proceed to an approximation of the first order by taking V'' into account. We assume that the eigenfunctions ψ_i and the eigenvalues E_i of the equation

$$-\frac{\hbar^2}{2m}\nabla^2\psi + V'(xyz)\psi = E\psi \tag{192}$$

are known. Then, as is easily shown, (191) can be solved by the functions

$$\psi_{ik}(x_1 \cdot \cdot \cdot z_2) = \psi_i(x_1 y_1 z_1)\psi_k(x_2 y_2 z_2)$$

or, more simply,

$$\psi_{ik} = \psi_i(1)\psi_k(2)$$

with the eigenvalues $E_{ik} = E_i + E_k$. To prove this we multiply the equations

$$-\frac{\hbar^2}{2m}\nabla_1{}^2\psi_i(1) + V'(1)\psi_i(1) = E_i\psi_i(1)$$

$$-\frac{\hbar^2}{2m}\nabla_2{}^2\psi_k(2) + V'(2)\psi_k(2) = E_k\psi_k(2)$$

by $\psi_k(2)$ and $\psi_i(1)$ respectively and add, obtaining

$$-\frac{\hbar^2}{2m}(\nabla_1{}^2 + \nabla_2{}^2)\psi_{ik} + [V'(1) + V'(2)]\psi_{ik} = E_{ik}\psi_{ik}$$

a relation by which the statement is proved.

But evidently (191) can be solved just as well by the function

$$\psi_{ki} = \psi_k(x_1 y_1 z_1)\psi_i(x_2 y_2 z_2) = \psi_k(1)\psi_i(2)$$

to which the same eigenvalue $E_{ki} = E_i + E_k$ belongs. Thus the two-body problem, in the zero-order approximation here considered, is degenerated; for any eigenvalue E_{ik} there exist two eigenfunctions ψ_{ik} and ψ_{ki} which arise from the possibility of giving two different occupations to the stationary states ψ_i and ψ_k. Therefore we must correlate this solution of the zero order to a system of principal axes which, for any eigenvalue E_{ik}, where $i \neq k$, contains two axes which are normal to each other. The space that is scaffolded by the two axes contains the directions of all states which do not differ in energy but only in the occupation of the i and k states.

From the zero-order approximation we proceed to the solution for the system which is perturbed by the interaction V'' of the particles. The perturbation will nullify the degeneration by establishing two normal principal axes in the E_{ik} space, the eigenvalues of which, $E_{ik} +$

ϵ_{ik}' and $E_{ik} + \epsilon_{ik}''$, are slightly different. Concerning the new eigenvalues, we can determine the correction terms, ϵ_{ik}, according to Section 36, by making diagonal the part V'' of the perturbation which belongs to the E_{ik} space. Now, according to Section 30, the elements of V'' in K_0 are given by

$$v_{11} = \int \psi_{ik}*V''\psi_{ik}\,dv \qquad v_{12} = \int \psi_{ik}*V''\psi_{ki}\,dv$$
$$v_{21} = \int \psi_{ki}*V''\psi_{ik}\,dv \qquad v_{22} = \int \psi_{ki}*V''\psi_{ki}\,dv \qquad (193)$$

If in v_{11} we interchange the variables $x_1y_1z_1$ and $x_2y_2z_2$, the integral retains its value since the effect is only another notation of the integration variables; the procedure leaves V'' and dv unchanged (V'' being symmetric in the indices 1 and 2) but changes ψ_{ik} into ψ_{ki}. Thus we get $v_{11} = v_{22}$ and $v_{12} = v_{21}$. According to Section 25 the correction terms ϵ_{ik} are now to be determined by the determinant equation

$$\begin{vmatrix} v_{11} - \epsilon_{ik} & v_{12} \\ v_{12} & v_{22} - \epsilon_{ik} \end{vmatrix} = 0$$

the solutions of which are $\epsilon_{ik} = v_{11} \pm v_{12}$. Therefore the eigenvalues of the system are

$$E_{ik}' = E_{ik} + v_{11} + v_{12} \qquad \text{and} \qquad E_{ik}'' = E_{ik} + v_{11} - v_{12} \quad (194)$$

In order to obtain the corresponding eigenfunctions of the perturbed system we must transfer to that coordinate system K of the E_{ik} space wherein V'' is diagonal. The passage to K changes ψ_{ik} and ψ_{ki} into two other functions σ' and σ'' which represent vectors in the directions of the new axes. σ' and σ'' are connected with the ψ functions by linear transformations

$$\sigma' = s_{11}\psi_{ik} + s_{12}\psi_{ki} \qquad \sigma'' = s_{21}\psi_{ik} + s_{22}\psi_{ki}$$

corresponding to the transformation equation $\mathbf{x}' = S\mathbf{x}$. According to these equations, σ' is a vector whose components, when referred to the original system K_0, are s_{11} and s_{12}, whereas σ'' is the vector with components s_{21} and s_{22}. As σ' is transformed by V'' into $\epsilon_{ik}'\sigma'$, we have

$$v_{11}s_{11} + v_{12}s_{12} = \epsilon_{ik}'s_{11} = (v_{11} + v_{12})s_{11}$$
$$v_{21}s_{11} + v_{22}s_{12} = \epsilon_{ik}'s_{12} = (v_{11} + v_{12})s_{12}$$

Both equations give $s_{11} - s_{12} = 0$, and therefore $s_{11} = s_{12} = \alpha$. Similarly $s_{21} = -s_{22} = \beta$, and thus for σ' and σ'' we have

$$\sigma' = \alpha(\psi_{ik} + \psi_{ki}) \qquad \sigma'' = \beta(\psi_{ik} - \psi_{ki}) \qquad (195)$$

Finally, we require that the functions σ' and σ'' as well as ψ_{ik} and ψ_{ki} be normalized so that $\int \sigma'^*\sigma' \, dv = \int \sigma''^*\sigma'' \, dv = 1$. Then, from (195), because of the orthogonality of ψ_{ik} and ψ_{ki}, we obtain

$$2\alpha^*\alpha = 2\beta^*\beta = 1$$

and therefore

$$\alpha = \beta = \frac{1}{\sqrt{2}}$$

We can state the result as follows: In the two-body problem the eigenfunctions, because of the perturbation V'', are no longer ψ_{ik} and ψ_{ki} but $\sigma' = (1/\sqrt{2})(\psi_{ik} + \psi_{ki})$ and $\sigma'' = (1/\sqrt{2})(\psi_{ik} - \psi_{ki})$, the corresponding eigenvalues being $E_{ik}' = E_{ik} + v_{11} + v_{12}$ and $E_{ik}'' = E_{ik} + v_{11} - v_{12}$.

39. Symmetric and Antisymmetric Solutions. Let us here recall the epistemological principle that, in order to consider the theory as having any meaning at all, any of its statements can be tested by experiment. This point is important when we apply the theory which has been developed to a system in which the particles are indistinguishable. The conclusion was reached that, when we carry out a measurement of the energy of a system, we shall find the value E_{ik}' with a certain probability and the value E_{ik}'' with another probability. Let us consider first the simple case where only the two eigenvalues of a certain E_{ik} space have probabilities that differ from zero. Then the state can be described in the form

$$u(x_1 \cdots z_2) = x'\sigma'(x_1 \cdots z_2) + x''\sigma''(x_1 \cdots z_2) \quad (196)$$

wherein we designate the components of the representing vector in the direction of the principal axes E_{ik}' and E_{ik}'' by x' and x''. The decisive point here is that, in the dependence on $x_1 \cdots z_2$, u^*u gives the probability of finding particle 1 at $P_1(x_1y_1z_1)$ and particle 2 at $P_2(x_2y_2z_2)$. But, on the assumption that the particles are indistinguishable, all that we can arrive at by experimental means is the probability W of finding one of the particles at P_1 and simultaneously the other at P_2. When this fact is given by a measurement, it can as well mean that 1 is at P_1 and 2 at P_2 as that 1 is at P_2 and 2 at P_1. Thus each of these two possibilities has the same probability, $W/2$, and accordingly we can give the following postulate: A theory of the many-body problem is acceptable only if it furnishes the same probability for the configuration $x_1y_1z_1x_2y_2z_2$ as it does for $x_2y_2z_2x_1y_1z_1$ or, in other words, if the probability function $|u(x_1y_1z_1x_2y_2z_2)|^2$ is symmetric in the indices 1 and 2. If $|u(x_1y_1z_1x_2y_2z_2)|^2$ differed from

$|u(x_2y_2z_2x_1y_1z_1)|^2$, the theory would hold that one of the configurations 1 at P_1 and 2 at P_2 and 1 at P_2 and 2 at P_1 would have a greater probability than the other, a situation that could not be tested by experiment.

We wish to examine now whether (196) satisfies the above postulate. We have

$$u^*u = \tfrac{1}{2}x'^*x'(\psi_{ik}^* + \psi_{ki}^*)(\psi_{ik} + \psi_{ki})$$
$$+ \tfrac{1}{2}x''^*x''(\psi_{ik}^* - \psi_{ki}^*)(\psi_{ik} - \psi_{ki})$$
$$+ \tfrac{1}{2}x''^*x'(\psi_{ik}^* - \psi_{ki}^*)(\psi_{ik} + \psi_{ki})$$
$$+ \tfrac{1}{2}x'^*x''(\psi_{ik}^* + \psi_{ki}^*)(\psi_{ik} - \psi_{ki}) \qquad (197)$$

The first two terms remain unchanged when the indices 1 and 2 are interchanged, whereas the terms with x''^*x' and x'^*x'' reverse signs. This forces us to impose a supplementary condition on the theory by the assumption: There is in reality no state for which both the components x' and x'' differ from zero, but the system is with certainty either in the state σ' (x'' being zero) or in the state σ'' (x' being zero). In both cases the mixed terms with x''^*x' and x'^*x'' (which terms make u^*u non-symmetric) vanish. In what follows, σ' will be called symmetric and σ'' antisymmetric.

It is easy to see how the considerations are to be generalized when, in addition to σ' and σ'' of the E_{ik} space, we consider also the eigenfunctions of the other spaces. If, to be more accurate, we denote the eigenfunctions by σ_{ik}' and σ_{ik}'', any state of the system can be represented by

$$u(x_1 \cdot \cdot \cdot z_2) = \sum_{i,k<i} x_{ik}'\sigma_{ik}' + \sum_{i,k<i} x_{ik}''\sigma_{ik}'' + \sum_i x_{ii}\sigma_{ii} \qquad (198)$$

where σ_{ii} represent the function $\psi_i(1)\psi_i(2)$ of the eigenvalues $2E_i$ which occurs only once. The requirement that u^*u be symmetric in 1 and 2 then leads to the conclusion that either all the x_{ik}'' components be zero or all the x_{ik}' components together with the x_{ii} terms vanish. The x_{ii} terms must be included with the x_{ik}' ones because $\psi_{ii} = \psi_i(1)\psi_i(2)$ does not invert the sign when 1 and 2 are interchanged; therefore σ_{ii} must be considered a symmetric eigenfunction. So we may state the theorem: *A system of indistinguishable particles is observed only in those states in which u is made up of symmetric eigenfunctions only or of antisymmetric ones only.*

It must be emphasized, however, that this theorem holds only for those systems wherein the particles are indistinguishable from each other.   If by experiment a distinction is possible, the unsymmetric u have a meaning also.   We are then no longer entitled to permit only symmetric or antisymmetric eigenfunctions to enter the function u, for then there is no contradiction in it being possible for experiment to describe a state, for example, by the expression

$$u = x_{ik}{}'\sigma_{ik}{}' + x_{ik}{}''\sigma_{ik}{}''$$

with $x_{ik}{}'$ and $x_{ik}{}'' \neq 0$.   Although it is true that this implies different probabilities for the configurations P_1P_2 and P_2P_1, these configurations can indeed be distinguished experimentally, so that there is reason in speaking of the states ψ_{ik} and ψ_{ki}.   A state corresponds to ψ_{ik} if an energy measurement carried out on both the particles separately gives the values E_i and E_k for the first and second particle respectively, whereas the inverse correlation of the same energy values indicates a state ψ_{ki}.

It is interesting to consider from another point of view a system with two distinguishable particles.   Let us assume that we know the system to be in a certain state ψ_{ik} at time t.   In order to find the vector representing the state we must substitute ψ_{ik} for u in (198).   Then we see that the equation, in order to be fulfilled, requires that all the x components that do not belong to the E_{ik} space be zero, whereas $x_{ik}{}' = x_{ik}{}'' = 1/\sqrt{2}$, since we then obtain

$$\psi_{ik} = \tfrac{1}{2}(\psi_{ik} + \psi_{ki}) + \tfrac{1}{2}(\psi_{ik} - \psi_{ki})$$

It is a question now of what will become of the state $x_0{}' = x_0{}'' = 1/\sqrt{2}$ (omitting the subscripts and indicating by the index 0 the correlation to $t = 0$) when the system is left alone.   This question is answered by the dynamical law, $(\hbar/i)(d\mathbf{x}/dt) = H\mathbf{x}$, from which it follows that for the time-dependence of the components x' and x'' we have

$$x' = x_0{}' e^{(i/\hbar)E_{ik}{}'t} \qquad x'' = x_0{}'' e^{(i/\hbar)E_{ik}{}''t}$$

and therefore u, in its time-dependence, is

$$u(x_1 \cdots z_2, t) = \tfrac{1}{2}(\psi_{ik} + \psi_{ki})e^{(i/\hbar)E_{ik}{}'t} + \tfrac{1}{2}(\psi_{ik} - \psi_{ki})e^{(i/\hbar)E_{ik}{}''t}$$

$$= \tfrac{1}{2}\psi_{ik}(e^{(i/\hbar)E_{ik}{}'t} + e^{(i/\hbar)E_{ik}{}''t})$$

$$+ \tfrac{1}{2}\psi_{ki}(e^{(i/\hbar)E_{ik}{}'t} - e^{(i/\hbar)E_{ik}{}''t}) \tag{199}$$

This means that the probability of finding the system in the state ψ_{ik} at time t is

$$\frac{1}{4} \left(e^{(i/\hbar)E_{ik'}t} + e^{(i/\hbar)E_{ik''}t} \right) \left(e^{-(i/\hbar)E_{ik'}t} + e^{-(i/\hbar)E_{ik''}t} \right)$$

$$= \frac{1}{4} \left[2 + 2 \cos \frac{1}{\hbar} \left(E_{ik'} - E_{ik''} \right)t \right]$$

$$= \cos^2 \frac{1}{2\hbar} \left(E_{ik'} - E_{ik''} \right)t = \cos^2 \frac{v_{12}}{\hbar} t \qquad (200)$$

whereas the probability of the state ψ_{ki} is $\sin^2 (v_{12}/\hbar)t$. Hence the probabilities of ψ_{ik} and ψ_{ki} change periodically between 0 and 1, having a period $\tau = h/2v_{12}$. If at $t = 0$ the system is with certainty in the state ψ_{ik}, then at $t = h/4v_{12}$ it will with certainty be in the state ψ_{ki}. This phenomenon can be described as a "place exchange" between the particles, the word "place" meaning the coordination of the particles to a certain stationary state. At times an interpretation has been suggested that the particles change positions once within the interval $h/4v_{12}$. Such an interpretation is, however, not quite correct. It must not be assumed that the exchange takes place in a discontinuous way, but rather that the transition from ψ_{ik} to ψ_{ki} is the continuous process described by (199). According to this description the system, in the time $h/4v_{12}$, passes through a sequence of states *which are not defined with respect to the positions of the particles*. When the system is in a state for which neither x' nor x'' is zero, it would be incorrect to say that it is in the state ψ_{ik} with the probability x'^*x' and in the state ψ_{ki} with the probability x''^*x'', because, actually, it can only be maintained that a measurement of the energies, made on the two particles, provides the results ψ_{ik} and ψ_{ki} with the stated probabilities. But we destroy the state in question by the measurement, forcing the system to assume one of the states ψ_{ik} and ψ_{ki}. And the meaning of x'^*x' and x''^*x'' is that they determine the probabilities of the system favoring ψ_{ik} or ψ_{ki}.

40. The Exclusion Principle Relative to a Combination of Symmetric and Antisymmetric States. We return here to systems of indistinguishable particles. As we have seen, such systems can exist only in states that are represented by a sum of symmetric eigenfunctions only or antisymmetric functions only. However, in order to be sure that this assumption complies with a consistent theory, we have to examine the change which a system undergoes according to the law $(\hbar/i)(d\mathbf{x}/dt) = H\mathbf{x}$. The question is whether it could not be possible that a system, starting from an admissible state at $t = 0$, changes in such a way that it occupies states in which symmetric and antisymmetric components are mixed. It is seen at once that for an unperturbed system this is impossible, for, since $x = x_0 e^{(i/\hbar)Et}$, a component will remain zero if it is zero at $t = 0$. However, we can prove also that *by the emission or absorption of light a transition from a symmetric into an antisymmetric state or its reverse cannot be induced.* To show this we take into consideration the fact that according to Section 20 the probability of a transition from the symmetric state σ_{ik}' into the antisymmetric state σ_{lm}'' depends on the integral

$$\int (x_1 + x_2)\sigma_{ik}'^* \sigma_{lm}'' \, dv \tag{201}$$

the integral being extended over the six-dimensional configuration space. From the correspondence principle it is readily understood that now we must substitute the sum $x_1 + x_2$ for x; for, in the case of two particles, the expectation value of the electric moment is given by the integral $e \int (x_1 + x_2)u^*u \, dv$ which when resolved furnishes the term

$$x_{ik}'^* x_{lm}'' e^{(i/\hbar)(E_{lm}'' - E')t} e \int (x_1 + x_2)\sigma_{ik}'^* \sigma_{lm}'' \, dv$$

If the integral in this expression is zero, the quantum-mechanical interpretation is that a transition $\sigma_{(ik)}' \rightleftarrows \sigma_{(lm)}''$ never occurs, either in the direction in which the transition is connected with the emission of light or in the other direction, which leads to absorption. In this case, expression (201) is truly zero, for the expression remains the same when the indices 1 and 2 are interchanged, the interchange meaning only another notation of the integration variables. Thus

$$\int (x_1 + x_2)\sigma_{ik}'^*(1,\,2)\sigma_{lm}''(1,\,2) \, dv$$
$$= \int (x_2 + x_1)\sigma_{ik}'^*(21)\sigma_{lm}''(21) \, dv$$

Because $\sigma_{ik}'(12) = \sigma_{ik}'$ (21) and $\sigma_{lm}''(12) = -\sigma_{lm}''$ (21) this can be true only if the integral is zero.

Accordingly we come to the conclusion that a system which is in a symmetric or an antisymmetric state will retain its character for the entire future. That is all that we may maintain if quantum mechanics is true. The further question is whether there are, for different samples of the same system, both symmetric and antisymmetric states, or is only one of the two types realized and, if so, which of these can be determined by experiment only. As we shall see later on, it happens that the character depends on the spin of the particles and is symmetric or antisymmetric depending on whether the spin is an integer or half-integer multiple of $\hbar$.

41. The Helium Atom.   As an illustration we consider the neutral He atom.   For a long time it has been known that the He spectrum corresponds to two systems of terms which never (more precisely, very seldom) combine and which are called ortho and para terms.   There is no doubt about how this fact is to be interpreted: The two electrons of the atom must in some way be distinguishable, the mark of distinction being the direction of spin.   The function u, which represents the state of the atom, is therefore composed of symmetric and antisymmetric eigenfunctions which are to be identified with the ortho and para terms.   That there actually is a weak combination between the two types of terms is due to the fact that, according to the rigorous theory, the integrals (201) are not exactly zero but only very small.

To carry out this idea we must find out first how the two classes of states and the two observed types of terms must be coordinated.   For this purpose we compare the ground states of the para and ortho series. The experimental evidence shows that the lowest energy level (denoted by $1S$) of the para type lies far below the lowest ortho level, $2s$.   This fact suggests the following interpretation: In the zero-order approximation each of the two electrons moves in the same way as it would in an H atom of which the nucleus is doubly charged.   According to the theory of the H atom, the lowest level will, therefore, come about if both the electrons are in the ground state, $n = 1$, $m = l = 0$ (cf. Section 18).   If we designate by ψ_1 the eigenfunction of the H atom which corresponds to this state (according to Section 18 it would be more precise to write ψ_{100}), the lowest energy term of He corresponds to the state $\sigma_{11} = \psi_1(1)\psi_1(2)$, which state belongs to the symmetric class, and so we must infer that *the para levels are to be coordinated to the symmetric and the ortho levels to the antisymmetric states.*   This conclusion is confirmed by an examination of the next lowest energy levels which must arise when one of the electrons is moving on the orbit $n = 1$, $l = m = 0$, and the other on the orbit $n = 2$, $l = m = 0$. Then the corresponding eigenfunctions are

$$\sigma'(12) = \frac{1}{\sqrt{2}}\,\psi_1(1)\psi_2(2) + \psi_1(2)\psi_2(1)$$

$$\sigma''(12) = \frac{1}{\sqrt{2}}\,\psi_1(1)\psi_2(2) - \psi_1(2)\psi_2(1)$$

(202)

of which, if our interpretation is correct, the first represents a para and the second an ortho state.   As the energies of the two states have nearly the same value, the first ortho S term should coincide approximately with the second para S term, and they actually do.   From the observed spectrum it is to be inferred that the para term must lie a little higher than the ortho term. This conclusion is also in agreement with the theory according to which the energies of the symmetric and antisymmetric eigenfunctions are

$$E_{12}' = E_1 + E_2 + v_{11} + v_{12} \quad \text{and} \quad E_{12}'' = E_1 + E_2 + v_{11} - v_{12}$$

respectively. Thus the difference is $2v_{12}$, for which the theory gives a positive value.

There is, however, still another point to be explained: *The term arrangement of para helium is a triplet system, whereas the ortho terms are single.* The spin of the electron must be taken into account to explain this fact. The electron has an angular momentum of its own. When the component of this momentum in an arbitrary direction z is measured, the result is either $+\hbar/2$ or $-\hbar/2$, the probabilities of either depending on the internal state of the electron. Accordingly this state can be described by a function $\chi(m)$, the argument m being capable only of the values $+\frac{1}{2}$ and $-\frac{1}{2}$. $\chi(+\frac{1}{2})$ determines by $|\chi(+\frac{1}{2})|^2$ the probability of finding the value $+\hbar/2$ for the z component of spin, whereas $\chi(-\frac{1}{2})$ belongs to $-\hbar/2$.

The function $\chi(m)$ can be pictured as a unit vector $\mathbf{x}$ which lies in a two-dimensional "spin space" and which, when referred to a certain normal coordinate system K, has the components $x_1 = \chi(+\frac{1}{2})$ and $x_2 = \chi(-\frac{1}{2})$. When the vector $\mathbf{x}$ has the direction of one of the two axes (in this case $\mathbf{x}$ may be designated by $\mathbf{x}^+$ and $\mathbf{x}^-$ respectively), it signifies a state in which the values $+\hbar/2$ and $-\hbar/2$ respectively for the z component of the angular momentum are found with certainty. The components of $\mathbf{x}^+$ are $x_1 = \chi(+\frac{1}{2}) = 1$ and $x_2 = \chi(-\frac{1}{2}) = 0$, and those of $\mathbf{x}^-$ are $\chi(+\frac{1}{2}) = x_1 = 0$ and $x_2 = \chi(-\frac{1}{2}) = 1$. As $\mathbf{x}^+$ and $\mathbf{x}^-$ are orthogonal, the product $(\mathbf{x}^+\mathbf{x}^-) = 0$.

We can now represent the state of an electron with energy E by the product of two vectors one of which, when resolved relative to the principal axes belonging to the xyz coordinates of the particle, is given by $\psi_i(xyz)$ and refers to the position of the electron, while the other $\chi(m)$ corresponds to the spin. $|\psi_i(xyz)\chi(m)|^2$ is the probability that a simultaneous measurement of position and spin will give the results xyz and m. $\psi_i(xyz)\mathbf{x}^+$ and $\psi_i(xyz)\mathbf{x}^-$ denote states in which m is found with certainty to be $+\hbar/2$ and $-\hbar/2$ respectively. No difficulty is encountered in applying this formalism to the case of two particles. We must consider, for example,

$$[\psi_i(1)\psi_k(2) + \psi_i(2)\psi_k(1)]\mathbf{x}^+(1)\mathbf{x}^+(2)$$

a representation of a state in which the electrons belong to the i

and k levels respectively, whereas the z component of spin has the value $+\hbar/2$ for both electrons.   When the spin is $+\hbar/2$ for one electron and $-\hbar/2$ for the other, we must take $\mathbf{x}^+(1)\mathbf{x}^-(2) + \mathbf{x}^+(2)\mathbf{x}^-(1)$ as a factor of σ_{ik}'.   This leads to eight different states in all, four of which are symmetric and four antisymmetric.   The first are given by

$$\sigma_{ik}'\mathbf{x}^+(1)\mathbf{x}^+(2)$$
$$\sigma_{ik}'\mathbf{x}^-(1)\mathbf{x}^-(2)$$
$$\sigma_{ik}'[\mathbf{x}^+(1)\mathbf{x}^-(2) + \mathbf{x}^+(2)\mathbf{x}^-(1)] \tag{203}$$
$$\sigma_{ik}''[\mathbf{x}^+(1)\mathbf{x}^-(2) - \mathbf{x}^+(2)\mathbf{x}^-(1)]$$

The other four are given by

$$\sigma_{ik}''\mathbf{x}^+(1)\mathbf{x}^+(2)$$
$$\sigma_{ik}''\mathbf{x}^-(1)\mathbf{x}^-(2)$$
$$\sigma_{ik}''[\mathbf{x}^+(1)\mathbf{x}^-(2) + \mathbf{x}^+(2)\mathbf{x}^-(1)] \tag{203'}$$
$$\sigma_{ik}'[\mathbf{x}^+(1)\mathbf{x}^-(2) - \mathbf{x}^+(2)\mathbf{x}^-(1)]$$

All eight states are orthogonal to each other, as is seen from the product $(\mathbf{x}^+\mathbf{x}^-) = 0$.   When 1 and 2 are interchanged, the first four remain unaltered but the latter four reverse signs.

Now we can readily understand the peculiarities of the helium spectrum.   First of all, we know that the probability for a transition between a symmetric and an antisymmetric state vanishes; the probability differs from zero only for transitions within the same group. Thus the exclusion principle is not to be applied to the σ_{ik}' and σ_{ik}'' functions but to the whole of the solutions (203) and (203').   This means that within the antisymmetric group (as will be seen, this is the only group realized in nature) the fourth solution may be combined with the other three, so that we can now understand how transitions between σ_{ik}' and σ_{ik}'' are possible in helium.   The reason is that σ_{ik}' and σ_{ik}'' are not, by themselves, the eigenfunctions of the system but have to be connected with the spin function χ.   Therefore we cannot deduce the character of the state from the character of σ.   The para function σ_{ik}' may describe an antisymmetric state, and the antisymmetric ortho function σ_{ik}'' may describe a symmetric one.

It is to be seen further that, if all eight eigenfunctions of (203) and (203') were realized, the theory would require that four different ortho and as many para terms occur in nature.   Actually, however, only three terms of the first kind and one of the second exist.   From this fact it must be inferred that, of the eight solutions, (203) and (203'), only the four of the antisymmetric group are realized. As three of these are of the ortho and one of the para type, our assumption (corresponding to the rule formulated at the end of the preceding section) leads just to the observed multiplicity of terms. However, the difference of the three ortho terms is small, owing to the weak magnetic interaction of the electrons caused by spin. This triplet structure of the ortho system was discovered after Heisenberg had predicted it theoretically.

Among the para terms, that of the ground state is of particular importance because it measures the ionization potential of the atom. The fact that Kellner and Hylleraas obtained for the potential a value that differs from the experimental one only by a few parts per thousand verifies the accuracy of the quantum-mechanical He model.

42. Systems of Many Similar Particles. Method of Particle Picture. At this point we are going to generalize our considerations by applying them to systems that contain an arbitrary number n of particles. As an example, we might take an atom the nucleus of which is surrounded by more than two electrons, but we could just as well consider a gas, regardless of whether its particles are material corpuscles or light quanta. However, we shall simplify the problem by assuming that an eventual interaction of the particles can be disregarded. In addition we assume that the mechanical nature of every particle is described by the same Hamiltonian H, so that the vector $\mathbf{x}$ of any particle satisfies the equation $(\hbar/i)(d\mathbf{x}/dt) = H\mathbf{x}$. No special assumptions are made regarding the kind of function, so that for H too there may be substituted energy operators that correspond to the relativistic wave equations of the next chapter.

At first we imagine that the particles are distinguishable and marked $1, 2, \cdots, n$. To avoid confusion we must use a carefully designed notation. For any particle there is a certain number of observables q which can be measured simultaneously and which have eigenspectra that may be assumed to be discrete. We denote by K_0 the coordinate system in which all the (commutative) q terms are diagonal. Any axis of K_0 corresponds to certain q values in the sense that a vector $\mathbf{x}$ the direction of which coincides with the axis is transformed by the operator Q, which corresponds to the coordinate q, into $\alpha\mathbf{x}$; the factor α is the eigenvalue of Q belonging to the considered axis. Any axis of K_0 may, therefore, be characterized by the totality of the corresponding eigenvalues. We simplify the notation by labeling the axes by the numbers $k = 1, 2, \cdots$ and setting down for any k the corresponding eigenvalues α. Then we may denote by $\mathbf{x}_k$ a unit vector which has the direction of the kth axis and indicate by an upper index i, for example $\mathbf{x}_k{}^i$, that the vector is meant to represent the state of the ith particle.

We pass now from the single particle to the whole system. We extend the system K_0 of the single particle to a system K_1 which combines n $K_0{}^{(i)}$ systems in such a way that any axis of K_1 defines a state k_1 of the first particle, a state k_2 of the second, and so on to the state k_n of the nth particle. This means that any unit vector $\mathbf{X}$, defined by an axis of K_1, is a product† of n unit vectors, $\mathbf{x}_{k_1}{}^{(1)}\mathbf{x}_{k_2}{}^{(2)} \cdots \mathbf{x}_{k_n}{}^{(n)}$; that is,

$$\mathbf{X} = \mathbf{x}_{k_1}{}^{(1)}\mathbf{x}_{k_2}{}^{(2)} \cdots \mathbf{x}_{k_n}{}^{(n)} \tag{204}$$

Thus a unit vector $\mathbf{X}$ of the kind that represents the direction of the axis $k_1, k_2, \cdots, k_n$ of K_1 represents a total state in which the first particle is in the state k_1, the second in k_2, and so on.

When we apply any permutation to the upper or lower indices in (204) we get another state that belongs to the single states $k_1, k_2, \cdots, k_n$ as well, differing from (204) only in the coordination of these states to the particles. If in the sequence of indices $k_1, k_2, \cdots, k_n$ (which need not differ one from the other) the value 1 occurs n_1 times, the value 2 n_2 times, and so on, there are $n!/n_1!n_2! \cdots$ different states $\mathbf{X}_1, \mathbf{X}_2, \cdots$ all of which belong to the same single states $k_1, k_2, \cdots k_n$. Thus any state of the kind $k_1, k_2, \cdots, k_n$ can be represented in the form

$$\mathbf{X} = a_1\mathbf{X}_1 + a_2\mathbf{X}_2 + \cdots \tag{205}$$

where $|a_i|^2$ represents the probability that the states $k_1, k_2, \cdots, k_n$ are coordinated to the particles in the manner required by $\mathbf{X}_i$.

Now let us assume that the particles are indistinguishable. Then (205) has a meaning only if all the probabilities $|a_i|^2$ have the same value. Otherwise, in contradiction to the possibilities of observation, a certain individual coordination of the k states to the particles would be maintained. We now learn from experience that in nature the condition that $|a_i|^2$ be a constant is realized in two different ways:

(i) For particles the spin of which is either zero or an integral multiple of $\hbar$, all the a_i terms have the same value; consequently the only states possible are those of the sort,

$$\mathbf{X} = a(\mathbf{X}_1 + \mathbf{X}_2 + \cdots) \tag{206}$$

† Only a product and not a sum can be considered, for our formalism requires that the component of $\mathbf{X}$ in the direction of a K_1 axis defines by the square of its magnitude the probability of finding the first particle in k_1, the second in k_2, and so on. However, this probability equals the product and not the sum of the single probabilities.

The principle of symmetric states then holds for the system, and the statistics of Bose-Einstein must be applied.

(ii) For particles with a half-integer spin, a will be positive or negative depending on whether $\mathbf{X}_i$ results from $\mathbf{X}_1 = \mathbf{x}_{k_1}{}^{(1)}\mathbf{x}_{k_2}{}^{(2)}$, $\cdots$ with $k_1 < k_2 < k_3 < \cdots$ by an even or odd number of permutations applied to the k_i. For such particles $\mathbf{X}$ is given by

$$\mathbf{X} = a(\mathbf{X}_1 - \mathbf{X}_2 + \mathbf{X}_3 - \cdots) \tag{207}$$

In this case the principle of antisymmetric states holds and the Fermi-Dirac statistics must be applied. $\mathbf{X}$ may be represented by the determinant

$$\mathbf{X} = a \begin{vmatrix} \mathbf{x}_{k_1}{}^{(1)} & \mathbf{x}_{k_1}{}^{(2)} & \cdots & \mathbf{x}_{k_1}{}^{(n)} \\ \mathbf{x}_{k_2}{}^{(1)} & \mathbf{x}_{k_2}{}^{(2)} & \cdots & \mathbf{x}_{k_2}{}^{(n)} \\ \cdots & \cdots & \cdots & \cdots \\ \cdots & \cdots & \cdots & \cdots \\ \cdots & \cdots & \cdots & \cdots \end{vmatrix} \tag{207'}$$

The factor a in (206) and (207) is to be chosen so that $|\mathbf{X}|^2 = 1$. If the $\mathbf{X}_i$ are already normalized—that is, if $(\mathbf{X}_i\mathbf{X}_k) = \delta_{ik}$—then, in the case represented by (206), from $|\mathbf{X}|^2 = 1$ we obtain the equation $|a|^2(n!/n_1!n_2! \cdots) = 1$ and therefore $a = \sqrt{n_1!n_2! \cdots/n!}$. On the other hand, because of (207'), an antisymmetric $\mathbf{X}$ is possible only if all the k_i states differ, so that $\mathbf{X}$ is composed of $n!$ terms and a is given by $a = 1/\sqrt{n!}$.

Thus we cannot characterize a state of the kind (206) or (207) by specifying the state k_i for every individual particle but can give only the description that n_1 particles (we do not know which) are in the state 1, n_2 particles in the state 2 and so on. The n_i must, of course, satisfy the condition that $\sum n_i = n$ and, for an antisymmetric system, can have only the values 1 and 0.

Once again it becomes necessary to change the coordinate system in the Hilbert space. We have extended the original system K_0, which was adapted to a single particle, to a system K_1, which was made sufficient for n particles by providing an axis for any sequence of states $k_1, k_2, \cdots, k_n$ coordinated to the particles 1, 2, $\cdots$, n. But, since the particles are indistinguishable, the totality of all states resulting from $k_1, k_2, \cdots, k_n$ by applying a permutation to the k_i terms now reduces to a single state, (206) or (207), and this fact forces us to simplify K_1 to a system K wherein the axes are characterized by an infinite sequence of numbers $n_1, n_2, \cdots$. This has to be understood in the sense that the axis $n_1, n_2, \cdots$ corresponds to a state in which n_1 particles are in state 1, n_2 particles in state 2, and so on.   If we denote the respective unit vectors by $\mathbf{X}_{n_1 n_2 \ldots}$, any state of the total system can be described by coordinates $x_{n_1 n_2 \ldots}$ in the form

$$\mathbf{X} = \sum_{n_1 n_2 \cdots} x_{n_1 n_2 \ldots} \mathbf{X}_{n_1 n_2 \ldots} \tag{208}$$

and $|x_{n_1 n_2 \ldots}|^2$ gives the probability that a measurement, carried out on all particles, finds n_1 of them in state 1, n_2 of them in state 2, and so on.   The components $x_{n_1 n_2 \ldots}$ of the vector must now be marked by a sequence of numbers n_1, n_2, $\cdots$ the whole of which now replaces the index i.

The representation expressed by (208) includes all statements that can be made in quantum mechanics about the possible states of a system of indistinguishable particles, and the only thing we must yet investigate is the law according to which the vector $\mathbf{X}$ changes with time.   We know this law to be

$$\frac{\hbar}{i} \frac{d\mathbf{X}}{dt} = \mathbf{H}\mathbf{X} \tag{209}$$

where $\mathbf{H}$ denotes the Hamiltonian operator of the total system. $\mathbf{H}$ is a matrix the elements of which, when referred to the coordinate system K, are to be written in the form $\mathbf{H}_{n_1 n_2 \ldots n_1' n_2' \ldots}$, so that from (209) we obtain

$$\frac{\hbar}{i} \frac{dx_{n_1 n_2 \ldots}}{dt} = \sum_{n_1' n_2' \cdots} \mathbf{H}_{n_1 n_2 \ldots n_1' n_2' \ldots} x_{n_1' n_2' \ldots} \tag{209$'$}$$

The question here is how to determine $\mathbf{H}$ from the operator H which holds for a single particle.   This question will be answered first for the symmetric system.   In this case the probability of finding the first particle in the state k_1, the second in k_2, and so on is given by $|x_{k_1}^{(1)}|^2$, $|x_{k_2}^{(2)}|^2 \cdots$.   The state considered is of the kind n_1, n_2, $\cdots$ if in the sequence k_1, k_2, $\cdots$, k_n the values 1, 2, $\cdots$ occur n_1, n_2, $\cdots$ times respectively.   As the probability of another distribution of the same single states has the same value and the number of distributions is $n!/n_1! n_2! \cdots$, we have

$$|x_{n_1 n_2 \ldots}|^2 = \frac{n!}{n_1! n_2! \cdots} |x_{k_1}^{(1)}|^2 |x_{k_2}^{(2)}|^2 \cdots |x_{k_n}^{(n)}|^2$$

Therefore

$$x_{n_1 n_2 \ldots} = \sqrt{\frac{n!}{n_1! n_2! \cdots}}\, x_{k_1}^{(1)} x_{k_2}^{(2)} \cdots x_{k_n}^{(n)} \tag{210}$$

Recalling that for a single particle

$$\frac{\hbar}{i}\frac{dx_\alpha^{(i)}}{dt} = \sum_\beta H_{\alpha\beta}x_\beta^{(i)} \tag{211}$$

we obtain, upon differentiating (210) relative to time,

$$\frac{\hbar}{i}\frac{dx_{n_1 n_2 \cdots}}{dt} = \sum_\alpha H_{\alpha\alpha}n_\alpha x_{n_1 n_2 \cdots}$$

$$+ \sum_{\beta \neq \alpha} H_{\alpha\beta}\sqrt{n_\alpha(n_\beta + 1)}\, x_{n_1 n_2 \cdots n_\alpha -1 \cdots n_\beta+1 \cdots} \tag{212}$$

Equation (212) is arrived at in the following way: First we take those factors in the product (210) for which k_i has an arbitrarily given value α. According to the definition of the numbers n_1, n_2, $\cdots$, the number of these factors is n_α. When we differentiate the factors relative to time, we obtain

(i) because of the terms $H_{\alpha\alpha}x_\alpha^{(i)}$ in (211), the product (210) multiplied n_α times by $H_{\alpha\alpha}$: $H_{\alpha\alpha}n_\alpha x_{n_1 n_2}\cdots$. This explains the first term on the right-hand side of (212).

(ii) because of the term $H_{\alpha\beta}x_\beta^{(i)}$, a product in which the factor x_α no longer occurs n_α times but $n_\alpha - 1$ times, whereas the number of x_{k_i} terms, with $k_i = \beta$, is increased from n_β to $n_\beta + 1$, that is, a product which, according to (210), belongs to $x_{n_1 n_2 \cdots n_\alpha -1 \cdots n_\beta+1}\cdots$. As the factor of the product we find $H_{\alpha\beta}n_\alpha\sqrt{n!/n_1!n_2!}\cdots$. If we take n_α into the root, one factor n_α is cancelled by the last factor of $n_\alpha!$ in the denominator, thus reducing it to $(n_\alpha - 1)!$. If, in addition, we multiply numerator and denominator by $n_\beta + 1$, the factor $n_\beta!$ of the denominator is increased to $(n_\beta + 1)!$ and we obtain

$$\sqrt{\frac{n!n_\alpha(n_\beta+1)}{n_1!n_2!\cdots(n_\alpha-1)!\cdots(n_\beta+1)!}}$$

as a factor. But this is $\sqrt{n_\alpha(n_\beta+1)}$ times the factor which, according to (210), belongs to $x_{n_1 n_2 \cdots n_\alpha-1 \cdots n_\beta+1}\cdots$. Thus, because of $H_{\alpha\beta}$, we obtain the term $H_{\alpha\beta}\sqrt{n_\alpha(n_\beta+1)}\,x_{n_1 n_2 \cdots n_\alpha-1 \cdots n_\beta+1}\cdots$.

On comparing (212) with (209') we now see that the diagonal elements of H are given by

$$\mathrm{H}_{n_1 n_2 \cdots n_1 n_2 \cdots} = \sum_\alpha n_\alpha H_{\alpha\alpha} \tag{213}$$

For any n_α term in this sum, that value is to be taken which occurs in the diagonal element $\mathrm{H}_{n_1 n_2 \cdots n_1 n_2 \cdots}$ as index. On the other hand, the non-diagonal elements are

$$\mathrm{H}_{n_1 n_2 \cdots n_1' n_2' \cdots} = H_{\alpha\beta} \sqrt{n_\alpha(n_\beta + 1)} \quad \text{or} \quad 0 \qquad (214)$$

the first value holding for $n_\alpha' = n_\alpha - 1$, $n_\beta' = n_\beta + 1$, with all the other n_i' terms being equal to the n_i. In all other cases the second value holds.

In a quite similar way H can be evaluated for an antisymmetric system. Here we shall be satisfied with the result only. For the diagonal elements of H, (213) is again valid but the non-diagonal elements are given by

$$\mathrm{H}_{n_1 n_2 \cdots n_1' n_2' \cdots} = \pm H_{\alpha\beta} n_\alpha \quad \text{or} \quad 0$$

The value $\pm H_{\alpha\beta}$ holds for $n_\alpha = 1$, $n_\alpha' = 0$, $n_\beta = 0$, $n_\beta' = 1$, all the other n_i' being equal to the n_i. The positive or negative value is taken depending on whether those n_i terms between n_α and n_β have the value unity an even or an odd number of times.

There remains to be considered the case wherein a continuous spectrum of eigenvalues belongs to the simultaneously measurable coordinates $q_1, q_2, \cdots, q_s$ by which the state of a single particle is defined. Then the state $\mathbf{x}$ of the particle can be described by a function $\psi(q_1 \cdots q_s)$, which by $|\psi|^2 dq_1 \cdots dq_s$ gives the probability of finding for the q_i, when they are measured simultaneously, values between q_i and $q_i + dq_i$. In what follows we shall use $\psi(q)$ to represent $\psi(q_1 \cdots q_s)$, wherein q is the single variable that includes all the q_i terms. Now let us assume that there are n particles the states of which are described by $\psi_1(q)\psi_2(q) \cdots$, the ψ_i being either identical or different functions. If we denote by $q^{(i)}$ the variable q which belongs to the ith particle, the probability that a measurement for the first particle gives a value $q^{(1)}$, for the second particle a value $q^{(2)}$, and so on, is given by the square of the magnitude of the function

$$\Psi(q^{(1)}q^{(2)} \cdots q^{(n)}) = \psi_1(q^{(1)})\psi_2(q^{(2)}) \cdots \psi_n(q^{(n)})$$

When in this function the indices of two ψ_i functions, say 1 and 2, are interchanged, we again obtain a function of the $q^{(i)}$ which, however, gives a different probability for the result $q^{(1)}q^{(2)} \cdots q^{(n)}$. This state differs from the preceding one in that the particles 1 and 2 have interchanged their states ψ_1 and ψ_2. However, since the particles are indistinguishable, we can never judge which of the particles belongs to which ψ_i, so that only those $\Psi(q^{(1)}q^{(2)} \cdots q^{(n)})$ have meaning which are symmetric or antisymmetric in the $q^{(i)}$ terms. This requirement is fulfilled by

$$\Psi = \sum_P \psi_1(q^{(1)})\psi_2(q^{(2)}) \cdots \psi_n(q^{(n)})$$

the sum being understood in the sense that any permutation is applied to the indices of the ψ_i and that the terms are taken either all with the same sign or positive and negative alternately.

In order to calculate H, the operator that regulates the time change of Ψ by $(\hbar/i)(d\Psi/dt) = H\Psi$, we start with the ψ_i functions. If H_i is the energy operator for the ψ_i state, we have

$$\frac{\hbar}{i}\frac{d}{dt}\psi_i(q^{(k)}) = H_i\psi_i(q^{(k)})$$

Thus it follows that

$$\frac{d\Psi}{dt} = \sum_P \frac{d\psi_1}{dt}\psi_2(q^{(2)}) \cdots + \sum_P \psi_1(q^{(1)})\frac{d\psi_2(q^{(2)})}{dt} \cdots + \cdots$$

After the permutations have been applied, the first term gives $(i/\hbar)H_1\psi$, and so we obtain

$$\frac{\hbar}{i}\frac{d\Psi}{dt} = \sum_i H_i\Psi \quad \text{or} \quad H = \sum_i H_i \tag{215}$$

43. Systems of Many Similar Particles. Method of Wave Picture. In the preceding section on the treatment of the many-body problem a method was applied in which we used the concepts of the particle picture only, explaining the state of the total system from the states of its individual particles. According to quantum mechanics, however, the behavior of a particle can also be interpreted by the picture of a wave motion, and this leads to another (mathematically equivalent) solution of the many-body problem, a method consisting essentially of a quantization of the wave motion that corresponds to a single particle.

To develop the method we do not consider a whole system, but rather a single particle, again assuming a discrete eigenspectrum of the observables q which, we imagine, characterize the state of the particle. In the Hilbert space, the coordinate system denoted by K_0 in Section 42 is then scaffolded by the unit vectors $\mathbf{x}_k$ and any state $\mathbf{x}$ can be represented in the form $\mathbf{x} = \sum x_k\mathbf{x}_k$. If we resolve $\mathbf{x}$ and $\mathbf{x}_k$ relative to the axes of the coordinate system belonging to the coordinates xyz of the particle, $\mathbf{x}$ and $\mathbf{x}_k$ become associated with the functions $\psi(xyzt)$ and $\psi_k(xyz)$, the relation being given by

$$\psi(xyzt) = \sum_k x_k(t)\psi_k(xyz) \tag{216}$$

The coordinates x_k are written as functions of t because they change with time according to

$$\frac{\hbar}{i} \frac{dx_k}{dt} = \sum_i H_{ki} x_i \tag{217}$$

where $\|H_{ki}\|$ is the energy matrix of a single particle referred to K_0.

If the function $\psi(xyzt)$ is interpreted as an excitation of some kind or other, ψ represents a wave motion the wave surfaces of which at time t_0 are given by $\psi(xyzt_0) =$ constant. Thus the meaning of equations (216) and (217) is that the wave can be resolved into parts $\psi_k(xyz)$ which appear in the total wave with intensities given by the $x_k(t)$ factors. We shall show now that the quantization of the wave motion leads to a formalism that is closely related to the solution of the many-body problem.

If the $\psi_k(xyz)$ functions are given, the wave motion evidently can be described by the time-dependence of the x_k terms; hence these can be considered generalized coordinates of the system. If we wish to apply the methods of quantum mechanics to the system, it will be necessary to give equations (217) the form of canonical equations by deriving them from the Hamiltonian H. If H is known as a function of the x_k terms and the conjugate momenta p_k, we can carry out the quantization by translating x_k and p_k into matrices chosen in such a way that they satisfy the commutation relation.

We begin by determining the function H. The condition H must satisfy is that equation (217) be identical with

$$\frac{dx_k}{dt} = \frac{\partial H}{\partial p_k} \qquad \frac{dp_k}{dt} = -\frac{\partial H}{\partial x_k} \tag{218}$$

We can achieve this by choosing H to be

$$H = \frac{i}{\hbar} \sum H_{ik} x_k p_i \tag{219}$$

For from (218) we get

$$\frac{dx_k}{dt} = \frac{i}{\hbar} \sum_i H_{ki} x_i \qquad \frac{dp_k}{dt} = -\frac{i}{\hbar} \sum_i H_{ik} p_i = -\frac{i}{\hbar} \sum_i H_{ki}{}^* p_i$$

The second equation becomes the conjugate complex of (217) if we put $p_k = (\hbar/i) x_k{}^*$. Thus we obtain

$$H = \sum H_{ik} x_i{}^* x_k \tag{220}$$

The next step in the procedure is to translate the x coordinates and the momenta p into matrices. This means that we must subject the already quantized equations (216) and (217) to a second quantization, for which we need a new Hilbert space equipped with a coordinate system K, this system having no relation to K_0 of the preceding discussions. If we denote the matrix belonging to x_k by X_k, the matrix corresponding to $x_k{}^*$ is the Hermitean conjugate matrix $\tilde{X}_k$; for $x_k + \tilde{x}_k$ is real and thus the corresponding matrix must be Hermitean, this condition being satisfied only by $X_k + \tilde{X}_k$. The coordinate and momentum, therefore, are to be represented by X_k and $(\hbar/i)\tilde{X}_k$, which are required to fulfill the relations

$$X_i\tilde{X}_k - \tilde{X}_kX_i = E\delta_{ik}$$
$$X_iX_k - X_kX_i = 0 \qquad (220)$$
$$\tilde{X}_i\tilde{X}_k - \tilde{X}_k\tilde{X}_i = 0$$

We obtain for H, using the matrices X_i and $\tilde{X}_i$,

$$H = \sum_{ik} H_{ik}\tilde{X}_iX_k \qquad (221)$$

The coordinate system K of the Hilbert space to which the matrices X_i and $\tilde{X}_i$ are referred can be chosen arbitrarily, and we choose it in such a way that $\tilde{X}_iX_i$ becomes diagonal. Then a certain eigenvalue of $\tilde{X}_iX_i$ can be correlated to any axis of K for any i value. If we imagine that the eigenvalues of $\tilde{X}_iX_i$ are marked by 1, 2, $\cdots$, any axis of K can be designated by n_1, n_2, $\cdots$, meaning that the axis belongs to the n_1th eigenvalue of $\tilde{X}_1X_1$, to the n_2th eigenvalue of $\tilde{X}X_2$, and so on. It is easily seen that the solutions of (220) satisfying the condition that $\tilde{X}_iX_i$ be diagonal are given by†

$$x^{(i)}{}_{n_i,\,n_i+1} = \sqrt{n_i + 1} \qquad \tilde{x}^{(i)}{}_{n_i,\,n_i-1} = \sqrt{n_i} \qquad (222)$$

with all the other elements being zero.

† If a matrix A is referred to a coordinate system K the axes of which are marked by several indices, the elements of A must be written in the form $a_{n_1n_2\cdots n_1'n_2'\cdots}$. The multiplication rule then requires that the elements of the product AB be defined by

$$(AB)_{n_1n_2\cdots n_1'n_2'\cdots} = \sum a_{n_1n_2\cdots n_1''n_2''\cdots}b_{n_1''n_2''\cdots n_1'n_2'\cdots}$$

this sum to be extended over all combinations $n_1''n_2''\cdots$. For example, in (223) all $\tilde{x}_{n_1n_2\cdots n_i\cdots n_1''n_2''\cdots n_i''\cdots} = 0$ except $\tilde{x}_{n_1n_2\cdots n_i\cdots n_1n_2\cdots n_i-1\cdots}$, and similarly all $x_{n_1''n_2''\cdots n_i''\cdots n_1n_2\cdots n_i\cdots} = 0$ except $x_{n_1n_2\cdots(n_i-1)\cdots n_1n_2\cdots n_i\cdots}$.

For the sake of simplicity the elements $x^{(i)}$ of X are marked only by those n_i, n_i' indices which are different, so that $x^{(i)}{}_{n_i, n_{i+1}}$ is an abbreviation of $x^{(i)}{}_{n_1 n_2 \cdots n_i \cdots n_1 n_2 \cdots n_{i+1}} \cdots$. From (222) we get for the product $\tilde{X}_i X_i$ the diagonal elements

$$(\tilde{X}_i X_i)_{n_1 n_2 \cdots n_1 n_2 \cdots} = n_i \tag{223}$$

whereas all non-diagonal elements are zero.   In numbering the axes of K we may, therefore, use the eigenvalues of $\tilde{X}_i X_i$ directly.

Let us now denote by $\mathbf{X}$ the vector that represents the state of the system, and let its components relative to the n_1, n_2, $\cdots$ axes of K be $x_{n_1 n_2 \cdots}$. If $\mathbf{X}$ has the direction of one of these axes, the product $x_i^* x_i = |x_i|^2$ is given by that eigenvalue of $\tilde{X}_i X_i$ which belongs to the axis, that is, by a whole number n_i. $|x_i|^2$ is the square of the amplitude of the ith partial wave and thus measures its intensity, so that $\mathbf{X}$ indicates a wave motion in which the first, second, and so on partial wave appear in strengths n_1, n_2, $\cdots$. If $\mathbf{X}$ does not coincide with an axis of K, the component $x_{n_1 n_2 \cdots}$, by its square $|x_{n_1 n_2 \cdots}|^2$ determines the probability that the measurement of the partial waves finds the strengths n_1, n_2, $\cdots$ respectively.

For the elements of the Hamiltonian $\mathrm{H} = \sum H_{ik} \tilde{X}_i X_k$, we obtain now

$$\mathrm{H}_{n_1 n_2 \cdots n\ n_2 \cdots} = \sum H_{\alpha\alpha} n_\alpha$$

$$\mathrm{H}_{n_1 n_2 \cdots n_1' n_2' \cdots} = H_{\alpha\beta} \sqrt{n_\alpha(n_\beta + 1)} \quad \text{or} \quad 0 \tag{224}$$

The first value holds for $n_\alpha' = n_\alpha - 1$, $n_\beta' = n_\beta + 1$, all the other n_i' terms being equal to the n_i.   The second value holds in all other cases.   Thus we arrive at the important result: *The operator* H, *which, according to* $(\hbar/i)(d\mathbf{X}/dt) = \mathrm{H}\mathbf{X}$, *regulates the time rate of change of the wave motion, turns out to be identical with the operator that belongs to a symmetric system of particles according to (213) and (214).*   Thus in a system of particles which is capable only of symmetric states, the quantization of the wave motion, carried out with the aid of the commutation relation (220), leads to the same formalism as the quantization of the particle picture.   Although quite different in content, the two methods are mathematically equivalent, so that the many-body problem may be treated just as well by the wave picture as by the particle picture.   In order to return to the particle picture, we need only apply a re-interpretation by considering the square of the amplitude $|x_i|^2$ of the ith partial wave as the number n_i of the particles which are in the ith state.

The wave picture method may also be applied to systems observed only in antisymmetric states, the difference merely being that the relations

$$X_i \tilde{X}_k + \tilde{X}_k X_i = E\delta_{ik} \qquad X_i X_k + X_k X_i = 0 \qquad \tilde{X}_i \tilde{X}_k + \tilde{X}_k \tilde{X}_i = 0$$

must be substituted for (220). This case will not be considered in detail here.

It should be noticed that a Hamiltonian operator of the form $\sum H_{ik}\tilde{X}_i X_k$ permits the system to be changed in time only in such a way that the number of particles remains constant. For it follows from $(\hbar/i)(d\mathbf{X}/dt) = \mathbf{H}\mathbf{X}$ that, if we resolve the vector $\mathbf{X}$ relative to the axes of K,

$$\frac{\hbar}{i}\frac{dx_{n_1 n_2 \cdots}}{dt} = \sum_{ikn_1'n_2' \cdots} H_{ik}(\tilde{X}_i X_i)_{n_1 n_2 \cdots n_1'n_2' \cdots} x_{n_1'n_2' \cdots} \qquad (225)$$

$|x_{n_1 n_2 \cdots}|^2$ is the probability of finding n_1 particles in state 1, n_2 in state 2, and so on. Now let us assume that at t_0 the system is in the state $n_1^0, n_2^0 \cdots$. Then, on the right-hand side of (225), only terms with $n_1' = n_1^0$, $n_2' = n_2^0$ and so on will occur, since only the $x_{n_1^0 n_2^0 \cdots}$ term is not equal to zero. However, according to (222), $(\tilde{X}_i X_k)_{n_1 n_2 \cdots n_1'n_2' \cdots}$ differs from zero only for $n_i = n_i^0 + 1$, $n_k = n_k^0 - 1$, all other n_α terms equaling the n_α^0. This means that, because of $H_{ik}(\tilde{X}_i X_k)$, only such components can be had wherein $n_1 + n_2 + \cdots = n_1^0 + n_2^0 \cdots$, the only effect of $(\tilde{X}_i X_k)$ being that the occupation number of the ith state is increased by 1, whereas that of the kth state is diminished by 1.

Later on we shall come across systems the Hamiltonian of which contains terms with X_i only or $\tilde{X}_i$ only. Such terms signify the possibility that particles are created or annihilated.

The equivalence of a quantized wave motion with a many-particle system is of decisive importance for the theory of wave fields. Our considerations have been concerned with a special wave field corresponding to equations (216) and (217). However, the method can be generalized on a large scale. If an arbitrary wave field is given whose excitation, in so far as it depends on x, y, z, t, is defined by $\psi(xyzt)$, then ψ, with the help of a system of orthogonal functions $f_i(xyz)$, can always be expanded into a series, $\sum x_i(t)f_i(xyz)$, and in the coefficients x_i of the expansion we obtain generalized coordinates the values of which define the state of the system for any time t. We can correlate certain momenta p_i to the x_i terms. If the energy of the field is expressed in terms of x_i and p_i, we obtain the Hamiltonian H from which the field equations can be derived in the form

$$\frac{dx_i}{dt} = \frac{\partial H}{\partial p_i} \qquad \frac{dp_i}{dt} = -\frac{\partial H}{\partial x_i}$$

If we succeed in selecting x_i in such a way that H takes on the form $\sum H_{ik}x_i{}^*x_k$, then, according to the theorem proved, the quantized wave field is equivalent to a system of particles; this means that the measurement of all observables that can be ascertained simultaneously with the $|x_i|^2$ terms leads to the same result as if the wave field were a system of particles. Later on we shall adopt this method in the treatment of all wave fields, especially those corresponding to the light quantum and the meson.

44. Statistics of Bose-Einstein and Fermi-Dirac. According to quantum mechanics only symmetric or antisymmetric states for a gas are allowable. Any of these states X is characterized by the numbers n_1, n_2, $\cdots$ of the particles that are in the single states $1, 2, \cdots$. Because the particles are indistinguishable, the question as to which of them belong to what states is meaningless. This situation necessitates a drastic departure from ordinary ideas in judging the a priori probability of a state. Classical physics would have estimated the probability from the number of different possibilities of coordinating to the particles the single states of which the total state is composed. In contradiction to this method, quantum mechanics gives to any symmetric or antisymmetric state, represented by a vector X in the Hilbert space, the same weight. As far as quantum mechanics is concerned, it is irrelevant, for example, that a total state composed of different single states can be realized in $n!$ different ways, whereas in the case of n identical states there is only one method of realization. This is no reason for quantum mechanics giving the first state a greater weight than the second, because the two states represented by a unit vector in the isotropic Hilbert space are considered to be perfectly equivalent.

To clarify this important difference between classical and quantum mechanics, we consider the simple case where two particles are present, the possible states of which can be given by a set of x_k vectors. Classical statistics would look at this as follows: When we investigate the particles at time t, we find either two identical or two different x_k states. A total state of the first kind, $X = x_k{}^{(1)}x_k{}^{(2)}$, can be realized in only one way, since an interchange of the two particles leaves X unchanged. For the states $X = x_k{}^{(1)}x_k{}^{(2)}$, the weight is therefore to be 1. On the other hand, there are two different total states, $X = x_i^{(1)}x_k^{(2)}$ and $X = x_i^{(2)}x_k^{(1)}$ for which the single states i and k are different; hence the weight of these states is 2. In other words, according to classical statistics, the probability of finding the particles should be twice as great in different states as in identical states. Quantum mechanics looks at it differently. If only symmetric states for the gas are permissible (which may be assumed), a total state with two different x_k cannot be realized in two different ways, but only by $X = x_i^{(1)}x_k^{(2)} + x_i^{(2)}x_k^{(1)}$, so that a total state of this kind has the same weight as a state $x_k^{(1)}x_k^{(2)}$. Thus the a priori probability is the same whether the two eigenstates composing the total state are different or not.

We can now generalize these considerations by investigating a system made up of n particles which may be assumed to be capable of symmetric states only. Then all the states described by the symmetric functions σ' have the same a priori probability. In any of the states n eigenfunctions x_{k1}, x_{k2}, $\cdots$ are realized all of which need not differ one from the other but may agree in groups. Then a certain state can be characterized in the simplest way by arraying the single states x_k in a row and setting the number n_k of the particles occupying x_k below any x_k. Of course, the sum of all the n_k terms must equal n. Then the scheme is, for example,

$$\begin{array}{ccccccc} x_1 & x_2 & x_3 & x_4 & x_5 & x_6 & \cdots \\ n_k \quad 0 & 3 & 7 & 0 & 2 & 1 & \cdots \end{array}$$

It means that the first and fourth eigenstates are unoccupied, whereas there are 3, 7, 2, and 1 particles in the second, third, fifth, and sixth states respectively. These data are sufficient for determining a certain X uniquely. When we apply a permutation to the numbers of the second row or exchange them for other numbers of the same sum, we obtain the description of another state, and now we may formulate the principle of quantum-mechanical statistics in the following way: *For a given n, any occupation of the x_k states has, a priori, the same probability.* This principle was enunciated in 1924 by S. N. Bose, who saw no other way to derive Planck's law for black-body radiation when the cavity radiation is considered a gas of light quanta.

Thus the new idea of Bose was to characterize a state X of the system only by the numbers $n_1, n_2, \cdots$ of the particles in the single states x_1, $x_2, \cdots$ and to ascribe the same a priori probability to any sequence $n_1, n_2, \cdots$, no matter by how many different individual coordinations of particles and states the same sequence $n_1, n_2, \cdots$ can be realized. In classical statistics the weight of a state $n_1, n_2, \cdots$ was judged solely by the number of these individual coordinations. The state of the kind n_1, n_2, $\cdot \cdot \cdot$ was determined by numbering the particles from 1 up to n, then arraying the numbers in a row and specifying, with the help of the numbers in a second row the states in which the particles were found. In this way was obtained a certain individual occupation of the single states which is of the kind n_1, n_2, $\cdot \cdot \cdot$ if in the second row the number 1 occurred n_1 times, the number 2 n_2 times, and so on. By applying all possible permutations to the numbers of the second row, all individual coordinations which correspond to the same sequence n_1, n_2, $\cdot \cdot \cdot$ were obtained. The number of different permutations is $n!/n_1!n_2! \cdot \cdot \cdot$, and this number was considered the probability W with which nature realizes a state of the kind n_1, n_2, $\cdot \cdot \cdot$. For a given n, W could have any value between 1 (valid for the case where all n_i vanish except one, which equals n) and $n!$, if no n_i is greater than 1. According to Bose, any occupation n_1, n_2, $\cdot \cdot \cdot$ has the same probability.

Instead of the occupation of the eigenstates, let us consider now that of the energy levels E_k, meaning by E_k the energies of a single particle. In the applications of the theory, we are always concerned with systems that are degenerated, and consequently we shall assume r_1 different eigenvectors, x_1', x_1'', x_1''', $\cdot \cdot \cdot$, $x_1^{(r_1)}$, all belonging to E_1, r_2 vectors, x_2', x_2'', x_2''', $\cdot \cdot \cdot$ belonging to E_2, and so on. Then a certain eigenstate X of the gas can be described by the scheme

$$
\begin{array}{ccc}
E_1 & E_2 & E_i \\
x_1'x_1'' \cdot \cdot \cdot x_1^{(r_1)} & x_2'x_2'' \cdot \cdot \cdot x_2^{(r_2)} & x_i'x_i'' \cdot \cdot \cdot x_i^{(r_i)} \\
n_1'n_1'' \cdot \cdot \cdot n_1^{(r_1)} & n_2'n_2'' \cdot \cdot \cdot n_2^{(r_2)} & n_i'n_i'' \cdot \cdot \cdot n_i^{(r_i)} \\
n_1 & n_2 & n_i
\end{array}
\qquad (226)
$$

where n_i represents the sums $n_i = n_i' + n_i'' + \cdot \cdot \cdot + n_i^{(r_i)}$. On examining the first and last rows we see from the scheme that, in the X state considered, n_1 particles have the energy E_1, n_2 the energy E_2, and so forth. The state, however, is not yet defined by these numbers. This can be done only by means of the detailed information given by the other two rows in which the n_i are assigned to the different eigenstates of the same energy E_i. Thus for a given n_1, n_2, $\cdot \cdot \cdot$, that is, for a given occupation of the energy levels, there exist as many different states $X = \sigma'$ of a gas as there are different ways of allotting the n_i terms, so that, since all the X states have the same a priori probability, the number Z of allotments must be considered the probability of the occupation n_1, n_2, $\cdot \cdot \cdot$. Thus, if, on the basis of Bose's statistics, we wish to find the most probable energy distribution of a gas, the first thing we must do is to evaluate the number Z. This can be done as follows: When n_i is resolved into n_i', n_i'', $\cdots$, $n_i^{(r_i)}$, we say that the resolution is of the kind N_0, N_1, $\cdots$, N_{n_i}, if among the n_i', n_i'' $\cdots$ terms the number 0 occurs N_0 times, the number 1 N_1 times, until finally the number n_i occurs N_{n_i} times. It should be pointed out that there is no $n_i^{(k)} > n_i$, and also that N_{n_i} can only be 0 or 1. Now the question arises, in how many ways can n_i be resolved in a given manner, N_0, N_1 $\cdots$, N_{n_i}? It can be seen easily that there are $r_i!/N_0!N_1! \cdots N_{n_i}!$ ways, because, if n_i', n_i'', $\cdots$, $n_i^{(r_i)}$ is of the kind N_0, N_1, $\cdots$, N_{n_i}, the manner of resolution does not change when in (226) all possible permutations are applied to the n_i', n_i'', $\cdots$, $n_i^{(r_i)}$ terms. But an exchange of those particular $n_i^{(k)}$ the value of which is 0 (there are N_0 of such) is without effect, and the same holds for those $n_i^{(k)}$ which equal 1, 2, $\cdots$. Thus $r_i!$ is to be divided by $N_0!N_1! \cdots N_{n_i}!$

The number Z_{n_i} of all the possible allotments $n_i'n_i'' \cdots n_i^{(r_i)}$ of n_i is given by the sum,

$$Z_{n_i} = \sum \frac{r_i!}{N_0!N_1! \cdots N_{n_i}!}$$

in which all resolutions of n_i into $N_0 0 + N_1 1 + \cdots + N_{n_i} n_i$ are to be taken into account. If r_i is a very great number, the expression for the sum can be simplified. In this case the largest fraction, $(r_i!/N_0!N_1! \cdots N_{n_i}!)$ that occurs in the sum exceeds the others to such an extent that we may neglect them and obtain

$$Z_{n_i} = \frac{r_i!}{N_0!N_1! \cdots N_{n_i}!}$$

in which the values $N_0 \cdots N_{n_i} (N_0 0 + N_1 1 + N_2 2 + \cdots N_{n_i} n_i = n_i)$ are to be taken for which the fraction becomes a maximum. If we evaluate Z_{n_i} in this way for every n_i, the product of all the Z_{n_i} is

$$Z = \prod_i \frac{r_i!}{N_0^{(i)}!N_1^{(i)}! \cdots N_{n_i}^{(i)}!}$$

and it gives the number of entirely different ways of realizing the occupations n_1, n_2, $\cdots$ of the energy levels. In other words, Z is the probability of the energy distribution n_1, n_2, $\cdots$.

Thus, for a given number n of particles and a given total energy E, we shall have to proceed in the following way: We have to determine those numbers, $N_0^{(i)} N_1^{(i)} \cdots N_{n_i}^{(i)}$ ($i = 1, 2, \cdots$) by which, under the conditions

$$n = \sum_i n_i = \sum_i (N_1^{(i)} + 2N_2^{(i)} + \cdots n_i N_{n_i}^{(i)})$$

and

$$E = \sum_i n_i E_i = \sum_i E_i(N_1^{(i)} + 2N_2^{(i)} + \cdots n_i N_{n_i}^{(i)})$$

the probability

$$Z = \prod_i \frac{r_i!}{N_0{}^i! N_1^{(i)}! \cdots N_{n_i}^{(i)}!}$$

is made a maximum. From the $N_k^{(i)}$ numbers we then find the occupation numbers of the energy levels E_i to be

$$n_i = N_1^{(i)} + 2N_2^{(i)} + \cdots + n_i N_{n_i}^{(i)}$$

The foregoing considerations are easily adapted to the case of a gas that exists in antisymmetric states only. Then the states of equal probability are those which are described by the antisymmetric eigenvectors $\mathbf{X} = \sigma''$. In any of the σ'' functions, n different $\mathbf{x}_k$ are realized, so that (226) may be applied again, the difference being, however, that for $n_i'n_i'' \cdots$ only the values 0 and 1 are admitted, since a multiple occupation of the $\mathbf{x}_k$ states is excluded. On the other hand, the n_i terms may assume any values not greater than r_i. Owing to the limitation of $n_i'n_i'' \cdots$ to values of 0 and 1, it follows that only $N_0^{(i)}$ and $N_1^{(i)}$ can be different from zero, so that the probability Z of the occupation $n_1 n_2 \cdots$ may now be written

$$Z = \prod_i \frac{r_i!}{N_0^{(i)}! N_1^{(i)}!} \tag{227}$$

In order to find the most probable energy distribution of the gas we must make (227) a maximum under the conditions

$$n = \sum_i n_i = \sum_i N_1^{(i)}$$

$$E = \sum_i n_i E_i = \sum_i N_1^{(i)} E_i$$

PROBLEMS

1. Show that, owing to the exclusion principle, the states ns, np, nd, and nf of an atom (where n is the principal quantum number denoted in Chapter 2 by $n + l + 1$, and the letters s, p, d, and f mean $l = 0, 1, 2, 3$) can be occupied by no more than 2, 6, 10, and 14 electrons.

2. Use this result for the explanation of the periodic system.

3. Show that the Bose statistics, when applied to a cavity radiation, leads to Planck's radiation law. Begin by dividing the momentum space of the photon into cells $\Delta\xi \, \Delta\eta \, \Delta\zeta$, a procedure suggested by the uncertainty relations. Apply the method of Section 44, and find the maximum of Z under the conditions $E = $ constant, and $\sum_k n_k^{(i)} = r_i$. (It would be better to use $\log_e Z$ instead of Z.) Finally, use Boltzmann's relation for the entropy $S = k \log_e Z$. The result of the calculation is

$$E = \sum d\nu \, \frac{8\pi\nu^3 h}{c^3} \, V \, \frac{1}{e^{h\nu/kT} - 1}$$

4. In the same way show that, for a gas that satisfies the principle of antisymmetry, the number of particles with an energy between ϵ and $\epsilon + d\epsilon$ is given by

$$\frac{4\sqrt{2}\,\pi m^{3/2}\epsilon^{1/2}}{h^3} \, V \, \frac{d\epsilon}{e^{(\epsilon/kT)+\gamma^T} - 1}$$

6

RELATIVISTIC WAVE EQUATIONS

45. Particles with Spin ½. Dirac's Equation. The wave equation (27), introduced by Schroedinger, does not satisfy the requirement for relativistic invariance, as is evident from its asymmetry in the coordinates xyz and the time t. This asymmetry originates in the application of the non-relativistic expression $p^2/2m = -(\hbar^2/2m)\nabla^2$ for the kinetic energy of a particle. In order to obtain an invariant equation we must start out with the relativistic equation

$$H = c \sqrt{m^2c^2 + p^2} \tag{228}$$

for the energy of a particle on which no force acts, and solve the problem of how to interpret the relation in terms of wave mechanics. If the wave function $\psi(xyzt)$ is used again to represent the state of the particle in the sense of the transformation theory, $\psi^*\psi$ must have the significance of a probability density; because $\psi(xyz)$, being the projection of the vector $\mathbf{x}$ on the principal axis xyz, should, by the square of its magnitude, determine the probability of the particle being found at the point xyz. Now, in relativistic theory, the density is not a scalar quantity but a part of a four-vector which satisfies a continuity equation. Thus the problem would be to find a function (i) that corresponds to an invariant differential equation, and (ii) from which a four-vector can be formed which will satisfy a continuity equation and which has a temporal component of the form $\psi^*\psi$. As Dirac has shown, these requirements can be complied with when the problem deals with particles with spin ½$\hbar$. But the attempt to establish a relativistic wave equation for particles with spin 0 or $\hbar$ succeeds only if we drop the condition of a probability density which is always positive. Under no circumstance is it then possible to interpret $\psi^*\psi$ as a density. This means that the function ψ may no longer be considered a vector, and accordingly the wave equation has to be understood in a sense far different from the non-relativistic Schroedinger equation. It refers no longer to a particle but rather describes a wave motion having no connection with the idea of a particle, therefore requiring a new interpretation. It will turn out that the equa-

165

tion does allow an interpretation in which the idea of particles can be used, but only after it has been quantized.   This can be accomplished with the aid of the method already adopted in Section 43.

A systematic investigation† shows that there exists a relativistic wave equation for particles with any given spin.   We shall, however, confine ourselves to the spins 0, ½, and 1, which are of special importance in the quantum mechanics of wave fields.   Historically the first relativistic equation was that introduced by Dirac.   We prefer to begin with that equation since it is still closely connected with the plan of the non-relativistic theory.

As before, we consider the wave function $\psi(xyzt)$ a description of a vector **x** which changes with time according to $(\hbar/i)\,d\mathbf{x}/dt = H\mathbf{x}$, where H is the energy operator of the particle considered.   When we resolve **x** into its components $\psi(xyz)$, relative to the principal system K of the coordinates xyz, we obtain the wave equation

$$\frac{\hbar}{i}\frac{\partial\psi}{\partial t} = H\psi \tag{229}$$

First let us consider a particle subject to no force and attempt to make (229) invariant by taking the relativistic expression (228) for H; to change the expression into an operator we again substitute $-(\hbar/i)(\partial/\partial x)$ for p_x and therefore $-\hbar^2\nabla^2$ for p^2.   Since a radical then appears on the right-hand side of the expression, Dirac decided to remove this inconvenient term by setting $\sqrt{m^2c^2 + p^2} = \alpha_1 p_x + \alpha_2 p_y + \alpha_3 p_z + \beta mc$.   The quantities α_1, α_2, α_3, β then must be determined in such a manner that when the right-hand side is squared we obtain $m^2c^2 + p^2$. We cannot achieve this by ordinary numbers, but we succeed if we consider $\alpha_1\alpha_2\alpha_3\beta$ to be matrices the discussion of which we shall defer for the present, assuming only that they are commutative with the momentum components.   On the other hand, they are not supposed to be commutative with one another, and hence when squaring we must take the factors in the proper order.   Then we get

$$(\alpha_1 p_x + \alpha_2 p_y + \cdots)^2 = \alpha_1{}^2 p_x{}^2 + \alpha_2{}^2 p_y{}^2 + \alpha_3{}^2 p_z{}^2 + \beta^2 m^2 c^2$$
$$+ (\alpha_1\alpha_2 + \alpha_2\alpha_1)p_x p_y + \cdots + (\alpha_1\beta + \beta\alpha_1)p_x mc + \cdots$$

Now we see that the right-hand side becomes $m^2c^2 + p^2$ if we choose $\alpha_1\alpha_2\alpha_3\beta$ (for β the notation α_4 may be used for the moment) in such a way that the following relations hold:

$$\alpha_i\alpha_k + \alpha_k\alpha_i = 2\delta_{ik} \qquad \left(\delta_{ik} = \begin{array}{l} 1 \text{ for } i = k \\ 0 \text{ for } i \neq k \end{array}\right) \tag{230}$$

† P. A. M. Dirac, *Proc. Roy. Soc. London*, **A155**, 447 (1936).

for then we shall have

$$\alpha_1{}^2 = \alpha_2{}^2 = \cdots = 1$$

and

$$\alpha_1\alpha_2 + \alpha_2\alpha_1 = 0 \qquad \alpha_1\beta + \beta\alpha_1 = 0, \quad \text{etc.}$$

The only question then is whether we can really find four quantities that satisfy (230). That we can is proved easily. First we define four matrices with two rows by

$$1 = \begin{bmatrix} 1 & 0 \\ 0 & 1 \end{bmatrix} \qquad \gamma_1 = \begin{bmatrix} 0 & 1 \\ 1 & 0 \end{bmatrix} \qquad \gamma_2 = \begin{bmatrix} 0 & i \\ -i & 0 \end{bmatrix} \qquad \gamma_3 = \begin{bmatrix} 1 & 0 \\ 0 & -1 \end{bmatrix}$$
$$(231)$$

From these we form two four-row matrices,

$$\alpha_i = \begin{bmatrix} 0 & \gamma_i \\ \gamma_i & 0 \end{bmatrix} \qquad \beta = \begin{bmatrix} 1 & 0 \\ 0 & -1 \end{bmatrix} \tag{232}$$

Then, using rule (120), we can verify that equations (230) are fulfilled. Now we attempt to base the theory on a Hamiltonian operator of the form

$$H = c \sum_{i=1}^{3} \alpha_i p_i + mc^2\beta = -\frac{\hbar}{i} c \sum_{i=1}^{3} \alpha_i \frac{\partial}{\partial x_i} + mc^2\beta \tag{233}$$

(we shall use the notation $x_1x_2x_3$ for xyz). We then obtain the wave equation

$$\frac{\partial \psi}{\partial t} = -c \sum_{i=1}^{3} \alpha_i \frac{\partial \psi}{\partial x_i} + \frac{i}{\hbar} mc^2\beta\psi \tag{234}$$

which is of the first order in both t and the coordinates $x_1x_2x_3$.

The next question is how the four-row matrices (232) which occur in the equation are to be interpreted. Evidently their significance can only be that, besides the coordinates $x_1x_2x_3$ a fourth observable ρ, called the spin coordinate, is to be associated with the particle; in a way that is still to be explained, it describes the *internal state* of the particle and can assume four values only. In order to represent this fourth coordinate in the geometric formalism of the theory, we have to amplify the coordinate system K of the Hilbert space. Up to this point any axis of K belonged to certain values of xyz. At the present stage, however, the values of x, y, and z do not define the state of the particle uniquely but require a specification of the internal state. This forces us to change any xyz axis of K into a four-dimensional sub-space, in which, by four orthogonal axes, a coordinate system K_1 is scaffolded.

It is this sub-space to which the matrices α_i and β refer.　(They depend, of course, on the choice of K_1 and undergo a transformation when we exchange K_1 for another system K_1'.)　The four axes of K_1 define four unit vectors $\mathbf{x}_1\mathbf{x}_2\mathbf{x}_3\mathbf{x}_4$ corresponding to four states all of which belong to the same values of xyz but differ, as we shall see, from one another by the spin and the sign of the energy.　This means that, because of the spin coordinate ρ, instead of one wave function $\psi(xyzt)$, four functions must now be introduced which may be distinguished from one another by an index ρ; thus a vector $\mathbf{x}$ representing a certain state of the particle needs four functions ψ_1, ψ_2, ψ_3, ψ_4 for its description.　The meaning of the ψ_ρ functions is this: $|\psi_1|^2$ determines the probability of finding the particle, by a simultaneous measurement of position and spin, at the point xyz in an internal state corresponding to the number $\rho = 1$.　By means of an operator A, $\mathbf{x}(\psi_1\psi_2\psi_3\psi_4)$ transforms into another vector $\mathbf{x}'(\psi_1'\psi_2'\psi_3'\psi_4')$, the linear connection of $\mathbf{x}$ and $\mathbf{x}' = A\mathbf{x}$ being effected by equations of the kind

$$\psi_\rho' = \sum_{\sigma=1}^{4} A_{\rho\sigma}\psi_\sigma \tag{235}$$

The $A_{\rho\sigma}$ form a matrix and comprise certain differential operators which can act on the ψ_σ functions.　An example of such is the operator H defined by (233) the elements of which are

$$H_{\rho\sigma} = -\frac{\hbar}{i}c \sum_i \alpha_{\rho\sigma}{}^{(i)} \frac{\partial}{\partial x_i} + mc^2\beta_{\rho\sigma}$$

For $\partial\psi_\rho/\partial t$ from (234), we obtain

$$\frac{\partial\psi_\rho}{\partial t} = \sum_\sigma \frac{i}{\hbar} H_{\rho\sigma}\psi_\sigma = \sum_\sigma \left(-c \sum_i \alpha_{\rho\sigma}{}^{(i)} \frac{\partial\psi_\sigma}{\partial x_i} + \frac{i}{\hbar} mc^2\beta_{\rho\sigma}\psi_\sigma\right)$$

Multiplying by $\psi_\rho{}^*$ and summating over all ρ gives

$$\sum_\rho \psi_\rho{}^* \frac{\partial\psi_\rho}{\partial t} = \sum_{\rho\sigma} \left(-c \sum_i \psi_\rho{}^*\alpha_{\rho\sigma}{}^{(i)} \frac{\partial\psi_\sigma}{\partial x_i} + \frac{i}{\hbar} mc^2\psi_\rho{}^*\beta_{\rho\sigma}\psi_\sigma\right)$$

Passing to the complex conjugate equation, we have, since

$$\alpha_{\rho\sigma}{}^* = \alpha_{\sigma\rho} \quad \text{and} \quad \beta_{\rho\sigma}{}^* = \beta_{\sigma\rho},$$

$$\sum_\rho \psi_\rho \frac{\partial\psi_\rho{}^*}{\partial t} = \sum_{\rho\sigma} \left(-c \sum_i \psi_\rho\alpha_{\sigma\rho}{}^{(i)} \frac{\partial\psi_\sigma{}^*}{\partial x_i} - \frac{i}{\hbar} mc^2\psi_\rho\beta_{\sigma\rho}\psi_\sigma{}^*\right)$$

When the indices ρ and σ are interchanged in this equation (which only means another notation of the indices), the summation of the two equations gives

$$\frac{\partial}{\partial t}\sum_{\rho}\psi_{\rho}^*\psi_{\rho} = -c\sum_{i}\frac{\partial}{\partial x_i}\sum_{\rho\sigma}\psi_{\rho}^*\alpha_{\rho\sigma}^{(i)}\psi_{\sigma}$$ (236)

a relation that has the form of the continuity equation

$$\frac{\partial\rho}{\partial t} = -\operatorname{div}\mathbf{i}$$ (237)

so that

$$\rho = \sum_{\rho}\psi_{\rho}^*\psi_{\rho}$$

may be interpreted as the probability density and

$$\mathbf{i} = c\sum_{\rho\sigma}\psi_{\rho}^*\vec{\alpha}_{\rho\sigma}\psi_{\sigma} = c(\psi,\,\vec{\alpha}\psi)$$ (238)

as a probability current. The arrow placed over α means that the three quantities, α_1, α_2, α_3, are taken together as a matrix vector; thus $(\psi,\,\vec{\alpha}\psi)$ is to be understood as a vector with the components $(\psi,\,\alpha_i\psi)$. The product is to be read in the sense of (113).

We have already remarked that α_i and β must, somehow, define the internal state of the particle. In fact, as we shall see, the phenomenon of the spin can be derived from them. Unexpectedly, however, they simultaneously determine the *velocity* of the particle. According to (163), the equation $dA/dt = (i/\hbar)(AH - HA)$ holds for any observable of a system, where A is the matrix associated with the observable. When we apply this relation to one of the x_i coordinates, taking into account that x_i and α_i are commutative, from (233) we obtain

$$\frac{dx_i}{dt} = -c\alpha_i\left(x_i\frac{\partial}{\partial x_i} - \frac{\partial}{\partial x_i}x_i\right) = c\alpha_i$$ (239)

Thus we have not, as in non-relativistic theory, $dx_i/dt = p_i/m$; rather dx_i/dt is a matrix and its measurement should, therefore, always furnish one of the eigenvalues of the matrix. These eigenvalues, evaluated according to Section 25 for all the α_i, turn out to be $+1$ and -1, so that, according to Dirac's theory, an electron should be expected to be moving always with the velocity c of light. The explanation of this seemingly absurd result is, as Schroedinger was able to show, that on the progressing motion of the electron (which alone can be measured) there is superposed an oscillating motion consisting of very rapid vibrations which the electron performs about its path of propagation.   The value $c\alpha_i$ refers to the total motion and does not, therefore, measure the velocity of advance of the electron, which velocity may have any value less than c.

Let us now investigate the phenomenon of spin.   This will be explained in the following way: In non-relativistic theory the operator of the angular momentum $\mathbf{r} \times \mathbf{p} = (-\hbar/i) \; \mathbf{r} \times \mathbf{grad}$ is commutative with H, so that the principal axes of H and $\mathbf{r} \times \mathbf{p}$ coincide, the consequence being that in a stationary state the angular momentum as well as the energy remains constant.   In Dirac's theory this commutability of H and $\mathbf{r} \times \mathbf{p}$ disappears, for we have

$$
\begin{aligned}
H(\mathbf{r} \times \mathbf{p})_x - (\mathbf{r} \times \mathbf{p})_x H = -\hbar^2 c &\left[\left(\alpha_1 \frac{\partial}{\partial x} + \alpha_2 \frac{\partial}{\partial y} + \alpha_3 \frac{\partial}{\partial z} \right) \left(y \frac{\partial}{\partial z} - z \frac{\partial}{\partial y} \right) \right. \\
&\left. - \left(y \frac{\partial}{\partial z} - z \frac{\partial}{\partial y} \right) \left(\alpha_1 \frac{\partial}{\partial x} + \alpha_2 \frac{\partial}{\partial y} + \alpha_3 \frac{\partial}{\partial z} \right) \right] \\
= -\hbar^2 c &\left(\alpha_2 \frac{\partial}{\partial z} - \alpha_3 \frac{\partial}{\partial y} \right) \qquad (240)
\end{aligned}
$$

This means that in a stationary state $\mathbf{r} \times \mathbf{p}$ does not remain constant. The reason for this is that now $\mathbf{r} \times \mathbf{p}$ alone does not represent the total angular momentum but has to be taken together with a second term which originates in the internal motion of the particle.   In order to determine this supplementary angular momentum we consider the matrices

$$
\sigma_1 = i\alpha_2\alpha_3 \qquad \sigma_2 = i\alpha_3\alpha_1 \qquad \sigma_3 = i\alpha_1\alpha_2 \qquad (241)
$$

and investigate the operator $(\hbar/2)\vec{\sigma}$ ($\vec{\sigma}$ denotes a vector with the components σ_i). $(\hbar/2)\vec{\sigma}$ is not commutative with H either, for on taking (230) into account we find

$$
\begin{aligned}
\frac{\hbar}{2} (H\sigma_1 - \sigma_1 H) = -\frac{\hbar^2}{2} c &\left[\left(\alpha_1 \frac{\partial}{\partial x} + \alpha_2 \frac{\partial}{\partial y} + \alpha_3 \frac{\partial}{\partial z} \right) \alpha_2\alpha_3 \right. \\
&\left. - \alpha_2\alpha_3 \left(\alpha_1 \frac{\partial}{\partial x} + \alpha_2 \frac{\partial}{\partial y} + \alpha_3 \frac{\partial}{\partial z} \right) \right] \\
= \hbar^2 c &\left(\alpha_2 \frac{\partial}{\partial z} - \alpha_3 \frac{\partial}{\partial y} \right)
\end{aligned}
$$

Comparing this result with (240), we see that the quantity $\mathbf{r} \times \mathbf{p}$ +

$(\hbar/2)\vec{\sigma}$ is commutative with H and therefore must be taken as the total angular momentum of the particle. The part $(\hbar/2)\vec{\sigma} = \mathbf{s}$ is due to the spin. For the magnitude of $\mathbf{s}$ we obtain, from (232),

$$\mathbf{s}^2 = \frac{\hbar^2}{4}(\sigma_1{}^2 + \sigma_2{}^2 + \sigma_3{}^2) = \frac{3}{4}\hbar^2 \mathbf{1}$$

Thus a measurement of $\mathbf{s}^2$ furnishes the value $\frac{3}{4}\hbar^2$ in any state of the particle. On the other hand, the components of $\mathbf{s}$, because $H\sigma_i - \sigma_i H \neq 0$, have no fixed values in any stationary state; this holds only for $\mathbf{r} \times \mathbf{p} + \mathbf{s}$. However, for a sufficiently slow motion, we can, by neglecting terms of the order of magnitude v^2/c^2, simplify the expression for the energy to $mc^2 + p^2/2m$. When we substitute this expression for H in $H\sigma_i - \sigma_i H$ (H is the operator of non-relativistic theory), the difference becomes zero. σ_i then commutes with H. However, this does not mean that all the components of $\mathbf{s}$ then take on fixed values in a stationary state. For the σ_i are not commutative with one another and therefore cannot be measured simultaneously. Always only one component of $\mathbf{s}$ can be measured, for example, $s_z = (\hbar/2)\sigma_3$. From (232), for $\sigma_3 = i\alpha_1\alpha_2$, we obtain the diagonal matrix

$$\sigma_3 = \begin{bmatrix} 1 & 0 & 0 & 0 \\ 0 & -1 & 0 & 0 \\ 0 & 0 & 1 & 0 \\ 0 & 0 & 0 & -1 \end{bmatrix}$$

This means that, in the four states the vectors of which have the directions of the principal axes of the spin space, the observable s_z is twice equal to $+\hbar/2$ and twice equal to $-\hbar/2$. Thus Dirac's theory furnishes twice as many states as are required by the spin, from which it may be inferred that, besides the spin, there still must be another observable with two possible values and consequently the two axes belonging to the same spin differ with respect to the values of this observable. It turns out that this observable is to be found from the *sign of the energy*. To prove this we assume that the representation of the α_i terms and β is chosen in such a way that all α_i are real, whereas β is imaginary. In order to attain such a representation we must exchange the coordinate system of the spin space for another one. A matrix A then becomes $A' = SAS^{-1}$. The desired effect can be achieved, for example, by means of the transformation matrix $S = (i/\sqrt{2})\alpha_1\alpha_3(\alpha_2 + \beta)$.

Now let us assume that $\psi_\rho(\rho = 1, 2, 3, 4)$ represents a stationary state of the positive energy E. Then we have $H\psi = E\psi$ and thus, because of (233),

$$E\psi_\rho = -\frac{\hbar}{i}c\sum_\sigma\left(\sum_i\alpha_{\rho\sigma}{}^{(i)}\frac{\partial\psi_\sigma}{\partial x_i} - \frac{i}{\hbar}mc^2\beta_{\rho\sigma}\psi_\sigma\right)$$

Passing to the complex conjugate equation we obtain, since now $\alpha_{\rho\sigma}{}^* = \alpha_{\rho\sigma}$, $\beta_{\rho\sigma}{}^* = -\beta_{\rho\sigma}$,

$$-E\psi_\rho{}^* = -\frac{\hbar}{i}c\sum_\sigma\left(\sum_i\alpha_{\rho\sigma}{}^{(i)}\frac{\partial\psi_\sigma{}^*}{\partial x_i} - \frac{i}{\hbar}mc^2\beta_{\rho\sigma}\psi_\sigma{}^*\right)$$

This equation, however, implies that $\psi_\rho{}^*(\rho = 1, 2, 3, 4)$ represents a state of negative energy $-E$. Thus any state of positive energy is associated with the existence of a state the energy of which is negative. The states of negative energy arise from the fact that in the relativistic expression (228) for energy the root may be taken with the negative as well as the positive sign; therefore they exist in classical theory. But they do not play any part in that theory because the continuous manner in which the states change there with time makes their realization impossible, and so they may be disregarded as being meaningless. In quantum mechanics, however, these states are not meaningless, for, according to the dynamical law (161), the passage from a state of positive energy into one of negative energy involves no difficulty whatever. This can be seen immediately from equation (184') with the help of which the probability of the passage induced by a perturbation acting on the system can be determined. The probability is proportional to the square of $|H_{nk}'|$, where k denotes a given initial state of positive energy and n a final state of negative energy. Therefore we cannot simply ignore the states of negative energy without destroying the theory, for by cancelling the states we reduce the four components of ψ to two and thus deprive the theory of its invariance. For a long time the theory was at a loss to explain the states, for no way could be found by which to give them a reasonable interpretation. In the next section the consequent explanation of them on the basis of Dirac's hole theory will be discussed.

At this point we shall not go into a rigorous proof of the relativistic invariance of Dirac's equation. The simplest way would be to interpret the four quantities ψ_1, ψ_2, ψ_3, ψ_4 as two pairs of spinors and apply the methods of spinor calculus, spinor calculus being merely an extension of tensor calculus. At once it would be seen that the four quantities, defined by (237) and (238), form a four-vector; this is necessary if (236) is to be Lorentz-invariant.

46. A Particle in an Electromagnetic Field. Dirac's Hole Theory. Thus far we have investigated only a particle subject to no force. Now let us consider a particle on which an electromagnetic field **EH** is acting, the field deriving from a scalar potential ϕ and a vector potential **A** by the equations

$$\mathbf{E} = -\text{grad } \phi - \frac{1}{c}\frac{d\mathbf{A}}{dt} \qquad \mathbf{H} = \text{curl } \mathbf{A}$$

The classical equation (228) for the Hamiltonian H then must be amplified by terms that contain ϕ and **A**. It can be shown that H then becomes

$$H = e\phi + c\sqrt{m^2c^2 + \left(\mathbf{p} - \frac{e}{c}\mathbf{A}\right)^2} \tag{242}$$

To prove this we write down the canonical equations

$$\frac{dx}{dt} = v_x = \frac{\partial H}{\partial p_x} = \frac{c\left(p_x - \frac{e}{c}A_x\right)}{\sqrt{m^2c^2 + \left(\mathbf{p} - \frac{e}{c}\mathbf{A}\right)^2}}$$

$$\tag{243}$$

$$\frac{dp_x}{dt} = -\frac{\partial H}{\partial x} = -e\frac{\partial \phi}{\partial x} + \frac{c\left(p_x - \frac{e}{c}A_x\right)\frac{e}{c}\frac{\partial A_x}{\partial x} + \cdots}{\sqrt{m^2c^2 + \left(\mathbf{p} - \frac{e}{c}\mathbf{A}\right)^2}}$$

$$= -e\frac{\partial \phi}{\partial x} + \frac{e}{c}\left(v_x\frac{\partial A_x}{\partial x} + v_y\frac{\partial A_y}{\partial x} + v_z\frac{\partial A_z}{\partial x}\right)$$

If $d\mathbf{A}/dt$ signifies the change of the potential **A** of the moving particle, we have

$$\frac{dA_x}{dt} = \frac{\partial A_x}{\partial t} + \frac{\partial A_x}{\partial x}v_x + \frac{\partial A_x}{\partial y}v_y + \frac{\partial A_x}{\partial z}v_z$$

where $\partial A_x/\partial t$ is the time rate of change of A_x at a fixed point. Multiplying this equation by $-e/c$ and adding it to the p_x equation, we obtain

$$\frac{d}{dt}\left(p_x - \frac{e}{c}A_x\right)$$

$$= -e\frac{\partial \phi}{\partial x} - \frac{e}{c}\frac{\partial A_x}{\partial t} + \frac{e}{c}\left[v_y\left(\frac{\partial A_y}{\partial x} - \frac{\partial A_x}{\partial y}\right) - v_z\left(\frac{\partial A_x}{\partial z} - \frac{\partial A_z}{\partial x}\right)\right]$$

$$= e\left(E_x + \frac{1}{c}[\mathbf{v} \times \mathbf{H}]_x\right) \tag{244}$$

On the other hand, from (243) and the two corresponding y and z equations, squaring and adding, we get

$$\mathbf{p} - \frac{e}{c}\mathbf{A} = \frac{m\mathbf{v}}{\sqrt{1 - \frac{v^2}{c^2}}}$$

Thus (244) becomes

$$\frac{d}{dt}\frac{m\mathbf{v}}{\sqrt{1 - v^2/c^2}} = e\left(\mathbf{E} + \frac{1}{c}\mathbf{v} \times \mathbf{H}\right)$$

This result shows that (242) is correct. Thus for an electromagnetic field ϕ, $\mathbf{A}$ the operator $-(\hbar/i)(\partial/\partial x_i)$ of the wave equation must be replaced by $-(\hbar/i)(\partial/\partial x_i) - (e/c)A_i$, and the operator $(\hbar/i)(\partial/\partial t)$ by $(\hbar/i)(\partial/\partial t) - e\phi$. Then we obtain

$$\frac{\hbar}{i}\frac{\partial \psi_\rho}{\partial t} = e\phi\psi_\rho - c\sum_\sigma\left[\sum_i \alpha_{\rho\sigma}{}^{(i)}\left(\frac{\hbar}{i}\frac{\partial}{\partial x_i} + \frac{e}{c}A_i\right) - mc\beta_{\rho\sigma}\right]\psi_\sigma \quad (245)$$

Although the explanation of spin as a relativity effect is an undoubted success for Dirac's theory, it had to be accepted on the assumption that there are states of negative energy. In these states the electron should have energy between $-mc^2$ and $-\infty$ and therefore should behave like a body of negative mass, that is, when a force acts on it it should move in a direction opposite to the force. Because an electron of this sort was never observed, there arose a clash between theory and experience which could be remedied only with the help of a supplementary principle excluding the states of negative energy. For this purpose Dirac suggested the assumption that, when no field is acting, all the states of negative energy are occupied. Then, because of the exclusion principle that holds for electrons, no electron is able to assume a state of negative energy. It is further assumed that electrons occupying negative energy states are unable to produce an external field. What we observe are always only the deviations of nature from the kind of charge distribution wherein all states of negative energy are occupied and all states of positive energy are unoccupied. In other words, we always measure the resulting charge if from all the actually existing charges those of the previously defined "zero state" are subtracted. The same is assumed to hold for energy and momentum also. For example, if a state of negative energy is unoccupied, the hole has the same effect as a particle of positive charge, positive energy, and momentum of opposite direction. Since the mass as well as the energy becomes positive, the hole behaves like a positron, which differs from an electron in the sign of its charge only. Regarding its production, we have to imagine that an electromagnetic field, that of a photon for example, is able to have an effect on the electrons of negative energy. The effect may be that the electron passes from a state of negative to one of positive energy. Then the hole, representing a positron, is created by the passage and, in addition, an ordinary electron, that is, a pair of electrons, will appear. As the energy of the electron is increased by the passage from a value less than $-mc^2$ to one greater than $+mc^2$, then for the production of a pair an energy of at least $2mc^2$ is required. Conversely, an energy greater than or equal to $2mc^2$ is liberated when a pair is annihilated by a process whereby an electron drops back into a state of negative energy, in this way filling the hole so that both electrons disappear again. Experience, in fact, shows that the creation of a pair takes place only if an amount of energy $h\nu$ equal at least to $2mc^2$ is available and that, correspondingly, the annihilation of a pair is accompanied by the emission of light the frequency of which is equal to or greater than $2mc^2/h$.

We are confronted with certain difficulties when we attempt to give the hole theory a consistent formulation. Without going into these difficulties, we shall merely point out that when we adopt the assumptions of that theory we are no longer in a position to consider Dirac's equation as the formulation of a one-body problem. If the conception of the hole theory is correct, we are not permitted to confine the considerations to only one electron, since only the deviations from a zero state, as characterized by the occupation of all negative energy states, are observable. This means that, in any case, the negative energy electrons must be considered. As a consequence, equation (237) no longer may be interpreted as a particle density, because, owing to the possibility of pair creations, the number of observable particles in a sufficiently rapidly varying field does not remain constant and hence there can be no defined particle density. Therefore we are obliged to interpret $\rho = (\psi, \psi)$ as a charge density which has a defined value since it is not changed by the creation or annihilation of a pair.

Thus, from a rigorous standpoint, we cannot establish a relationship between Dirac's theory and the concept of a particle. Such becomes possible only after the theory has been quantized (cf. Chapter 7). Dirac's equation corresponds to a one-body problem only when there is no field permitting the production of pairs; then ψ may be taken as the vector representing the state of a single particle and (ψ, ψ) as the probability of finding the particle at a given point. Then the sea of electrons has only the effect that the electromagnetic field, by *virtual* creations and annihilations of pairs, takes on properties which contradict those of classical electrodynamics and which can be described only by non-linear equations, according to which it is possible, for example, for light to be scattered by light.

47. Particles with Spin 0. The Equation of Klein and Gordon. The simplest wave equation corresponding to the relativistic equation (228) for energy, is obtained if, as in Schroedinger's theory, a scalar function ψ is taken, and if, in the relation $H^2 = c^4 m^2 + c^2 p^2$, $H = (\hbar/i)(\partial/\partial t)$ and $\mathbf{p} = -(\hbar/i)$ grad, giving

$$-\frac{\hbar^2}{c^2} \frac{\partial^2 \psi}{\partial t^2} = m^2 c^2 \psi - \hbar^2 \nabla^2 \psi$$

If we let $\square$ represent $-(1/c^2)(\partial^2/\partial t^2) + \nabla^2$, we obtain

$$\square \psi = \frac{m^2 c^2}{\hbar^2} \psi \qquad (246)$$

This second-order equation can be easily resolved into two equations of the first order. From this point on we shall use the variable $x_4 = ict$ instead of t. The advantage of this is that the metric fundamental form for the four-dimensional world becomes $x_1^2 + x_2^2 + x_3^2 + x_4^2$, thus making it unnecessary to distinguish between covariant and contravariant tensors (cf. Section 48). By taking the four-dimensional gradient we can then derive from ψ a four-vector with components $\partial \psi/\partial x_\alpha$ ($\alpha = 1, 2, 3, 4$). By way of definition we put this vector equal to another four-vector χ multiplied by κ, where $\kappa = mc/\hbar$; thus

$$\frac{\partial \psi}{\partial x_\alpha} = \kappa \chi_\alpha \qquad (247)$$

The divergence of χ is a scalar, and (246) may be written in the form

$$\frac{\partial \chi_\alpha}{\partial x_\alpha} = \kappa \psi \qquad (247')$$

(We follow the usual convention in considering an expression in which two identical indices occur as a sum and α assumes all values from 1 to 4.) When an electromagnetic field ϕ, $\mathbf{A}$ acts on the particle, according to Section 46 the operators $(\hbar/i)(\partial/\partial t)$ and $-(\hbar/i)(\partial/\partial x_i)$ are to be changed to $(\hbar/i)(\partial/\partial t) - e\phi$ and $-(\hbar/i)(\partial/\partial x_i) - (e/c)A_i$ respectively. We can simplify this directive by combining $\mathbf{A}$ and ϕ to a four-vector Φ with $\Phi_i = A_i$ ($i = 1, 2, 3$) and $\Phi_4 = i\phi$. Then, for any index α, the operator $(\hbar/i)(\partial/\partial x_\alpha)$ is to be changed to $(\hbar/i)(\partial/\partial x_\alpha) +$

$(e/c)\Phi_\alpha$, and (246) becomes

$$\sum \left(\frac{\hbar}{i}\frac{\partial}{\partial x_\alpha} + \frac{e}{c}\Phi_\alpha\right)^2 \psi = -m^2c^2\psi \tag{248}$$

The problem now is to find the meaning of the wave function ψ. For this purpose we must try to form a four-vector s_α from ψ which, because of (248), satisfies the continuity equation $\partial s_\alpha/\partial x_\alpha = 0$, and the time component of which may therefore be viewed as representing a density. Such a vector is found in

$$s_\alpha = ia\left(\psi^*\frac{\partial \psi}{\partial x_\alpha} - \psi\frac{\partial \psi^*}{\partial x_\alpha}\right) - \frac{2ea}{c\hbar}\Phi_\alpha\psi^*\psi \tag{249}$$

where a denotes a real factor which remains to be determined. It is clear at once that the expression corresponds to a four-vector because the first two terms transform like a gradient and the third one like Φ. Furthermore it is seen readily that the divergence $\partial s_\alpha/\partial x_\alpha$ vanishes because of (248). To show this, all we must do is to multiply the equation

$$\sum \left(-\frac{\hbar}{i}\frac{\partial}{\partial x_\alpha^*} + \frac{e}{c}\Phi_\alpha^*\right)^2 \psi^* = -m^2c^2\psi^*$$

by ψ and subtract it from (248), which has been multiplied by ψ^*. The equation $\partial s_\alpha/\partial x_\alpha = 0$ results. Conforming to the requirements of its physical interpretation, the vector (249) is real in its space components but the fourth component is imaginary. As the latter is to be considered as $ic\rho$ (this is evident from the equation $\partial s_\alpha/\partial x_\alpha = 0$, which then becomes $\partial\rho/\partial t = -\text{div }\mathbf{s}$, $\mathbf{s}$ being a vector with components $s_1 s_2 s_3$), ρ is given by

$$\rho = -\frac{ia}{c^2}\left(\psi^*\frac{\partial \psi}{\partial t} - \psi\frac{\partial \psi^*}{\partial t}\right) - \frac{2ea}{c^2\hbar}\phi\psi^*\psi \tag{249'}$$

As the wave equation is of the second order, the derivative $\partial\psi/\partial t$ may be chosen arbitrarily for a given instant so that (249') may take on both positive and negative values. Thus ρ cannot signify a particle density, for which negative values are without meaning, but must be considered a charge density. Hence there is in the scalar wave field no probability of finding the particle when its position is measured at a given point, and as a result we can no longer look upon ψ as a vector representing the state of a particle. This means that (248) requires an interpretation quite different from that of the non-relativistic equation of Schroedinger. However, before going into this matter, let us determine first the expressions for the energy and momentum of the field which result from (248). We shall confine ourselves to the case $\phi = \mathbf{A} = 0$, so that ψ satisfies equation (246). The equation corresponds to a certain Lagrangian function L, from which it can be derived by $\delta \int L \, dt = 0$. If we set $L = \int \bar{L} \, dv$ (where $\bar{L}$ denotes the Lagrangian per unit volume), $\bar{L}$ (aside from an arbitrary factor) is found to be

$$\bar{L} = -\left(\kappa \psi^* \psi + \frac{1}{\kappa} \frac{\partial \psi^*}{\partial x_\alpha} \frac{\partial \psi}{\partial x_\alpha}\right) = -\kappa(\psi^* \psi + \chi_\alpha^* \chi_\alpha) \tag{250}$$

in which $\bar{L}$ is expressed in terms of ψ and ψ^*, which, being functions of $xyzt$, determine the momentary state of the field and thus take on the significance of generalized coordinates. In order to derive the field equations, ψ and ψ^* must be chosen in such a way that $\int L \, dt$ takes on a maximum or minimum value, that is, $\int \delta L \, dt$ must be equal to zero for any infinitesimal variation $\delta \psi$ and $\delta \psi^*$ which vanishes at the boundaries of the field at the given time. This is fulfilled if ψ satisfies (246), for on integrating by parts we get

$$\delta \int L \, dt = -\int \int \left[\kappa(\delta\psi^* \psi + \psi^* \delta\psi) \right.$$

$$\left. + \frac{1}{\kappa} \left(\frac{\partial \delta\psi^*}{\partial x_\alpha} \frac{\partial \psi}{\partial x_\alpha} + \frac{\partial \psi^*}{\partial x_\alpha} \frac{\partial \delta\psi}{\partial x_\alpha} \right) \right] dt \, dv$$

$$= -\int \int \left[\left(\kappa\psi - \sum \frac{1}{\kappa} \frac{\partial^2 \psi}{\partial x_\alpha^2} \right) \delta\psi^* \right.$$

$$\left. + \left(\kappa\psi^* - \sum \frac{1}{\kappa} \frac{\partial^2 \psi^*}{\partial x_\alpha^2} \right) \delta\psi \right] dt \, dv = 0$$

The momenta, which are canonically conjugate to ψ and ψ^* and which are designated by π and π^*, are found from (250) to be

$$\pi = \frac{\partial \bar{L}}{\partial (\partial\psi/\partial t)} = \frac{1}{\kappa c^2} \frac{\partial \psi^*}{\partial t} \qquad \pi^* = \frac{1}{\kappa c^2} \frac{\partial \psi}{\partial t}$$

As is known, the energy H of the system is obtained from $L = L(q\dot{q})$ by the relation $H = \sum p\dot{q} - L$. In the case at hand we find

$$H = \int \bar{H} \, dv$$

$$\tag{251}$$

$$\bar{H} = \frac{2}{\kappa c^2} \frac{\partial \psi^*}{\partial t} \frac{\partial \psi}{\partial t} - \bar{L} = -\frac{1}{\kappa} \frac{\partial \psi^*}{\partial x_4} \frac{\partial \psi}{\partial x_4} + \sum_{i=1}^{3} \frac{1}{\kappa} \frac{\partial \psi^*}{\partial x_i} \frac{\partial \psi}{\partial x_i} + \kappa \psi^* \psi$$

These expressions represent the energy density of the field. To determine the momentum density **g** we have to develop (251) to a symmetric tensor T of the second order in which (251) occurs as the term T_{44}. This tensor T, by T_{k4}/ic, gives the components g_k of the momentum density. Now, from ψ and ψ^*, we can form two symmetric tensors of the second order. One of these can be derived from the four-vectors grad ψ and grad ψ^* and is given by

$$T_{mn}' = \frac{\partial \psi^*}{\partial x_m} \frac{\partial \psi}{\partial x_n} + \frac{\partial \psi^*}{\partial x_n} \frac{\partial \psi}{\partial x_m}$$

The other is the product of the scalar $\psi^* \psi$ and the tensor δ_{mn} and is expressed by

$$T_{mn}'' = \psi^* \psi \, \delta_{mn}$$

The scalar function $\bar{L}$ may be used instead of $\psi^* \psi$ for the definition of T''. Then the combination of T' and T'' which fulfills the required condition is

$$T_{mn} = -\frac{1}{\kappa} \left(\frac{\partial \psi^*}{\partial x_m} \frac{\partial \psi}{\partial x_n} + \frac{\partial \psi^*}{\partial x_n} \frac{\partial \psi}{\partial x_m} \right) - \bar{L} \, \delta_{mn} \qquad (252)$$

For the components of **g** we obtain, from the above equation,

$$g_k = \frac{1}{ic} T_{k4} = \frac{1}{c^2 \kappa} \left(\frac{\partial \psi^*}{\partial x_k} \frac{\partial \psi}{\partial t} + \frac{\partial \psi^*}{\partial t} \frac{\partial \psi}{\partial x_k} \right) \qquad (253)$$

When a field of force $\phi, \mathbf{A}$ is acting in (252) and (253), we must, as in the passage from (246) to (248), change $\partial \psi / \partial x_k$ and $\partial \psi^* / \partial x_k$ into $\partial \psi / \partial x_k + (ie/\hbar c)\Phi \psi$ and $\partial \psi^* / \partial x_k - (ie/\hbar c)\Phi_k \psi^*$ respectively.

A scalar field can be correlated only to those particles which have a spin zero. Since the spin is to be considered an internal property of the particles and independent of the xyz coordinates, it can be represented only by means of a wave function which, in addition to depending on the coordinates xyz, depends on still another variable ρ. This means that ψ must consist of several components just as did the ψ of Dirac.

It is important to realize the physical significance of the wave equation (248). It has been emphasized already that this equation no longer permits an interpretation in the sense of non-relativistic quantum mechanics. As long as it is not quantized, it has no relation whatever with particles but controls the behavior of a field that is not purely symbolic but actually represents a physical reality. This is clear from the fact that, according to (249), (251), and (253), the field possesses charge, energy, and momentum and thus it can be measured relative to these observables.   It is only a question then as to whether wave fields corresponding to the assumed equation really exist, a question that must be answered in the affirmative.   All our experiences dealing with elementary particles lead to the conclusion that the particles must be related in some way to a wave field, since in certain experiments they conceal their corpuscular nature and behave as wave motions.   Accordingly it is reasonable to correlate a certain wave motion to any sort of particles and to suppose that this motion is defined by one of the relativistic equations under discussion in this chapter.

However, this picture of a wave motion represents only one aspect of actual experience because there are other experiments in which no undulatory properties are detected, the particles displaying a strictly corpuscular nature.   Such a situation compels the theory to associate the wave field with some symbolic mechanism based on the commutation relations and operating in such a way that the wave picture and the particle picture disappear alternately, the consequence being that the field assumes the strikingly ambiguous character which is observed in nature.   By methods to be developed in the next chapter, we shall see that the mechanism functions in such a way that the field is quantized.

48. Digression on Tensor Calculus. Pseudoscalar Wave Field.   In our further investigations the methods of tensor calculus will be of great help.   For this reason, we shall outline these methods briefly.   We fix our attention on a four-dimensional space in which an orthogonal coordinate system K may be established.   A *contravariant* tensor of the first order is defined by a set of four quantities, a^1, a^2, a^3, a^4, which may be either constants or functions of x_1, x_2, x_3, x_4, and which, when K is replaced by another coordinate system K', transform in the same way as the components of a four-vector.   Thus the components $a^{i'}$ of the tensor, when referred to K', are linear functions of a^i, that is, $a^{i'} = \alpha^{ik} a^k$, where α^{ik} represents the coefficients of the transformation $K \rightarrow K'$.   A tensor $a_1 a_2 a_3 a_4$ is called *covariant* if, when K is changed to K', the $a_i' = \alpha_{ik} a_k$ terms transform in such a way that the sum $a_i a^i$ changes to $a_i' a^{i'}$.   Since $a_i' a^{i'} = \alpha_{ik} \alpha^{im} a_k a^m$, the transformation coefficients α_{ik} must satisfy the condition $\alpha_{ik} \alpha^{im} = \delta_k{}^m = 1$ or 0, depending on whether $m = k$ or $m \neq k$.   We obtain $a_i' a^{i'} = \delta_k{}^m a_k a^m = a_m a^m$.

A *contravariant* tensor of the second order is defined as a set of sixteen quantities a^{ik}, which transform like the products $a^i b^k$, where a^i and b^k are the components of two tensors of the first order.   Thus $a^{ik'} = \alpha^{im} \alpha^{kn} a^{mn}$, which is to be summed up over m and n.   Similarly a covariant tensor of the second order a_{ik} transforms like $a_i b_k$; $a_{ik}' = \alpha_{im}\alpha_{kn}a_{mn}'$. It can be inferred from this definition that $a_{ik}a^{ik}$ is invariant, for we have

$$a_{ik}'a^{ik\prime} = \alpha_{im}\alpha_{kn}a_{mn}\alpha^{ip}\alpha^{ks}a^{ps} = \delta_m{}^p \delta_n{}^s a_{mn}a^{ps} = a_{mn}a^{mn}$$

A *mixed* tensor of the second order consists of sixteen quantities $a_i{}^k$ which transform like the products $a_i b^k$, so that $a_i{}^{k\prime} = \alpha_{im}\alpha^{kn}a_m{}^n$. It follows that $a_i{}^i$ is invariant because

$$a_i{}^{i\prime} = \alpha_{im}\alpha^{in}a_m{}^n = \delta_m{}^n a_m{}^n = a_m{}^m$$

A contravariant or covariant tensor of the second order is *symmetric* if $a^{ik} = a^{ki}$ or $a_{ik} = a_{ki}$ and *antisymmetric* if $a^{ik} = -a^{ki}$ or $a_{ik} = -a_{ki}$. These properties are not changed by a transformation, since

$$a^{ik\prime} = \alpha^{im}\alpha^{kn}a^{mn} = \alpha^{im}\alpha^{kn}a^{nm} = a^{ki\prime}$$

In a similar way it can be shown that $a^{ik\prime} = -a^{ki\prime}$ when $a^{ik} = -a^{ki}$. It is immediately evident how these definitions are to be extended to higher orders. The tensor of order 0 is defined as a scalar. A tensor of arbitrary order is said to be symmetric or antisymmetric depending on whether the exchange of two indices leaves the sign of a component the same or reverses it. There are two very useful rules in tensor calculus:

(i) When the components of a tensor of order i are multiplied by those of a tensor of order k, a tensor of the order $i + k$ results. This is a direct consequence of the transformation properties of tensors.

(ii) When, in a mixed tensor, an upper and lower index are set equal (then we must summate over the index), we obtain a tensor the order of which is reduced by 2.

To prove this let us consider the tensor $a_i{}^{km}$. Then $a_i{}^{im\prime} = \alpha_{in}\alpha^{ip}\alpha^{mr}a_n{}^{pr} = \delta_n{}^p\alpha^{mr}a_n{}^{pr} = \alpha^{mr}a_n{}^{nr}$, this relation implying that $a_i{}^{im}$ transforms like a^m. This procedure of making two indices equal for the purpose of lowering the order of a mixed tensor is called *contraction*. As an example, we have already had $a_i{}^i$ as invariant, that is, forming a tensor of order 0, which by contraction is derived from the tensor $a_i{}^k$.

Throughout our applications of tensor calculus we shall be concerned with tensor functions, that is, tensors the components of which are functions of x_1, x_2, x_3, x_4. We can speak of a tensor field. It is a matter of importance that from a given tensor field other fields may be derived by means of certain differential operators. For example, let us assume that $\phi(x_1 x_2 x_3 x_4)$ is a scalar function defining a tensor field of order 0. Then the increment of ϕ corresponding to the increase of $x_1 \cdots x_4$ to $x_1 + dx_1, \cdots, x_4 + dx_4$, is given by $d\phi = (\partial\phi/\partial x_1)\, dx_1 + \cdots + (\partial\phi/\partial x_4)\, dx_4$. Since its value does not depend on the coordinate system, $d\phi$ is invariant. Furthermore $dx_1 \cdots dx_4$ transform like a four-vector and therefore represent a contravariant tensor of the first order. From this invariance of $d\phi$ it follows that $\partial\phi/\partial x_1 \cdots \partial\phi/\partial x_4$ form a covariant tensor. Thus, from a tensor field of order 0, a covariant tensor field of order 1 can be derived by multiplying ϕ symbolically by $\partial/\partial x_i$. The result evidently is the gradient of ϕ.

The method applies also to tensor fields of higher order. $a^i(x_1 x_2 x_3 x_4)$ may be supposed to represent a contravariant field of the first order. With the help of an arbitrary tensor a_i the components of which have fixed values, we form the scalar function $a_i a^i(x_1 \cdots x_4) = \phi$ the increment of which is $d\phi = a_i(\partial a^i/\partial x_1)\, dx_1 + \cdots + a_i(\partial a^i/\partial x_4)\, dx_4$. Since $d\phi$ is invariant, $a_i(\partial a^i/\partial x_1) \cdots a_i(\partial a^i/\partial x_4)$ must be the components of a covariant tensor of the first order and $\partial a^i/\partial x_k$ the components of a mixed tensor $a_k{}^i$. By contraction we obtain from $\partial a^i/\partial x_k$ the scalar function $\partial a^i/\partial x_i$, which is identical with the divergence of the tensor function.

The distinction between covariant and contravariant tensors forms an essential feature of tensor calculus, since only by the combined effect of these two can invariant quantities be established. A covariant tensor can be coordinated to any contravariant tensor and vice versa, the two tensors being, in general, different. However, a suitable choice of the coordinates $x_1 x_2 x_3 x_4$ makes it possible to achieve equal tensors. To do so we take as the fourth coordinate $x_4 = ict$, and then the invariant expression $x_1{}^2 + x_2{}^2 + x_3{}^2 - c^2 t^2$ changes to $x_1{}^2 + x_2{}^2 + x_3{}^2 + x_4{}^2$, from which it follows that the contravariant tensor $x_1 x_2 x_3 x_4$ is associated with a covariant tensor of the same components. (On the other hand, $x_1 x_2 x_3 ct$ calls for $x_1, x_2, x_3, -ct$). We shall assume that x_4 is always ict; then we need not distinguish between covariant and contravariant tensors, it being sufficient to characterize tensors by lower indices.

Above all, in quantum mechanics, we are interested in antisymmetric tensors: they have the property that any component reverses sign when the indices are interchanged; thus $a_{ik} = -a_{ki}$ and $a_{ikl} = -a_{lki}$. In an antisymmetric tensor all components, such as a_{ii} or a_{iki}, having two equal indices must vanish, for these components remain unchanged when the two indices are interchanged. Thus in the four-dimensional world an antisymmetric tensor of the second order has not sixteen but only twelve components. These form six pairs of components having same magnitude but opposite signs, and thus the tensor is defined by the specification of six numbers. In an antisymmetric tensor of the third order only those a_{ikl} components having different i, k, l are not equal to zero, so that the tensor may be specified by four values which belong to a_{234}, a_{314}, a_{124}, a_{123}. These four quantities transform like the components $a_1 a_2 a_3 a_4$ of a four-vector, for the tensor a_{ikl} together with the covariant tensor (which, for $x_4 = ict$, is identical with the first one) defines the invariant $6(a_{234}^2 + \cdots + a_{123}^2)$ which is the same kind as the invariant $a_1^2 + \cdots + a_4^2$ of a tensor $a_1 \cdots a_4$. Thus an antisymmetric tensor of the third order behaves like a four-vector. However, there is no complete equivalence with a four-vector when the coordinate system is changed so that all space axes are inverted but the time axes remain the same. Then an ordinary four-vector changes the sign of every space component, leaving the time component unchanged. On the other hand, the vector $a_{234} a_{314} a_{124} a_{123}$ behaves in just the opposite manner, as, for example, a_{234} transforms like the product $x_1 x_2 x_4$. The antisymmetric tensor $a_{234} a_{314} a_{124} a_{123}$ on this account is called a *pseudovector*.

Finally we consider an antisymmetric tensor a_{iklm} of the fourth order, which is evidently the highest order because more than four indices cannot differ one from the other. Here we obtain a scalar, for now the totality of the components reduces to one member, $a_{1234} = -a_{2134} = \cdots$, and there follows from the invariance of $a_{iklm} a_{iklm}$ that of a_{1234}. Thus an antisymmetric tensor of the fourth order is a scalar which, like the pseudovector, is of a peculiar kind, for, whereas a true scalar remains unchanged when a spatial reflection is performed on the coordinate system, the quantity a_{1234} reverses its sign. For this reason it is called a pseudoscalar.

There is no difficulty in adapting the equations of the preceding section to the case of a pseudoscalar field. When we substitute an antisymmetric tensor function $\chi_{\alpha\beta\gamma\delta}$ for ψ instead of (247), we obtain

$$\frac{\partial \chi_{\alpha\beta\gamma\delta}}{\partial x_\alpha} = \kappa \psi_{\beta\gamma\delta} \tag{254}$$

where $\psi_{\beta\gamma\delta}$ is a pseudovector. Equation (254) is an invariant one since we have seen that from any tensor field another field of an order reduced by one can be derived by differentiation and contraction. In (254) the summation is over the index α, but, as all terms of $\chi_{\alpha\beta\gamma\delta}$ vanish except one, then (254) has precisely the same form as (247), the only difference being that a pseudoscalar and pseudovector replace scalar and vector.

By differentiating $\psi_{\beta\gamma\delta}$, a tensor of the fourth order, $\partial\psi_{\beta\gamma\delta}/\partial x_{\alpha}$, is obtained, which, however, is not antisymmetric, for when α is interchanged with another index, a quite different quantity results. We can, however, obtain an antisymmetric tensor by combining four tensors of the kind $\partial\psi_{\beta\gamma\delta}/\partial x_{\alpha}$ in a suitable way, and we obtain the equation

$$\frac{\partial\psi_{\beta\gamma\delta}}{\partial x_{\alpha}} - \frac{\partial\psi_{\alpha\gamma\delta}}{\partial x_{\beta}} + \frac{\partial\psi_{\alpha\beta\delta}}{\partial x_{\gamma}} - \frac{\partial\psi_{\alpha\beta\gamma}}{\partial x_{\delta}} = \kappa\chi_{\alpha\beta\gamma\delta} \tag{255}$$

Examination shows that the expression on the left-hand side is antisymmetric in all indices; therefore it represents a scalar. Equation (255) is the counterpart of equation (247′).

The rest of the theory is in perfect analogy to that which has been developed in the preceding section. Except for certain factors, all the previous expressions may be adopted. For example, for the Lagrangian function we obtain

$$L = -\kappa\left(\frac{1}{3!}\,\psi_{\alpha\beta\gamma}{}^{*}\psi_{\alpha\beta\gamma} + \frac{1}{4!}\,\chi_{\alpha\beta\gamma\delta}{}^{*}\chi_{\alpha\beta\gamma\delta}\right) \tag{256}$$

The factors $1/3!$ and $1/4!$ must be inserted because, as in Section 47, we have to take the products only once, whereas our index convention requires summation over all the permutations of the indices.

As long as the interaction of the field with the particles is omitted from consideration, both the scalar and pseudoscalar theories are perfectly equivalent, both describing the same field and differing only in the means of representation. This equivalence does not, however, apply to the interaction of the field with matter, a problem to be treated in Chapter 9. This interaction must be expressed by terms which are relativistically invariant, and an essential difference is introduced depending on whether the terms are derived from a scalar or a pseudoscalar field.

49. Particles with Spin 1. de Broglie and Proca's Equation.
As has been pointed out, the spin requires a resolution of the wave function ψ into several components, for a scalar function is incapable of describing the internal state of a particle. In Dirac's theory ψ was resolved into two pairs of spinors. de Broglie, and later Proca, tried to handle the spin in a different way by substituting a four-vector ψ, with components ψ_1, ψ_2, ψ_3, ψ_4. In this way an antisymmetric tensor $\chi_{\alpha\beta}$ can be derived from ψ by means of the equations

$$\frac{\partial\psi_{\beta}}{\partial x_{\alpha}} - \frac{\partial\psi_{\alpha}}{\partial x_{\beta}} = \kappa\chi_{\alpha\beta} \qquad \kappa = \frac{m_0 c}{\hbar} \tag{257}$$

where m_0 is the rest mass of the particles of the field; they appear when the field is quantized. These equations are in exact agreement with Maxwell's theory wherein, for a charge-free field, the field quantities $\chi_{\alpha\beta}' = \mathbf{EH}$ are derived from a four-potential $\Phi(\Phi_i = A_i, \Phi_4 = i\phi)$ by $\chi_{\alpha\beta}' = \partial\Phi_\beta/\partial x_\alpha - \partial\Phi_\alpha/\partial x_\beta$. But, whereas the $\chi_{\alpha\beta}'$ quantities satisfy the equations $\partial\chi_{\alpha\beta}'/\partial x_\alpha = 0$, it is now assumed that

$$\frac{\partial\chi_{\alpha\beta}}{\partial x_\alpha} = \kappa\psi_\beta \tag{258}$$

This equation is invariant because, from the operation on the left-hand side, a four-vector results. Owing to the equality $\chi_{\alpha\beta} = -\chi_{\beta\alpha}$, from (258) with $\kappa \neq 0$ we obtain

$$\frac{\partial\psi_\beta}{\partial x_\beta} = \frac{1}{\kappa}\frac{\partial^2\chi_{\alpha\beta}}{\partial x_\alpha\,\partial x_\beta} = 0 \tag{259}$$

On substituting in (258) for $\chi_{\alpha\beta}$ its value from (257), we obtain

$$\overline{\sum_\alpha}\frac{\partial^2\psi_\beta}{\partial x_\beta^2} - \frac{\partial}{\partial x_\beta}\frac{\partial\psi_\alpha}{\partial x_\alpha} = \sum_\alpha\frac{\partial^2\psi_\beta}{\partial x_\alpha^2} = \kappa^2\psi_\beta$$

so that for each ψ_α the Klein-Gordon equation holds provided $\kappa \neq 0$.

If the ψ_α are complex quantities, $a_\alpha + ib_\alpha$, where a_α and b_α are real, then analogously to the relation $x_4 = ict$, we consider ψ_4 a quantity of the form $i(a_4 + ib_4)$ and define ψ^* as a four-vector with components $a_k - ib_k$ $(k = 1, 2, 3)$ and $i(a_4 - ib_4)$. If $\partial\psi_\beta^*/\partial x_\alpha - \partial\psi_\alpha^*/\partial x_\beta$ is denoted by $\chi_{\alpha\beta}^*$, then (257), (258), and (259) hold for ψ_α^* and $\chi_{\alpha\beta}^*$ also, so that, for example,

$$\frac{\partial\chi_{\alpha\beta}^*}{\partial x_\alpha} = \kappa\psi_\beta^* \tag{258'}$$

The passage to the case where an electromagnetic field is present is accomplished as in Section 46 by substituting in (257) and (258) $\partial/\partial x_\alpha + (ie/c\hbar)\Phi_\alpha$ for $\partial/\partial x_\alpha$. Then instead of (258) we obtain

$$\left(\frac{\partial}{\partial x_\alpha} + \frac{ie}{c\hbar}\Phi_\alpha\right)\chi_{\alpha\beta}' = \kappa\psi_\beta$$

with

$$\kappa\chi_{\alpha\beta}' = \left(\frac{\partial}{\partial x_\alpha} + \frac{ie}{c\hbar}\Phi_\alpha\right)\psi_\beta - \left(\frac{\partial}{\partial x_\beta} + \frac{ie}{c\hbar}\Phi_\beta\right)\psi_\alpha \tag{260}$$

Similarly for (258') we obtain

$$\left(\frac{\partial}{\partial x_\alpha} - \frac{ie}{c\hbar}\Phi_\alpha\right)\chi_{\alpha\beta}'^* = \kappa\psi_\beta^*$$

with

$$\kappa \chi_{\alpha\beta}'^* = \left(\frac{\partial}{\partial x_\alpha} - \frac{ie}{c\hbar} \Phi_\alpha \right) \psi_\beta^* - \left(\frac{\partial}{\partial x_\beta} - \frac{ie}{c\hbar} \Phi_\beta \right) \psi_\alpha^*$$

We try to find a four-current with real space components $s_1 s_2 s_3$ and an imaginary time component s_4 which, because of (258) or (260), satisfy the condition $\partial s_\alpha / \partial x_\alpha = 0$. The simplest combination by which a four-vector is formed from the ψ_α and χ_α quantities is given by the expressions $\psi_\alpha \chi_{\alpha\beta}$. Therefore, on the assumption that there is no electromagnetic field, we put

$$s_\beta = ia(\psi_\alpha \chi_{\alpha\beta}^* - \psi_\alpha^* \chi_{\alpha\beta}) \tag{261}$$

If a is real, these expressions comply with the condition that s_1, s_2, s_3 be real and s_4 imaginary. They also satisfy the continuity equation, for we have

$$\frac{\partial s_\beta}{\partial x_\beta} = ia \left(\frac{\partial \psi_\alpha}{\partial x_\beta} \chi_{\alpha\beta}^* - \frac{\partial \psi_\alpha^*}{\partial x_\beta} \chi_{\alpha\beta} + \psi_\alpha \frac{\partial \chi_{\alpha\beta}^*}{\partial x_\beta} - \psi_\alpha^* \frac{\partial \chi_{\alpha\beta}}{\partial x_\beta} \right)$$

If the expressions (257) are substituted for $\chi_{\alpha\beta}$ and $\chi_{\alpha\beta}^*$, the first two terms cancel each other, in one of them the subscripts α and β being interchanged. Because of (258), the other two terms give zero. We obtain for the time component

$$s_4 = ic\rho = ia(\psi_\alpha \chi_{\alpha 4}^* - \psi_\alpha^* \chi_{\alpha 4}) \tag{262}$$

Thus ρ depends on the ψ_α quantities and their first derivatives. As the wave equation (258) for ψ_α is of second order, the first derivatives may assume any values; hence both positive and negative values are possible for ρ. Thus, again, the only interpretation of ρ is that of a charge density. When an electromagnetic field is present, $\chi_{\alpha 4}$ and $\chi_{\alpha 4}^*$ are to be changed to

$$\left(\frac{\partial}{\partial x_\alpha} + \frac{ie}{c\hbar} \Phi_\alpha \right) \psi_4 - \left(\frac{\partial}{\partial x_4} + \frac{ie}{c\hbar} \Phi_4 \right) \psi_\alpha$$

and

$$\left(\frac{\partial}{\partial x_\alpha} - \frac{ie}{c\hbar} \Phi_\alpha \right) \psi_4^* - \left(\frac{\partial}{\partial x_4} - \frac{ie}{c\hbar} \Phi_4 \right) \psi_\alpha^*$$

respectively.

In addition, we determine the energy and momentum densities, confining ourselves, for the sake of simplicity, to the case $\Phi = 0$. Here the field is described by (258), which, if ψ_α and ψ_α^* are considered generalized coordinates of the field, can be derived from the Lagrangian

$$\bar{L} = -\frac{\kappa}{2} \chi_{\alpha\beta}^* \chi_{\alpha\beta} - \kappa \psi_\alpha^* \psi_\alpha \tag{263}$$

The variation $\delta\psi_\beta$ of ψ_β gives

$$\delta\bar{L} = -\chi_{\alpha\beta}* \frac{\partial\,\delta\psi_\beta}{\partial x_\alpha} - \kappa\psi_\beta* \,\delta\psi_\beta$$

and this expression, when substituted in $\delta \int dt \int \bar{L}\, dv = 0$, results in (258). For the momenta π_α and $\pi_\alpha*$ of ψ_α and $\psi_\alpha*$, we find, from (263),

$$\pi_4 = \frac{\partial\bar{L}}{\partial\,(\partial\psi_4/\partial t)} = \frac{1}{ic}\frac{\partial\bar{L}}{\partial\,(\partial\psi_4/\partial x_4)} = 0 \qquad \pi_4* = 0$$

$$\pi_i = \frac{\partial\bar{L}}{\partial\,(\partial\psi_i/\partial t)} = -\frac{1}{ic}\chi_{4i}* \qquad\qquad \pi_i* = -\frac{1}{ic}\chi_{4i} \tag{264}$$

Since $H = \sum p(dq/dt) - L$, we obtain for the energy

$$H = \int \left(-\chi_{4\alpha}* \frac{\partial\psi_\alpha}{\partial x_4} - \chi_{4\alpha} \frac{\partial\psi_\alpha*}{\partial x_4} - \bar{L} \right) dv \tag{265}$$

If, for $\partial\psi_\alpha/\partial x_4$, we substitute $\kappa\chi_{4\alpha} + \partial\psi_4/\partial x_\alpha$ we get

$$\chi_{4\alpha}* \frac{\partial\psi_\alpha}{\partial x_4} + \chi_{4\alpha} \frac{\partial\psi_\alpha*}{\partial x_4} = 2\kappa\chi_{4\alpha}*\chi_{4\alpha} + \chi_{4\alpha}* \frac{\partial\psi_4}{\partial x_\alpha} + \chi_{4\alpha} \frac{\partial\psi_4*}{\partial x_\alpha}$$

When the last two terms are integrated by parts, we obtain, because of (258), $+\kappa \int 2\psi_4*\psi_4\, dv$, and then (265) becomes

$$H = \int \left(-2\kappa\chi_{4\alpha}*\chi_{4\alpha} - 2\kappa\psi_4*\psi_4 + \frac{\kappa}{2}\chi_{\alpha\beta}*\chi_{\alpha\beta} + \kappa\psi_\alpha*\psi_\alpha \right) dv$$

$$= \int \left[-\kappa\chi_{4\alpha}*\chi_{4\alpha} + \frac{\kappa}{2}\chi_{ik}*\chi_{ik} - \kappa(\psi_4*\psi_4 - \psi_i*\psi_i) \right] dv$$

The summation is from 1 to 4 over the index α and from 1 to 3 over k and i. Thus the energy density of the field is given by

$$\bar{H} = -\kappa\chi_{4\alpha}*\chi_{4\alpha} + \frac{\kappa}{2}\chi_{ik}*\chi_{ik} - \kappa(\psi_4*\psi_4 - \psi_i*\psi_i) \tag{266}$$

As ψ_4 and ψ_4* are defined by $i(a_4 + ib_4)$ and $i(a_4 - ib_4)$, then $\psi_4*\psi_4$ and $\chi_{4\alpha}*\chi_{4\alpha}$ are negative. Therefore (266) is always positive.

$\bar{H}$ can be developed to an energy-momentum tensor. To do this we must form a symmetric tensor of the second order of ψ_α and $\chi_{\alpha\beta}$ which agrees with $\bar{H}$ in the T_{44} element. This requirement is satisfied by the quantities

$$T_{mn} = -\kappa(\chi_{ma}*\chi_{na} + \chi_{na}*\chi_{ma}) - \kappa(\psi_m*\psi_n + \psi_n*\psi_m) - \bar{L}\,\delta_{mn} \tag{267}$$

which represent a tensor, since ψ_α and $\chi_{\alpha\beta}$ form a four-vector and a tensor respectively and $\bar{L}$, as is seen from (263), is an invariant. Equation (267) satisfies the condition that $T_{mn} = T_{nm}$, and in addition we have $T_{44} = \bar{H}$, as a comparison with (266) shows.

The Proca equations describe particles with spin 1. This could be shown by a straightforward evaluation of the angular momentum. The proof, however, turns out to be rather troublesome. Much simpler is the method based on an investigation by Dirac, who succeeded in developing the most general wave equation; it can be made specific for any value of the spin. It can be shown that, for spin 1, this equation agrees with the formalism proposed by Proca.

50. The Pseudovector Field. We were able to represent particles with spin 0 by both a scalar and a pseudoscalar wave field. In a similar way, for particles with spin 1, we can use a pseudovector function $\chi_{\alpha\beta\gamma}$ instead of the vector function. This function, being defined as an antisymmetric tensor of the third order, can, as we have seen, be specified by the four components χ_{234}, χ_{314}, χ_{124}, and $-\chi_{123}$ which, when the coordinate system is changed for another, transform like the components of a four-vector, the only difference being that a spatial reflection of the coordinate system does not change the spatial components of the vector. A tensor of the second order can be derived from a tensor of the third order by differentiation and contraction, and therefore we obtain the counterpart of (257) by setting

$$\frac{\partial \chi_{\alpha\beta\gamma}}{\partial x_\alpha} = \kappa\psi_{\beta\gamma} = \kappa\psi_{\alpha\delta}' \qquad (268)$$

$\psi_{\beta\gamma}$ is an antisymmetric second-order tensor and therefore represents a six-vector. $\psi_{\alpha\delta}'$ is the corresponding dual six-vector the components of which are given by $\psi_{\alpha\delta}' = \psi_{\beta\gamma}$ if $\alpha\delta\beta\gamma$ are obtained from the sequence 1, 2, 3, 4 by an uneven number of permutations. (This relationship between ψ and ψ' is not changed by a transformation.) Equation (268) then corresponds exactly to (257) of the preceding section. For example, we have the relation

$$\frac{\partial \chi_{\alpha 24}}{\partial x_\alpha} = \frac{\partial \chi_{124}}{\partial x_1} + \frac{\partial \chi_{324}}{\partial x_3} = \kappa\psi_{24} = \kappa\psi_{13}'$$

which agrees with (257) since χ_{124} and χ_{234} are the components χ_3' and χ_1' of the pseudovector $\chi_{\alpha\beta\gamma}$. We obtain from $\psi_{\alpha\beta}$, by differentiation, the tensor of the third order $\partial\psi_{\alpha\beta}/\partial x_\gamma$, which is not antisymmetric but can be developed to an antisymmetric tensor by adding $\partial\psi_{\beta\gamma}/\partial x_\alpha + \partial\psi_{\gamma\alpha}/\partial x_\beta$. The result is a pseudovector which must satisfy the relation

$$\frac{\partial \psi_{\beta\gamma}}{\partial x_\alpha} + \frac{\partial \psi_{\gamma\alpha}}{\partial x_\beta} + \frac{\partial \psi_{\alpha\beta}}{\partial x_\gamma} = \kappa\chi_{\alpha\beta\gamma}$$

which corresponds to (258). For example, if we choose 2, 3, 4 for α, β, γ, we obtain

$$\frac{\partial \psi_{12}'}{\partial x_2} + \frac{\partial \psi_{13}'}{\partial x_3} + \frac{\partial \psi_{14}'}{\partial x_4} = -\kappa\chi_1'$$

which agrees with (258).

The Lagrangian function L of a pseudovector field is found to be

$$\bar{L} = -\frac{\kappa}{2!}\,\psi_{\alpha\beta}{}^*\psi_{\alpha\beta} - \frac{\kappa}{3!}\,\chi_{\alpha\beta\gamma}{}^*\chi_{\alpha\beta\gamma}$$

We have pointed out that there is a physical difference between a scalar and a pseudoscalar field only if the interaction of the field with matter is to be considered. The same remark applies to the vector and pseudovector fields.

Vector fields are subject to the same interpretation as scalar fields: they represent a pure wave motion that has nothing to do with particles, and they describe only that aspect of reality which can be pictured by a wave field. The particles enter the picture only when the wave motion is quantized and, as a result of this operation, assume the property of a corpuscular radiation. There are, however, certain characteristic features of the particle picture which can be recognized in the wave picture. The fact that in the latter only a density which may be positive as well as negative can be defined can mean only that both positive and negative particles can exist in the particle picture, and it is the charge rather than the number of particle per unit volume that we can apprehend. The explanation of this must be that the number of particles has no definite value because of the possibility of pairs of positive and negative particles being created or annihilated. *It is characteristic of relativistic quantum mechanics that, in all its forms, it insists on processes of creation and annihilation of pairs.* Only Dirac's theory seemed at first to be an exception to this because it permits particles of negative energy only. Nevertheless, states of negative energy have to be considered, and the interpretation of these is possible only within the framework of a hole theory and leads to the assumption of processes presented to our observation as if pairs of particles were created or annihilated.

PROBLEMS

1. Solve the Dirac equation by the plane wave $\psi_i = u_i e^{(i/\hbar)(Et - \mathbf{p} \cdot \mathbf{r})}$. Show that for a given $\mathbf{p}$ and E there exist four solutions corresponding to $E > 0$, $E < 0$ and two directions of the spin.

2. Show that the components $\sigma_1 \sigma_2 \sigma_3$ of the spin $\vec{\sigma}$ defined by (240) satisfy the equations

$$\sigma_i \sigma_k + \sigma_k \sigma_i = 2\delta_{ik}$$

3. Prove the same for the matrices

$$\rho_1 = i\alpha_3 \alpha_2 \alpha_1 \qquad \rho_2 = \beta \alpha_3 \alpha_2 \alpha_1 \qquad \rho_3 = \beta$$

Show that these matrices commute with the σ_i.

4. Show that $\sigma_2 \sigma_3 - \sigma_3 \sigma_2 = 2i\sigma_1$, etc.

5. If $\mathbf{a}$ and $\mathbf{b}$ are two arbitrary vectors, it can be shown that

$$(\vec{\sigma} \cdot \mathbf{a})(\vec{\sigma} \cdot \mathbf{b}) = (\mathbf{a} \cdot \mathbf{b}) + i(\vec{\sigma} \cdot \mathbf{a} \times \mathbf{b})$$

6. By using the matrices ρ_1, ρ_2, ρ_3 of Problem 3, show that equation (245) can be transformed into

$$\left\{ \frac{1}{c}(E - e\phi) + \rho_1 \left[\sigma \cdot \left(\mathbf{p} - \frac{e}{c} \mathbf{A} \right) \right] + \rho_3 mc \right\} \psi = 0$$

7. On the left-hand side of the above equation apply the operator

$$\frac{1}{c}(E - e\phi) - \rho_1 \left[\sigma \cdot \left(\mathbf{p} - \frac{e}{c} \mathbf{A} \right) \right] - \rho_3 mc$$

and show, by using theorem 5 (formulated in Problem 5), that the result is

$$\left\{ \left(\frac{E - e\phi}{c} \right)^2 - \left(\mathbf{p} - \frac{e}{c} \mathbf{A} \right)^2 - m^2 c^2 + m \left(\frac{e\hbar}{mc} \sigma \cdot \text{curl } \mathbf{A} \right) \right.$$
$$\left. + m \left(\left[\rho_1 \sigma \times \frac{e\hbar}{2mc} \sigma \right] \cdot \mathbf{E} \right) \right\} \psi = 0$$

Interpret the last two terms as being due to an electric and a magnetic dipole.

8. Show that the Proca equation can be derived from $(\square - k^2)\psi_i = 0$, together with (256) and the condition $\sum (\partial \psi_i / \partial x_i) = 0$.

9. Discuss the difference in meaning between a non-relativistic and a relativistic wave equation.

7

QUANTIZATION

OF WAVE FIELDS

51. The Idea of Quantization. Our next task is to bring the theory of wave fields into contact with the concepts of quantum mechanics in order to find a way to introduce the particle idea. This can be achieved by interpreting the field quantities, which have been represented by certain tensors or spinors in the preceding chapter, as matrices which must satisfy certain commutation relations. In this way a field is given properties that can be expressed in terms of whole numbers, thus providing an explanation for the fact that a measurement, for example, of the charge always furnishes an integer multiple of a fundamental unit, so that the field is behaving like an assemblage of particles.

This quantization can be brought about by requiring the wave functions ψ_i and the corresponding momenta π_i, which are taken as matrices, to fulfill the commutation relations of (136). In the following, however, we prefer to transform ψ_i and π_i into a denumerable set of coordinates q_k and momenta p_k. For this purpose we first determine the Lagrangian function L from which the given wave equation can be derived by means of $\delta \int L \, dt = 0$. The next step is to expand the wave function in terms of an arbitrary set of orthogonal functions, $f_k(xyz)$:

$$\psi(xyzt) = \sum_k q_k(t) f_k(xyz)$$

the consequence being that the wave equation becomes an infinite system of equations for the $q_k(t)$ terms. L then becomes a function of the q_k terms, which are the generalized coordinates of the field, and of the derivatives dq_k/dt, that is, $L = L[q_k \, (dq_k/dt)]$. From this function the momenta p_k, which are conjugate to the coordinates q_k, can be determined by means of the relation $p_k = \partial L / \partial \, (dq_k/dt)$. Then for the Hamiltonian of the system we obtain

$$H = \sum \left(\frac{dq_k}{dt} \right) p_k - L \left[q_k \left(\frac{dq_k}{dt} \right) \right] = H(q_p p_k)$$

191

The wave equation can now be transcribed into

$$\frac{dq_k}{dt} = \frac{\partial H}{\partial p_k} \qquad \frac{dp_k}{dt} = -\frac{\partial H}{\partial q_k}$$

In order to quantize the system the quantities q_k and p_k must be replaced by matrices Q_k and P_k, which satisfy certain commutation relations. Care must be taken in setting down these relations. According to quantum mechanics, (136) certainly holds for real conjugate observables, which are represented by Hermitean matrices. But in the theory of wave fields we are frequently concerned with q_k and p_k terms which are complex, and hence we must investigate first whether we can apply (136) to this case as well. Let us assume that ψ is a real or complex wave function and that π, the conjugate momentum function, derives from the Lagrangian $L = \int dv\,\bar{L}$ by differentiation of $\bar{L}$ relative to $d\psi/dt$, that is, $\pi = \partial\bar{L}/\partial(d\psi/dt)$. We imagine that the field is enclosed in a cubic space of extension l, and assume that the field periodically extends beyond this space. Then ψ and π undergo a Fourier expansion if we choose the real functions $f_i = \sqrt{\frac{2}{l^3}} \frac{\sin}{\cos} \mathbf{k}_i \cdot \mathbf{r}$ as an orthogonal system. $\mathbf{k}_i$ denotes a vector the components of which are $2\pi/l$ times a whole number $n_1 n_2 n_3$, so that $\mathbf{k}_i \cdot \mathbf{r} = (2\pi/l)(n_1 x + n_2 y + n_3 z)$. The physical meaning of the expansions

$$\psi = \sum_i q_i f_i \qquad \pi = \sum_i p_i f_i \tag{269}$$

is that of a resolution of ψ and π into stationary waves that have the directions of the $\mathbf{k}_i$ vectors and a wavelength given by $|\mathbf{k}_i| = 2\pi/\lambda_i$. Two opposite directions are taken as one, so that only the directions of a hemisphere need be considered; therefore, for two of the n_i, we must take both the positive and negative whole numbers, but for the third only the positive numbers. The f_i functions form a complete orthogonal system by satisfying the condition $\int dv\, f_i f_k = \delta_{ik}$. The q_i and p_i terms are real or complex depending on whether ψ is real or complex. If complex, we pass from the complex q_i and p_i terms to the real coordinates $q_i^{(1)} q_i^{(2)}$ and real momenta $p_i^{(1)} p_i^{(2)}$ by means of the transformation

$$q_i = \frac{1}{\sqrt{2}}\left(q_i^{(1)} + iq_i^{(2)}\right) \qquad q_i^* = \frac{1}{\sqrt{2}}\left(q_i^{(1)} - iq_i^{(2)}\right)$$

$$p_i = \frac{1}{\sqrt{2}}\left(p_i^{(1)} - ip_i^{(2)}\right) \qquad p_i^* = \frac{1}{\sqrt{2}}\left(p_i^{(1)} + ip_i^{(2)}\right) \tag{270}$$

The factor $1/\sqrt{2}$ is necessary in order that $q_i^{(1)}p_i^{(1)}$ and $q_i^{(2)}p_i^{(2)}$ become conjugate together with $q_i p_i$. If $H(qpq^*p^*)$ is the Hamiltonian of the field (always assumed real), then, according to (270) we obtain

$$\frac{\partial H}{\partial p_i^{(1)}} = \frac{\partial H}{\partial p_i}\frac{\partial p_i}{\partial p_i^{(1)}} + \frac{\partial H}{\partial p_i^*}\frac{\partial p_i^*}{\partial p_i^{(1)}} = \frac{1}{\sqrt{2}}\left(\frac{\partial H}{\partial p_i} + \frac{\partial H}{\partial p_i^*}\right)$$

$$= \frac{1}{\sqrt{2}}\left(\frac{dq_i}{dt} + \frac{dq_i^*}{dt}\right) = \frac{dq_i^{(1)}}{dt}$$

so that the $q_i^{(1)}$ and $p_i^{(1)}$ also satisfy the canonical equations. The matrices $Q_i^{(1)}$, $P_i^{(1)}$, $Q_i^{(2)}$, $P_i^{(2)}$ which belong to $q_i^{(1)}p_i^{(1)}$ and $q_i^{(2)}p_i^{(2)}$ respectively must then fulfill the equations

$$[Q_i^j P_k^{j'}] = \frac{\hbar}{c}\,\delta_{ik}\delta_{jj'}E \qquad [Q_i^j Q_k^{j'}] = 0 \qquad [P_i^j P_k^{j'}] = 0 \quad (271)$$

(where such an expression as $[ab]$ signifies $ab - ba$). From this it follows that, for the complex matrices belonging to q_i and p_i,

$$[Q_i P_k] = \frac{1}{2}[Q_i^{(1)} + iQ_i^{(2)}, P_k^{(1)} - iP_k^{(2)}]$$

$$= \frac{1}{2}[Q_i^{(1)}P_k^{(1)}] + \frac{1}{2}[Q_i^{(2)}P_k^{(2)}] = \frac{\hbar}{i}\,\delta_{ik}E$$

$$[Q_i Q_k] = 0 \qquad [P_i P_k] = 0 \tag{272}$$

Thus the expansion (269) in terms of the real orthogonal functions $\sqrt{\dfrac{2}{l^3}}\,\begin{matrix}\sin\\\cos\end{matrix}\,\mathbf{k}_i\cdot\mathbf{r}$ leads to coordinates q_i and momenta p_i, for which (272) holds regardless of whether ψ is real or complex.

Frequently, however, it is convenient to expand ψ in terms of the complex functions $(1/\sqrt{l^3})e^{i\mathbf{k}_i\cdot\mathbf{r}}$. For this purpose we substitute $(1/2i)(e^{i\mathbf{k}_i\cdot\mathbf{r}} - e^{-i\mathbf{k}_i\cdot\mathbf{r}})$ for $\sin \mathbf{k}_i\cdot\mathbf{r}$ and $\frac{1}{2}(e^{i\mathbf{k}_i\cdot\mathbf{r}} + e^{-i\mathbf{k}_i\cdot\mathbf{r}})$ for $\cos \mathbf{k}_i\cdot\mathbf{r}$, the effect being a decomposition of the stationary waves into *running waves* in the directions k_i and $-k_i$. Instead of (269) we will have then

$$\psi = \frac{1}{\sqrt{l^3}}\sum q_i e^{i\mathbf{k}_i\cdot\mathbf{r}} \qquad \pi = \frac{1}{\sqrt{l^3}}\sum p_i e^{-i\mathbf{k}_i\cdot\mathbf{r}} \tag{273}$$

The summation is now to be extended over all directions i, not only over those of a hemisphere. Thus the range of the index i is from $-\infty$ to $+\infty$, the two indices $+i$ and $-i$ signifying two opposite directions. It is convenient, in the expansion of π, to coordinate p_i

to $e^{-i\mathbf{k}_i \cdot \mathbf{r}}$. The functions $u_i = (1/\sqrt{l^3})e^{i\mathbf{k}_i \cdot \mathbf{r}}$, like the f_i, form a normalized orthogonal system, since

$$\int u_i^* u_k \, dv = \delta_{ik} \tag{274}$$

For a real ψ, for any value i we have

$$q_{-i} = q_i^* \qquad p_{-i} = p_i^*$$

so that the two terms $q_{-i}e^{-i\mathbf{k}_i \cdot \mathbf{r}} + q_i e^{i\mathbf{k}_i \cdot \mathbf{r}}$ provides a real value.

In order to set up the commutation relations for the matrices Q_i, P_i of q_i and p_i, we form the commutator $[\psi\pi]$ and integrate over the field space. If we designate the matrices considered by Q_i' and P_i' in order to distinguish them from Q_i and P_i, we have

$$\int [\psi\pi] \, dv = \int \left[\sum_i Q_i' u_i, \sum_k P_k' u_k^* \right] dv$$

$$= \int \left[\sum_i Q_i f_i, \sum_k P_k f_k \right] dv$$

Hence, if we take into account (274), it follows that

$$\sum_i [Q_i' P_i'] = \sum_i [Q_i P_i] \tag{275}$$

The number of terms on the left-hand and right-hand sides is the same; for, although we summate on the right only over the directions of the hemisphere, every direction is to be taken twice, the function f_i appearing as sine and cosine. Therefore (275) requires that, since $[Q_i P_i] = (\hbar/i)E$, then $[Q_i' P_i']$ must also equal $(\hbar/i)E$. Correspondingly, from the fact that $[\psi\psi] = [\pi\pi] = 0$, it follows that $[Q_i' Q_{-i}']$ and $[P_i' P_{-i}']$ must vanish. Hence the matrices Q_i' and P_i' may, in general, be assumed to satisfy the relations

$$[Q_i' P_k'] = \frac{\hbar}{i} \delta_{ik} E \qquad [Q_i' Q_k'] = 0 \qquad [P_i' P_k'] = 0 \tag{276}$$

52. Quantization of a Scalar Field.

The procedure will be applied first to a scalar field. (The field may be pseudoscalar as well, but then a pseudoscalar and pseudovector must replace the scalar and the vector.) In this case, according to (250), the Lagrangian is given by

$$L = -\kappa \int (\psi^*\psi + \chi_\alpha^* \chi_\alpha) \, dv \tag{277}$$

[*Note:* χ_α^* signifies $(1/\kappa)(\partial\psi^*/\partial x_\alpha)$ and not $(1/\kappa)(\partial\psi/\partial x_\alpha)^*$.] In order to transform L into a function of the coordinates q_i and their derivatives dq_i/dt, we introduce the momentum field π, conjugate to ψ:

$$\pi = \frac{\partial \bar{L}}{\partial\,(d\psi/dt)} = \frac{1}{\kappa c^2}\frac{\partial\psi^*}{\partial t} \qquad \pi^* = \frac{1}{\kappa c^2}\frac{\partial\psi}{\partial t}$$

For the Hamiltonian of the field we then obtain

$$H = \int \left(\frac{d\psi}{dt}\pi + \frac{d\psi^*}{dt}\pi^*\right) dv - L$$

$$= \int \left(\kappa c^2 \pi^*\pi + \kappa\psi^*\psi + \frac{1}{\kappa}\frac{\partial\psi^*}{\partial x_i}\frac{\partial\psi}{\partial x_i}\right) dv$$

in which the summation of i is from 1 to 3 only.   If we expand ψ and π in terms of running waves, H becomes

$$H = \sum_i \left[\kappa c^2 p_i^* p_i + \left(\kappa + \frac{k_i{}^2}{\kappa}\right) q_i^* q_i\right] \qquad (278)$$

The canonical equations arising from H,

$$\frac{dq_i}{dt} = \frac{\partial H}{\partial p_i} = \kappa c^2 p_i^* \qquad \frac{dp_i}{dt} = -\frac{\partial H}{\partial q_i} = -\left(\kappa + \frac{k_i{}^2}{\kappa}\right) q_i^*$$

are identical with the field equations for they lead to the equations

$$\frac{d^2 q_i}{dt^2} = -\kappa c^2\left(\kappa + \frac{k_i{}^2}{\kappa}\right) q_i$$

from which, on returning to ψ with the help of (273), we arrive again at the equation

$$\frac{1}{c^2}\frac{\partial^2\psi}{\partial t^2} = (-\kappa + \nabla^2)\psi$$

The momentum $\mathbf{G}$ and the charge ϵ can be expressed in terms of q_i and p_i just as was the energy H.   If, for the sake of simplicity, we assume $\phi = A = 0$, then, according to (253) and (249′), the momentum and charge density are given by

$$g_\alpha = \frac{1}{\kappa c^2}\left(\frac{\partial\psi^*}{\partial x_\alpha}\frac{\partial\psi}{\partial t} + \frac{\partial\psi^*}{\partial t}\frac{\partial\psi}{\partial x_\alpha}\right)$$

$$\rho = -\frac{ia}{c^2}\left(\psi^*\frac{\partial\psi}{\partial t} - \psi\frac{\partial\psi^*}{\partial t}\right)$$

As we see, $\rho = 0$ for a field with a real ψ.   By integration, we find for

G and ϵ

$$\mathbf{G} = -\frac{i}{\kappa c^2} \sum_i \mathbf{k}_i \left[q_i^* \left(\frac{dq_i}{dt} \right) - \left(\frac{dq_i^*}{dt} \right) q_i \right]$$

$$\epsilon = -\frac{ia}{c^2} \sum_i \left[q_i^* \left(\frac{dq_i}{dt} \right) - \left(\frac{dq_i^*}{dt} \right) q_i \right]$$

We now quantize the field by transcribing q_i and p_i into the matrices Q_i and P_i, which satisfy the relations of (276). Since $q_i + q_i^*$ is real, the corresponding matrix must be Hermitean. To satisfy this condition we have to translate q_i^* into $\tilde{Q}_i$. We then obtain for H, **G**, and ϵ the matrices†

$$H = \sum_i \left[\kappa c^2 \tilde{P}_i P_i + \left(\kappa + \frac{k_i^2}{\kappa} \right) \tilde{Q}_i Q_i \right]$$

$$\mathbf{G} = -i \sum_i \mathbf{k}_i (\tilde{Q}_i \tilde{P}_i - Q_i P_i) \qquad (279)$$

$$\epsilon = -ia\kappa \sum_i (\tilde{Q}_i \tilde{P}_i - Q_i P_i)$$

We shall show now that there are matrices, Q_i and P_i, satisfying the required commutation relations with which, if the coordinate system K of the Hilbert space is suitably chosen, the matrices H, **G** and ϵ become diagonal simultaneously. For this purpose we introduce new matrices, A_i and B_i, which are defined by

$$Q_i = -i \sqrt{\frac{c\hbar}{2}} \frac{1}{\sqrt[4]{1 + k_i^2/\kappa^2}} (A_i - \tilde{B}_i)$$

$$\qquad (280)$$

$$P_i = \sqrt{\frac{\hbar}{2c}} \sqrt[4]{1 + \frac{k_i^2}{\kappa^2}} (\tilde{A}_i + B_i)$$

It is proved easily that all the requirements of (276) are fulfilled if the matrices A_i and B_i are chosen in such a way that

$$[A_i \tilde{A}_k] = \delta_{ik} E \qquad [B_i \tilde{B}_k] = \delta_{ik} E \qquad (281)$$

with all the other bracket terms such as $[A_i A_k]$, $[A_i B_k]$, $\cdots$ being equal to zero. Then we have, for example,

$$[Q_i P_k] = -\frac{i\hbar}{2} ([A_i \tilde{A}_k] - [\tilde{B}_i B_k] + [A_i B_k] - [\tilde{B}_i \tilde{A}_k]) = -i\hbar E$$

† Note that the succession of the factors in the formulas are not uniquely determined by the condition that H, **G**, and ϵ be Hermitean.

It can be shown in the same manner that the other relations are satisfied.

The relations expressed by (281) are exactly the same as those we encountered in Section 43 for the treatment of the many-body problem, the only difference being that here the relations involve two independent sequences of matrices, $A_i \tilde{A}_i$ and $B_i \tilde{B}_i$. This independence is made evident by the commutability of the pairs. As in Section 43, we now choose the coordinate system K of the Hilbert space relative to which all the products $\tilde{A}_i A_i$ and $\tilde{B}_i B_i$ are diagonal. Then any axis of K can be marked by two sequences of numbers, $n_1^+ n_2^+ n_3^+ \cdots$ and $n_1^- n_2^- n_3^- \cdots$, signifying that the axis belongs to the n_1^+-th eigenvalue of $\tilde{A}_1 A_1$, the n_2^+-th eigenvalue of $\tilde{A}_2 A_2$, and so on, and similarly to the n_1^--th eigenvalue of $\tilde{B}_1 B_1$, and so on. Then, according to Section 43, the eigenvalues of $\tilde{A}_i A_i$ and $\tilde{B}_i B_i$ are given by

$$(\tilde{A}_i A_i)_{\text{diag}} = (\tilde{A}_i A_i)_{\substack{n_1^+ n_2^+ \cdots \\ n_1^- n_2^- \cdots}} \Big|_{\substack{n_1^+ n_2^+ \cdots \\ n_1^- n_2^- \cdots}} = n_i^+ \qquad (\tilde{B}_i B_i)_{\text{diag}} = n_i^-$$

whereas all non-diagonal elements vanish.

If now, in the expressions (279), A_i and B_i are substituted for Q_i and P_i, we obtain

$$H = \sum_i \kappa c^2 \frac{\hbar}{2c} \sqrt{1 + \frac{k_i^2}{\kappa^2}} \, (A_i + \tilde{B}_i)(\tilde{A}_i + B_i)$$

$$+ \sum_i \kappa \frac{\hbar c}{2} \sqrt{1 + \frac{k_i^2}{\kappa^2}} \, (\tilde{A}_i - B_i)(A_i - \tilde{B}_i)$$

$$= \frac{1}{2} \sum_i \hbar c \sqrt{\kappa^2 + k_i^2} \, (A_i \tilde{A}_i + A_i B_i + \tilde{B}_i \tilde{A}_i + \tilde{B}_i B_i + \tilde{A}_i A_i$$

$$- B_i A_i - \tilde{A}_i \tilde{B}_i + \tilde{B}_i \tilde{B}_i)$$

Since, because of (281), $A_i \tilde{A}_i = E + \tilde{A}_i A_i$, the expression in parentheses reduces to $2\tilde{A}_i A_i + 2\tilde{B}_i B_i + 2E$, and with $\kappa = m_0 c/\hbar$, we obtain

$$H = \sum_i c \sqrt{m_0^2 c^2 + k_i^2 \hbar^2} \, (\tilde{A}_i A_i + \tilde{B}_i B_i + E) \qquad (282)$$

Now, according to (228), $c \sqrt{m_0^2 c^2 + k_i^2 \hbar^2}$ is the energy E_i of a particle with rest mass m_0 and momentum $k_i \hbar$. Therefore (282) represents H as a matrix diagonal in K the eigenvalues of which, belonging to the axes $n_1^+ n_2^+ \cdots n_1^- n_2^- \cdots$, are given by

$$\sum_i E_i(n_i^+ + n_i^- + 1)$$

The physical interpretation of this is that, when we measure the energy of the field (we make the vector representing the state take the direction of an axis $n_1{}^+ n_2{}^+ \cdots n_1{}^- n_2{}^- \cdots$), the result is the same as if the system were composed of particles which are capable only of energies $E_i = c \sqrt{m_0{}^2 c^2 + k_i{}^2 \hbar^2}$. The axis $n_1{}^+ n_2{}^+ \cdots n_1{}^- n_2{}^- \cdots$ represents a state in which $n_1{}^+ + n_1{}^-$ particles are observed to have an energy E_1, $n_2{}^+ + n_2{}^-$ to have an energy E_2, and so on.

A corresponding interpretation is possible for the momentum $\mathbf{G}$ and the charge ϵ. We find

$$\mathbf{G} = \tfrac{1}{2} \sum_i \mathbf{k}_i \hbar \left\{ (\tilde{A}_i - B_i)(A_i + \tilde{B}_i) + (A_i - \tilde{B}_i)(\tilde{A}_i + B_i) \right\}$$

$$= \sum_i \mathbf{k}\hbar (\tilde{A}_i A_i - \tilde{B}_i B_i)$$

$$\epsilon = a\kappa \sum_i \hbar (\tilde{A}_i A_i - \tilde{B}_i B_i) \tag{283}$$

$$= \sum_i e(\tilde{A}_i A_i - \tilde{B}_i B_i) \qquad \text{for } a = \frac{e}{m_0 c}$$

This means that in the state $n_1{}^+ n_2{}^+ \cdots n_1{}^- n_2{}^- \cdots$ the system has a total momentum $\sum_i \mathbf{k}_i \hbar (n_1{}^+ - n_1{}^-)$ and a charge $\epsilon = \sum_i e(n_1{}^+ - n_1{}^-)$. Thus the numbers that originate in the quantization permit the interpretation that $n_i{}^+$ is the number of particles having the charge $+e$, momentum $+\mathbf{k}_i \hbar$, and energy $c \sqrt{m_0{}^2 c^2 + k_i{}^2 \hbar^2}$, whereas $n_i{}^-$ counts the particles with charge $-e$, momentum $-\mathbf{k}_i \hbar$, and energy $c \sqrt{m_0{}^2 c^2 + k_i{}^2 \hbar^2}$. Particles of negative energy do not occur in the theory because the Hamiltonian can have positive values only.

When the field is real, we have $L = -\kappa \left(\psi^2 + \sum_\alpha \chi_\alpha{}^2 \right)$, hence $\pi = (2/\kappa c^2)(\partial \psi / \partial t)$. Formulas (279) must, therefore, be changed into

$$H = \sum_i \left(\frac{1}{4} \kappa c^2 \tilde{P}_i P_i + \left(\kappa + \frac{k_i{}^2}{\kappa} \right) \tilde{Q}_i Q_i \right)$$

$$\mathbf{G} = -i \sum_i \frac{\mathbf{k}_i}{2} (\tilde{Q}_i \tilde{P}_i - Q_i P_i)$$

$$\epsilon = -i \frac{a\kappa}{2} \sum_i (\tilde{Q}_i \tilde{P}_i - Q_i P_i)$$

In this case, Q_i, as defined in (280), is multiplied by $1/\sqrt{2}$, and P_i in the same expression by $\sqrt{2}$. Then we obtain

$$H = \sum_i \tfrac{1}{2}c\sqrt{m_0{}^2c^2 + k_i{}^2\hbar^2}\,(\tilde{A}_iA_i + \tilde{B}_iB_i + E)$$

$$\mathbf{G} = \sum_i \tfrac{1}{2}\mathbf{k}_i\hbar(\tilde{A}_iA_i - \tilde{B}_iB_i)$$

$$\epsilon = ia\kappa^{\tfrac{1}{2}} \sum_i (\tilde{A}_iA_i - \tilde{B}_iB_i)$$

For a real field we have $q_{-i} = q_i{}^*$, $p_{-i} = p_i{}^*$, and therefore $Q_{-i} = \tilde{Q}_i$, $P_{-i} = \tilde{P}_i$. In order to satisfy this condition we have to set

$$A_{-i} = B_i \quad\text{and}\quad B_{-i} = A_i \tag{284}$$

In the expression for H the terms arising from i and $-i$ then give

$$\tfrac{1}{2}c\sqrt{m_0{}^2c^2 + k_i{}^2\hbar^2}\,(\tilde{A}_iA_i + \tilde{B}_iB_i + \tilde{A}_{-i}A_{-i} + \tilde{B}_{-i}B_{-i})$$
$$= c\sqrt{m_0{}^2c^2 + k_i{}^2\hbar^2}\,(\tilde{A}_iA_i + \tilde{A}_{-i}A_{-i})$$

so that we get

$$H = \sum_i c\sqrt{m_0{}^2c^2 + k_i{}^2\hbar^2}\left(\tilde{A}_iA_i + \frac{E}{2}\right)$$

$$\mathbf{G} = \sum_i \mathbf{k}_i\hbar\tilde{A}_iA_i$$

$$\epsilon = 0$$

Thus the matrix B may be dropped in the case of a real field, and the coordinate system K of the Hilbert space may be reduced to a system the axes of which are marked by one sequence $n_1n_2 \cdots$ of numbers only. When the vector representing the state has the direction of an axis $n_1n_2 \cdots$, the field consists of $n_1n_2 \cdots$ uncharged particles with the energies $c\sqrt{m_0{}^2c^2 + k_1{}^2\hbar^2}$, $c\sqrt{m_0{}^2c^2 + k_2{}^2\hbar^2}$, $\cdots$ and momenta $\mathbf{k}_1\hbar$, $\mathbf{k}_2\hbar \cdots$ respectively.

53. Quantization of a Vector Field. For the quantization of a vector or pseudovector field it is convenient first to eliminate the time component ψ_4 from the equations, the corresponding momentum being zero according to (264) anyway. According to (258) and (264), we have

$$\psi_4 = \frac{1}{\kappa}\frac{\partial\chi_{\alpha4}}{\partial x_\alpha} = \frac{ic}{\kappa}\frac{\partial\pi_\alpha{}^*}{\partial x_\alpha} \qquad \psi_4{}^* = \frac{ic}{\kappa}\frac{\partial\pi_\alpha}{\partial x_\alpha}$$

and so the expression for $\bar{H}$ may be changed to

$$\bar{H} = \kappa c^2 \pi_i{}^* \pi_i + \frac{\kappa}{2} \chi_{ik}{}^* \chi_{ik} + \frac{c^2}{\kappa} \frac{\partial \pi_i{}^*}{\partial x_i} \frac{\partial \pi_k}{\partial x_k} + \kappa \psi_i{}^* \psi_i \qquad (285)$$

The summation over i is to be from 1 to 3 only. The components of the field momentum g_α are determined by the tensor (267) to be

$$g_\alpha = \frac{1}{ic} T_{\alpha 4} = \frac{i\kappa}{c} (\chi_{\alpha i}{}^* \chi_{4i} + \chi_{4i}{}^* \chi_{\alpha i}) + \frac{i\kappa}{c} (\psi_\alpha{}^* \psi_4 + \psi_4{}^* \psi_\alpha)$$

$$= \kappa (\chi_{\alpha i}{}^* \pi_i{}^* + \chi_{\alpha i} \pi_i) - \left(\psi_\alpha{}^* \frac{\partial \pi_i{}^*}{\partial x_i} + \psi_\alpha \frac{\partial \pi_i}{\partial x_i} \right) \qquad (286)$$

On the other hand, the charge density, according to (262), is given by the formula

$$\rho = ia(\psi_i \pi_i - \psi_i{}^* \pi_i{}^*) \qquad (287)$$

from which we see again that $\rho = 0$ for a real field.

The expressions (285), (286), and (287) contain only those quantities ψ_1, ψ_2, ψ_3 and the corresponding momenta π_1, π_2, π_3 which can be associated with the vector functions $\vec{\psi}$ and $\vec{\pi}$. In order to introduce denumerable coordinates, $\vec{\psi}$ and $\vec{\pi}$ are expanded in terms of a complete orthogonal system which now must consist of *vector* functions. To attain this end we multiply by the unit vector $\mathbf{e}_i$ the scalar functions $(1/\sqrt{l^3})e^{i\mathbf{k}_i \cdot \mathbf{r}}$ used in the preceding section. The product then represents a wave polarized in the direction of $\mathbf{e}_i$. The vector $\mathbf{k}_i$ defines the direction of propagation and has the components $(2\pi/l)n_1$, $(2\pi/l)n_2$, $(2\pi/l)n_3$, where n_1, n_2, n_3 denote whole (positive and negative) numbers. For a longitudinal wave, $\mathbf{e}_i$ has the same direction as $\mathbf{k}_i$ (thus making $\mathbf{e}_i \mathbf{k}_i = k_i$) and is designated by $\mathbf{e}_{i1}$, whereas, for a transverse wave, $\mathbf{e}_i$ is perpendicular to $\mathbf{k}_i$ (meaning that $\mathbf{e}_i \mathbf{k}_i = 0$). All directions perpendicular to $\mathbf{k}_i$ can be represented with the help of two directions $\mathbf{e}_{i2}$ and $\mathbf{e}_{i3}$ which are perpendicular to each other, so that for a given i there exist three vector functions, which may be designated by $u_{ij} = (1/\sqrt{l^3})\mathbf{e}_{ij}e^{i\mathbf{k}_i \cdot \mathbf{r}}$ $(j = 1, 2, 3)$. The $\vec{\psi}$ and $\vec{\pi}$ are represented by

$$\vec{\psi} = \frac{1}{\sqrt{l^3}} \sum_{ij} q_{ij} \mathbf{e}_{ij} e^{i\mathbf{k}_i \cdot \mathbf{r}} \qquad \vec{\pi} = \frac{1}{\sqrt{l^3}} \sum_{ij} p_{ij} \mathbf{e}_{ij} e^{-i\mathbf{k}_i \cdot \mathbf{r}} \qquad (288)$$

from which follows, for $\chi_{\alpha\beta}$,

$$\kappa\chi_{\alpha\beta} = \frac{\partial\psi_\beta}{\partial x_\alpha} - \frac{\partial\psi_\alpha}{\partial x_\beta} = \frac{1}{\sqrt{l^3}} \sum_{ij} q_{ij} i (\mathbf{e}_{ij}{}^{(\beta)} k_i{}^{(\alpha)} - \mathbf{e}_{ij}{}^{(\alpha)} k_i{}^{(\beta)}) e^{i\mathbf{k}_i \cdot \mathbf{r}}$$

if $\mathbf{e}_{ij}{}^{(\alpha)}$ and $k_i{}^{(\alpha)}$ denote the components of the vectors $\mathbf{e}_{ij}$ and $\mathbf{k}_i$ taken in the direction α. The expression in parentheses is a component of the product $\mathbf{e}_{ij} \times \mathbf{k}_i$ and, therefore, only for a transverse wave is not equal to zero. Accordingly the integration of $\frac{1}{2}\chi_{ik}{}^*\chi_{ik}$ over the cubic space gives the value

$$\frac{1}{\kappa^2} \sum_{ij} q_{ij}{}^* q_{ij} k_i{}^2 (1 - \delta_{j1})$$

where $\delta_{j1} = 1$ for $j = 1$, and 0 for $j = 2, 3$. On the other hand, we obtain for $\partial\pi_i/\partial x_i$

$$\frac{\partial\pi_i}{\partial x_i} = -\frac{i}{\sqrt{l^3}} \sum_{ij} p_{ij} (\mathbf{e}_{ij}{}^{(1)} k_i{}^{(1)} + \cdots) e^{-i\mathbf{k}_i \cdot \mathbf{r}}$$

$$= -\frac{i}{\sqrt{l^3}} \sum_{ij} p_{ij} (\mathbf{e}_{ij} \cdot \mathbf{k}_i) e^{-i\mathbf{k}_i \cdot \mathbf{r}}$$

so that for the integral of $(\partial\pi_i{}^*/\partial x_i)(\partial\pi_k/\partial x_k)$ we obtain

$$\sum_{ij} p_{ij}{}^* p_{ij} k_i{}^2 \, \delta_{j1}.$$

This gives us for H, $\mathbf{G}$, and ϵ

$$H = \sum_{ij} p_{ij}{}^* p_{ij} c^2 \left(\kappa + \frac{k_i{}^2}{\kappa} \delta_{j1} \right)$$

$$+ \sum_{ij} q_{ik}{}^* q_{ik} \left[\kappa + \frac{k_i{}^2}{\kappa} (1 - \delta_{j1}) \right]$$

$$\mathbf{G} = \sum_{ij} i\mathbf{k}_i (q_{ij} p_{ij} - q_{ij}{}^* p_{ij}{}^*)$$

(289)

$$\epsilon = \sum_{ij} ia(q_{ij} p_{ij} - q_{ij}{}^* p_{ij}{}^*)$$

In order to quantize the system we substitute the matrices Q_{ij} and P_{ij} for q_{ij} and p_{ij}, requiring that Q_{ij} and P_{ij} satisfy the relations

$$[Q_{ij} P_{kj'}] = \frac{\hbar}{i} \delta_{ik} \delta_{jj'} E \qquad [Q_{ij} Q_{kj'}] = 0 \qquad [P_{ij} P_{kj'}] = 0 \quad (290)$$

Passing again from Q_{ij} and P_{ij} to the new matrices A_{ij} and B_{ij}, which now are defined by the relations

$$Q_{ij} = - \sqrt{\frac{\hbar}{2}}\, i\, \sqrt[4]{\frac{c^2 \left(\kappa + \dfrac{k_i{}^2}{\kappa}\, \delta_{j1} \right)}{\kappa + \dfrac{k_i{}^2}{\kappa}\, (1 - \delta_{j1})}}\, (A_{ij} - \tilde{B}_{ij})$$

(291)

$$P_{ij} = \sqrt{\frac{\hbar}{2}}\, \sqrt[4]{\frac{\kappa + \dfrac{k_i{}^2}{\kappa}\, (1 - \delta_{j1})}{c^2 \left(\kappa + \dfrac{k_i{}^2}{\kappa}\, \delta_{j1} \right)}}\, (\tilde{A}_{ij} + B_{ij})$$

we have

$$[Q_{ij}P_{kj'}] = - \frac{\hbar i}{2}\, [A_{ij} - \tilde{B}_{ij'}\tilde{A}_{kj'} + B_{kj'}]$$

Thus the conditions of (290) are satisfied if

$$[A_{ij}\tilde{A}_{kj'}] = \delta_{ik}\, \delta_{jj'}E \qquad [B_{ij}B_{kj'}] = \delta_{ik}\, \delta_{jj'}E \tag{292}$$

with all other bracketed terms being equal to zero. The expressions of (289) now can be written

$$H = \sum_{ij} \frac{\hbar}{2} \sqrt{c^2 \left(\kappa + \frac{k_i{}^2}{\kappa}\, \delta_{j1} \right) \left[\kappa + \frac{k_i{}^2}{\kappa}\, (1 - \delta_{j1}) \right]} \times$$

$$[(A_{ij} + \tilde{B}_{ij})(\tilde{A}_{ij} + B_{ij}) + (\tilde{A}_{ij} - B_{ij})(A_{ij} - \tilde{B}_{ij})]$$

$$= \sum_{ij} \hbar c\, \sqrt{\kappa^2 + k_i{}^2}\, (\tilde{A}_{ij}A_{ij} + \tilde{B}_{ij}B_{ij} + E)$$

(293)

$$\mathbf{G} = \sum_{ij} \mathbf{k}\hbar(\tilde{A}_{ij}A_{ij} - \tilde{B}_{ij}B_{ij})$$

$$\epsilon = a \sum_{ij} (\tilde{A}_{ij}A_{ij} - \tilde{B}_{ij}B_{ij})$$

As we did in Section 52, we refer to that coordinate system K of the Hilbert space in which all the products $\tilde{A}_{ij}A_{ij}$ and $\tilde{B}_{ij}B_{ij}$ are diagonal. Any axis of K can then be marked by two sequences of numbers, $n_{ij}{}^+$ and $n_{ij}{}^-$, and the elements of the products $\tilde{A}_{ij}A_{ij}$ and $\tilde{B}_{ij}B_{ij}$ are given by

$$(\tilde{A}_{ij}A_{ij})_{\mathrm{diag}} = n_{ij}{}^+ \qquad (\tilde{B}_{ij}B_{ij})_{\mathrm{diag}} = n_{ij}{}^-$$

with all the non-diagonal elements being equal to zero. In a state represented by a vector having the direction of an axis $n_{ij}{}^+n_{ij}{}^-$, H, $\mathbf{G}$, and ϵ have the values

$$H = \sum_{ij} c \sqrt{m_0^2 c^2 + k_i^2 \hbar^2} \, (n_{ij}{}^+ + n_{ij}{}^-)$$

$$\mathbf{G} = \sum_{ij} \mathbf{k}_i \hbar (n_{ij}{}^+ - n_{ij}{}^-)$$

$$\epsilon = a \sum_{ij} (n_{ij}{}^+ - n_{ij}{}^-) = e \sum_{ij} (n_{ij}{}^+ - n_{ij}{}^-) \qquad \text{for } a = e$$

This means that, if the vector representing the state of the field has the direction of an axis of K, the field behaves like a system of $\sum_{ij} n_{ij}{}^+$ particles with a charge $+e$ and $\sum_{ij} n_{ij}{}^-$ particles with a charge $-e$. All the $n_{ij}{}^+$ and $n_{ij}{}^-$ particles which belong to the same axis i have the same energy $c \sqrt{m_0^2 c^2 + k_i^2 \hbar^2}$, and the momenta are $+\mathbf{k}_i \hbar$ and $-\mathbf{k}_i \hbar$ respectively. Because of the index j, two kinds of particles occur which may be transverse or longitudinal.

If ψ is real, we must again, as in Section 52, take two matrices, A_{ij} and B_{ij}, for which

$$A_{-ij} = B_{ij} \qquad B_{-ij} = A_{ij}$$

Then the charge is zero, and the terms with B_{ij} in H and $\mathbf{G}$ are to be cancelled.

As a final precaution, let us emphasize again that the relativistic wave equations must be understood in a sense entirely different from that of non-relativistic theory. The non-relativistic ψ has only the significance of a probability function which is represented by the picture of a wave motion. In contradistinction to this, the relativistic ψ refers to a real and not a symbolic wave field that possesses energy, momentum, and charge. This interpretation implies that the relativistic field, as long as it is not quantized, is not associated with the idea of particles, an idea which in non-relativistic quantum mechanics constitutes an essential supposition. The non-quantized relativistic theory is competent only for those experiments in which particles act like waves. Only in the quantized theory do particles appear because the quantization creates properties of the field which can be expressed only in terms of whole numbers. In this way the theory succeeds in explaining that peculiar ambiguity which is to be observed in matter and light. The consistent interpretation of this ambiguity is based on the recognition that quantities that are measured relative to the wave and the particle picture respectively are not commutative, the consequence being that, when a quantity referring to the wave picture is measured, all quantities associated with the particle picture become unobservable and vice versa.

8

QUANTUM ELECTRODYNAMICS

54. Classical Theory.   The Field as a Superposition of Plane Waves.   Now we shall apply the formalism of relativistic quantum mechanics to the process of light.   In Maxwell's theory this process is described by a set of wave equations which are adequate for a complete understanding of all those experiments in which light displays the nature of a wave motion.   But in other experiments light displays the properties of a corpuscular radiation, for in these any apparatus capable of measuring the energy and momentum of a radiation always registers integer multiples of certain fundamental unities.   This ambiguous nature of light cannot be understood on the basis of a pure wave theory.   However, a consistent explanation can be given if, on interpreting the field quantities as matrices, we quantize the wave equations.   The field retains its wave character but simultaneously takes on such qualities that in its interaction with matter it behaves like a corpuscular radiation.   Thus it is to be hoped that by this quantization we may arrive at a theory that is consistent with experimental facts.

As a beginning we shall develop the classical theory of light.   According to Maxwell and Lorentz, the field corresponding to a given charge and current distribution is described by the equations

$$\text{curl } \mathbf{E} = -\frac{1}{c}\frac{d\mathbf{H}}{dt} \qquad\qquad \text{div } \mathbf{E} = 4\pi\rho$$

$$\text{curl } \mathbf{H} = \frac{4\pi}{c}\rho\mathbf{v} + \frac{1}{c}\frac{d\mathbf{E}}{dt} \qquad \text{div } \mathbf{H} = 0 \tag{294}$$

If the last equation above is solved by setting

$$\mathbf{H} = \text{curl } \mathbf{A} \qquad (\mathbf{A} = \text{vector potential}) \tag{295}$$

the first becomes

$$\text{curl }\left(\mathbf{E} + \frac{1}{c}\frac{d\mathbf{A}}{dt}\right) = 0 \qquad \therefore\ \mathbf{E} = -\frac{1}{c}\frac{d\mathbf{A}}{dt} - \text{grad } \phi \tag{296}$$

where ϕ is the scalar potential.   From the other equations we then have

$$\text{div} \frac{d\mathbf{A}/dt}{c} + \nabla^2\phi + 4\pi\rho = 0 \tag{297}$$

$$\frac{1}{c}\ddot{\mathbf{A}} - \nabla^2\mathbf{A} + \text{grad}\left(\text{div } \mathbf{A} + \frac{1}{c}\frac{d\phi}{dt}\right) = \frac{4\pi}{c}\rho\mathbf{v} \tag{298}$$

The potentials $\mathbf{A}$ and ϕ, associated with a given field $\mathbf{EH}$, are not uniquely determined by (295) and (296); for, if $\mu(xyzt)$ is an arbitrary function of coordinates and time, $\mathbf{E}$ and $\mathbf{H}$ are not changed when $\mathbf{A}$ and ϕ are replaced by $\mathbf{A}' = \mathbf{A} + \text{grad } \mu$ and $\phi' = \phi - \mu/c$ (gauge invariance). Thus by choosing μ in a suitable way, we may cause the scalar potential to vanish. Then $\mathbf{E}$ becomes

$$\mathbf{E} = -\frac{1}{c}\frac{d\mathbf{A}}{dt}$$

whereas (297) and (298) become

$$\frac{1}{c}\text{div }\dot{\mathbf{A}} + 4\pi\rho = 0 \tag{297'}$$

$$\frac{1}{c^2}\ddot{\mathbf{A}} - \nabla^2\mathbf{A} + \text{grad div }\mathbf{A} = \frac{4\pi}{c}\rho\mathbf{v} \tag{298'}$$

Now for the continuous field quantity $\mathbf{A}(xyzt)$ substitute a denumerable set of coordinates $q(t)$ by expanding the potential $\mathbf{A}$ of the radiation in terms of the functions $\mathbf{e}_{ij}e^{i\mathbf{k}_i\cdot\mathbf{r}}$. (The radiation is imagined to be in a cubic cavity of extension l). In this manner the field is resolved into plane waves. Any of the vectors $\mathbf{k}_i$ is specified by three whole numbers, n_1, n_2, n_3, which may be positive or negative and which define the components of $\mathbf{k}_i$ by $k_i^{(\alpha)} = (2\pi/l)n_\alpha$. If we write the product $\mathbf{k}_i\cdot\mathbf{r} = (2\pi/l)(n_1x + n_2y + n_3z)$ in the form $(2\pi/\lambda_i)(\alpha x + \beta y + \gamma z)$, where λ_i is the wavelength and α, β, γ the direction cosines of $\mathbf{k}_i$, we obtain

$$\frac{1}{\lambda_i^2} = \frac{n_1^2 + n_2^2 + n_3^2}{l^2} \tag{299}$$

Letting ν_i be the frequency associated with λ_i, and defined by $2\pi/\tau$, τ being the period, then $c/\nu_i = \lambda_i/2\pi$, and thus

$$\nu_i = \frac{2\pi c}{l}\sqrt{n_1^2 + n_2^2 + n_3^2} \tag{300}$$

If we normalize the functions $\mathbf{e}_{ij}e^{i\mathbf{k}_i\cdot\mathbf{r}}$ by means of the factor $\sqrt{4\pi c^2/l^3}$, the functions

$$u_{ij} = \sqrt{\frac{4\pi c^2}{l^3}}\, \mathbf{e}_{ij} e^{i\mathbf{k}_i \cdot \mathbf{r}}$$

satisfy the condition

$$\int u_{ij}{}^* u_{kj'} = 4\pi c^2\, \delta_{ik}\, \delta_{jj'} \tag{301}$$

and we obtain for $\mathbf{A}$ the expansion

$$\mathbf{A} = \sum_{ij} q_{ij} u_{ij} \tag{302}$$

The index i refers to the direction of propagation of the plane wave u_{ij}, two opposite directions being denoted by i and $-i$. In (302) all positive and negative integer numbers must be considered. On the other hand, the index j determines the direction of polarization, $j = 1$ signifying a longitudinal wave and $j = 2, 3$ a transverse wave. For $j = 1$, $\mathbf{e}_{ij}$ has the direction of $\mathbf{k}_i$, and therefore $\mathbf{e}_{ij} \times \mathbf{k}_i = 0$; for $j = 2, 3$, $\mathbf{e}_{ij} \cdot \mathbf{k}_i = 0$. Consequently, in the case of a function u_{ij}, when $j = 1$, curl $u_{i1} = 0$; and when $j = 2, 3$, div $u_{ij} = 0$. In what follows we shall designate the longitudinal wave u_{i1} by u_l, and the transverse wave u_{i2} or u_{i3} by u_t. Thus, for all waves u_l, curl $u_l = 0$; for all waves u_t, div $u_t = 0$. Hence (302) may be written

$$\mathbf{A} = \mathbf{A}_l + \mathbf{A}_t = \sum_l q_l u_l + \sum_t q_t u_t$$

Substituting this value of $\mathbf{A}$ in (298′), keeping in mind that because of (300) we have for any value of u

$$\nabla^2 u_{ij} = -\frac{\nu_i{}^2}{c^2}\, u_{ij}$$

and also that, since curl curl $= -\nabla^2 +$ grad div, for any u_l

$$\text{grad } div\ u_l = \nabla^2 u_l$$

we obtain

$$\frac{1}{c^2} \sum_t (\ddot{q}_t + \nu_t{}^2 q_t) u_t + \frac{1}{c^2} \sum_l \ddot{q}_l u_l = \frac{4\pi}{c}\, \rho\mathbf{v}$$

On multiplying this by one of the $u_{ij}{}^*$ and integrating over the space of the enclosure, we obtain, because of (301),

$$\ddot{q}_t + \nu_t{}^2 q_t = \frac{1}{c} \int u_t{}^* \rho\mathbf{v}\, dv \tag{303}$$

$$\ddot{q}_l = \frac{1}{c} \int u_l{}^* \rho\mathbf{v}\, dv \tag{304}$$

It turns out then that the transverse and longitudinal q_{ij} terms satisfy two different differential equations. Whereas (303) agrees in form with the equation for the forced vibrations of an oscillator, equation (304) corresponds to the motion of a free point mass on which a force is acting. Because of this difference the transverse part of the field can be quantized; this is impossible for the longitudinal part of the field.

To evaluate the right-hand sides of (303) and (304) we assume that the matter consists of particles with charge e. Then we have for the point particles

$$\int u^*\rho \mathbf{v}\, dv = \sum_k e\mathbf{v}_k u^*(P_k)$$

where $\mathbf{v}_k$ denotes the velocity of the kth particle and $u(P_k)$ is the value of u at the point P_k occupied by that same particle.

The next step is to derive (303) and (304) as canonical equations from a Hamiltonian H. We maintain that H is given by the expression

$$H = \sum_{t>0} (p_t^* p_t + \nu_t^2 q_t^* q_t) + \sum_{l>0} p_l^* p_l$$

$$+ \sum_k c\sqrt{m^2 c^2 + \left[\mathbf{p}_k - \frac{e}{c}\mathbf{A}(P_k)\right]^2} \qquad (305)$$

the summation to be extended over the positive values of t and l only, that is, only over the directions of the hemisphere. The same holds for $\mathbf{A}$, which, we imagine, is expanded in the form

$$\sum_{t>0} (q_t u_t + q_t^* u_t^*) + \sum_{l>0} (q_l u_l + q_l^* u_l^*)$$

such an expansion being possible because $q_{-i} = q_i^*$ when $\mathbf{A}$ is real. The third term in the expression for H represents the energy of the particles, the quantity $\mathbf{A}(P_k)$ in this term signifying the value of $\mathbf{A}$ at the P_k position of the kth particle. Equation (305) is a function of qpq^*p^*, and also it depends on the coordinates $x_k y_k z_k$ and the momenta $\mathbf{p}_k$ of the particles. In order to prove that H represents the Hamiltonian of the system, we consider the canonical equations which result from (305):

$$\frac{dq_t}{dt} = \frac{\partial H}{\partial p_t} \qquad \frac{dp_t}{dt} = -\frac{\partial H}{\partial q_t} \qquad (a)$$

$$\frac{dq_l}{dt} = \frac{\partial H}{\partial p_l} \qquad \frac{dp_l}{dt} = -\frac{\partial H}{\partial q_l} \qquad (b)$$

$$\frac{dx_k}{dt} = \frac{\partial H}{\partial p_x{}^k} \qquad \frac{dp_x{}^k}{dt} = -\frac{\partial H}{\partial x_k} \qquad (c)$$

Taking into account (243), (a) and (b) above give

$$\frac{dq_t}{dt} = p_t^* \qquad \frac{dp_t}{dt} = -\nu_t^2 q_t^* + \sum_k \frac{e\left(\mathbf{p}_k - \frac{e}{c}\mathbf{A}\right)u_t}{\sqrt{m^2c^2 + \left(\mathbf{p}_k - \frac{e}{c}\mathbf{A}\right)^2}}$$

$$= -\nu_t^2 q_t^* + \sum_k \frac{e}{c}\mathbf{v}_k u_t(P_k) \tag{306}$$

$$\frac{dq_l}{dt} = p_l^* \qquad \frac{dp_l}{dt} = \sum_k \frac{e}{c}\mathbf{v}_k u_l(P)_k$$

From these equations we get the same values for $\ddot{q}_t$ and $\ddot{q}_l$ as from (303) and (304). The (c) equations determine the motion of the particles, as demonstrated in Section 47.

Instead of equation (305), the energy of the system can be represented also by

$$H = \sum_t \frac{1}{2}(p_t^* p_t + \nu_t^2 q_t^* q_t) + \sum_l \frac{1}{2} p_l^* p_l$$

$$+ \sum_k c \sqrt{m^2c^2 + \left(\mathbf{p}_k - \frac{e}{c}\mathbf{A}\right)^2} \tag{305'}$$

in which the summation is taken over both the positive and negative values of t and l.

55. Transformation of the Hamiltonian. The first two terms of $(305')$ represent the field energy, $U = (1/8\pi)\int dv\,(\mathbf{E}^2 + \mathbf{H}^2)$, for we have

$$u = \frac{1}{8\pi}\int\left[\frac{1}{c^2}\frac{d\mathbf{A}^2}{dt} + (\operatorname{curl}\mathbf{A})^2\right]dv$$

$$= \frac{1}{8\pi}\int\left[\frac{1}{c^2}\left(\sum\frac{dq}{dt}u\right)^2 + \left(\sum q\operatorname{curl}u\right)^2\right]dv$$

Because of (301) and (306) the first term on the right gives

$$\frac{1}{2}\sum\frac{dq^*}{dt}\frac{dq}{dt} = \frac{1}{2}\sum_t p_t^* p_t + \frac{1}{2}\sum_l p_l^* p_l$$

On the other hand, the second term can be transformed into

$$\tfrac{1}{2} \sum_t v_t^2 q_t^* q_t$$

We can effect this transformation with the help of the relations

$$\int \operatorname{curl} u_i \operatorname{curl} u_k \, dv = \int [u_i \operatorname{curl} u_k]_n \, df + \int (u_i \cdot \operatorname{curl} \operatorname{curl} u_k) \, dv$$

and

$$\operatorname{curl} \operatorname{curl} u_t = -\nabla^2 u_t = \frac{v_t^2}{c^2} u_t$$

keeping in mind the fact that the surface integral vanishes because of the periodicity of u and the derivatives of u.

It is important that the longitudinal part of the field energy $\tfrac{1}{2} \sum_l p_l^* p_l$ turns out to be identical with the energy corresponding to the Coulomb interaction. This can be proved with the help of (297'), according to which $(1/c) \operatorname{div} d\mathbf{A}/dt = -4\pi\rho$. Owing to the fact that $\operatorname{div} \mathbf{u}_t = 0$, we have

$$\operatorname{div} \frac{d\mathbf{A}}{dt} = \sum_l \frac{dq_l}{dt} \operatorname{div} u_l = \sum_l p_l^* \operatorname{div} u_l$$

On the other hand, because $\mathbf{e}_l \cdot \mathbf{k}_i = k_i = 2\pi/\lambda_i$, we have for $\operatorname{div} \mathbf{u}_l$

$$\operatorname{div} u_l = i \frac{2\pi}{\lambda_i} \sqrt{\frac{4\pi c^2}{l^3}} \, e^{i\mathbf{k}_i \cdot \mathbf{r}} = i \frac{v_i}{c} f_i$$

According to Fourier's theorem, $f_i = \sqrt{4\pi c^2/l^3} \, e^{i\mathbf{k}_i \cdot \mathbf{r}}$ forms a complete orthogonal system since any *scalar* periodical function can be represented in terms of it. (For *vector* functions the orthogonal system is given by the u_{ij} terms.) The f_i terms satisfy the normalization condition

$$\int f_i^* f_k \, dv = \delta_{ik} 4\pi c^2 \tag{307}$$

Equation (297') now becomes

$$\operatorname{div} \frac{d\mathbf{A}}{dt} = \sum_l \frac{i v_l}{c} p_l^* f_l = -4\pi\rho c$$

On multiplying this equation by f_l^* and integrating, we get

$$i v_l p_l^* = -\int \rho f_l^* \, dv = -\sum_k e f_l^*(P_k)$$

where $f_l{}^*(P_k)$ signifies the value of $f_l{}^*$ associated with the position P_k of the kth particle. Accordingly we obtain

$$\frac{1}{2}\sum_l p_l{}^* p_l = \frac{e^2}{2}\sum_l \sum_{ik} \frac{f_l{}^*(P_k)f_l(P_i)}{\nu_l{}^2}$$

In this expression the summation is over all i and k values, and thus any ik combination occurs twice $(i \neq k)$. Hence two particles, i and k, contribute

$$H_{ik} = e^2 \sum \frac{f_l{}^*(P_k)f_l(P_i)}{\nu_l{}^2}$$

which depends on the coordinates of the point P_i and P_k. If we consider H_{ik} a function of P_k, the point P_i being considered fixed, we obtain for $\nabla^2 H_{ik}$, since $\nabla^2 f = -(\nu^2/c^2)f$,

$$\nabla^2 H_{ik} = -\frac{e^2}{c^2}\sum_l f_l{}^*(P_k)f_l(P_i) = -\frac{e^2}{c^2}4\pi^2 c^2\, \delta(P_i - P_k) \quad (308)$$

The function $\delta(P_i - P_k)$ vanishes for $P_i \neq P_k$, but for $P_i = P_k$ it becomes infinite in such a way that the integral of $\delta(P_i - P_k)$, taken over an arbitrary small domain surrounding P_i, has the value unity.

From (308) it follows that $H_{ik} = e^2/r$, where r is the distance of the points P_i and P_k, for e^2/r considered as a function of P_k agrees with H_{ik} in satisfying the equation $\nabla^2(e^2/r) = 0$ for the case where P_i is not equal to P_k, but, when P_i is equal to P_k,

$$\int \nabla^2 \frac{e^2}{r}\, dv = \int dv\, \mathrm{grad}\, \frac{e^2}{r}\, dv = -\int \frac{e^2}{r^2}\, df = -4\pi e^2$$

Thus we get

$$\frac{1}{2}\sum_l p_l{}^* p_l = \sum_{i>k} \frac{e^2}{r_{ik}} \quad\quad\quad (309)$$

That is, $\frac{1}{2}\sum_l p_l{}^* p_l$ is identical with the Coulomb energy of the point charges contained in the field. The term with $i = k$ represents the longitudinal, or electrostatic, self-energy of the particles. For point particles this self-energy becomes infinite.

If we substitute $\sum e^2/r_{ik}$ for the second term in equation (305) of the Hamiltonian, the canonical equations (306) lose their validity, for in the equation for $dp_x{}^{(k)}/dt$, for example, a new term arising from (309) must be taken into account. It can be shown, however, that the equations of (306) remain valid (except for the second one, which becomes meaningless) when, after $\frac{1}{2} \sum p_l{}^*p_l$ has been replaced by $\sum e^2/r_{ik}$ in (305), in the third term only the transverse part of $\mathbf{A}$ $\left(\mathbf{A}_t = \sum q_l u_t\right)$ is taken so that the q_l coordinates as well as the p_l are eliminated from H. We then obtain for H

$$H = \frac{1}{2} \sum_t (p_t{}^*p_t + v_t{}^2 q_t{}^*q_t) + \sum_{i<k} \frac{e^2}{r_{ik}}$$
$$+ \sum_k c \sqrt{m^2c^2 + \left(\mathbf{p}_k - \frac{e}{c}\mathbf{A}_t\right)^2} \quad (310)$$

The equations for dq_t/dt and dp_t/dt in (306) then remain unchanged, whereas those for dq_l/dt and dp_l/dt are eliminated. On the other hand, we obtain for dx_k/dt and $dp_x{}^k/dt$

$$\frac{dx_k}{dt} = \frac{\partial H}{\partial p_x{}^{(k)}} = \frac{c\left(p_x{}^{(k)} - \frac{e}{c}A_x{}^{(t)}\right)}{\sqrt{m^2c^2 + \left(\mathbf{p} - \frac{e}{c}\mathbf{A}_t\right)^2}} \quad (311)$$

$$\frac{dp_x{}^{(k)}}{dt} = -\frac{\partial H}{\partial x_k} = -\frac{\partial}{\partial x_k} \sum \frac{e^2}{r_{ik}} + \frac{e\left(\mathbf{p}_k - \frac{e}{c}\mathbf{A}_t, \frac{\partial \mathbf{A}_t}{\partial x_k}\right)}{\sqrt{m^2c^2 + \left(\mathbf{p}_k - \frac{e}{c}\mathbf{A}_t\right)^2}}$$
$$= -\frac{\partial}{\partial x_k} \sum \frac{e^2}{r_{ik}} + \frac{e}{c}\left(\mathbf{v}_k, \frac{\partial \mathbf{A}_t}{\partial x_k}\right) \quad (312)$$

If we subtract from (312) the equation

$$\frac{e}{c}\frac{dA_x{}^{(t)}}{dt} = \frac{e}{c}\left(\frac{\partial A_x{}^{(t)}}{\partial t} + v_x{}^{(k)}\frac{\partial A_x{}^{(t)}}{\partial x_k} + v_y{}^{(k)}\frac{\partial A_x{}^{(t)}}{\partial y_k} + v_z{}^{(k)}\frac{\partial A_x{}^{(t)}}{\partial z_k}\right)$$

then, because $\mathbf{H} = \text{curl } \mathbf{A}$, we obtain

$$\frac{d}{dt}\left(p_x{}^{(k)} - \frac{e}{c}A_x{}^{(t)}\right) = -\frac{\partial}{\partial x_k} \sum \frac{e^2}{r_{ik}} - \frac{e}{c}\frac{\partial A_x{}^{(t)}}{\partial t} + \frac{e}{c}[\mathbf{v} \times \mathbf{H}]_x$$

Because of (311), the left-hand side is

$$\frac{d}{dt} \frac{m(d\bar{x}_k/dt)}{\sqrt{1 - v_k{}^2/c^2}}$$

On the right-hand side, according to (296), $-(1/c)(\partial A_x{}^{(t)}/\partial t)$ means the field strength $\mathbf{E}$ due to the transverse field and the first term determines that part of $e\mathbf{E}$ which is caused by the Coulomb forces, that is, by the longitudinal field. Again we obtain the equation of motion

$$\frac{d}{dt} \frac{m\mathbf{v}}{\sqrt{1 - v^2/c^2}} = e\left(\mathbf{E} + \frac{1}{c}\mathbf{v} \times \mathbf{H}\right)$$

by which the correctness of (310) is proved.

The significance of the three terms which, according to (310), compose the energy H, is immediately clear. The first term gives the energy of the transverse light waves, which can be treated like a system of oscillators. The second term refers to the Coulomb interaction between the particles, and the third part represents the kinetic energy of the particles together with the energy that is due to the interaction of matter with the light waves.

56. Quantization of the Field. The classical theory we have developed above can account only for the wave phenomena of light. In order to describe also those processes in which light displays the nature of corpuscles, the field must be quantized. For this purpose we consider first the field by itself. The Hamiltonian of the field is

$$H = \frac{1}{2}\sum_t (p_t{}^*p_t + \nu_t{}^2 q_t{}^*q_t) + \sum_{i<k} \frac{e^2}{r_{ik}} \tag{313}$$

In order to quantize the field we must transcribe the q and p factors into matrices Q and P. Now, in (313), only the transverse factors q_t and p_t occur, the corresponding longitudinal factors being completely eliminated since it has turned out that their energy contribution can be described by the Coulomb interaction of the particles. *Thus only the transverse and not the longitudinal part of the field can be quantized.* This corresponds to the evidence that only transverse waves display corpuscular properties. Therefore we only have to deal with the first term of (313), which upon quantization becomes

$$H = \tfrac{1}{2}\sum_t (\tilde{P}_t P_t + \nu_t{}^2 \tilde{Q}_t Q_t) \tag{314}$$

The summation is to be extended over both positive and negative t. According to (276), Q_t and P_t must satisfy the relations

$$[Q_t P_{t'}] = \frac{\hbar}{i}\, \delta_{tt'}\, E \qquad [Q_t Q_{t'}] = 0 \qquad [P_t P_{t'}] = 0 \qquad (315)$$

Following the method of Sections 52 and 53, we solve the problem by setting

$$Q_t = i\sqrt{\frac{\hbar}{2\nu_t}}\,(\tilde{A}_t - B_t) \qquad P_t = \sqrt{\frac{\hbar\nu_t}{2}}\,(A_t + \tilde{B}_t) \qquad (316)$$

As the field $\mathbf{A}$ is real, we have $Q_{-t} = \tilde{Q}_t$, $P_{-t} = \tilde{P}_t$ and, therefore, according to (284)

$$A_{-t} = B_t \qquad B_{-t} = A_t \qquad (317)$$

To satisfy the conditions of (315), it is necessary that

$$[A_t \tilde{A}_{t'}] = \delta_{tt'} E \qquad [B_t \tilde{B}_{t'}] = \delta_{tt'} E$$

with all other brackets being equal to zero. By substituting (316) in (314), we get

$$H = \frac{1}{2}\sum_t \frac{\hbar\nu_t}{2}\Big((\tilde{A}_t + B_t)(A_t + \tilde{B}_t) + (A_t - \tilde{B}_t)(\tilde{A}_t - B_t)$$

$$= \frac{1}{2}\sum_t \hbar\nu_t(\tilde{A}_t A_t + \tilde{B}_t B_t + E) = \sum_t \hbar\nu_t\Big(\tilde{A}_t A_t + \frac{E}{2}\Big) \qquad (318)$$

because, since $B_{-t} = A_t$, $\tilde{B}_{-t} = \tilde{A}_t$, and $\nu_{-t} = \nu_t$, the following transformation holds:

$$\sum_t \nu_t \tilde{B}_t B_t = \sum_t \nu_{-t}\tilde{A}_{-t}A_{-t} = \sum_t \nu_t \tilde{A}_t A_t$$

(In the last two sums the difference is in the arrangement of terms only.) In this manner we have arrived at a formalism that corresponds exactly to that of Section 43. If we refer the A_t terms (in Section 43 X_i stands for A_t) to that coordinate system K of the Hilbert space in which the products $\tilde{A}_t A_t$ are diagonal, the energy H is also diagonal in K and the eigenvalues of H are given by

$$\sum_t \hbar\nu_t(n_t + \tfrac{1}{2})$$

The interpretation is this: Whenever we carry out a measurement of the field energy, we always find an integer multiple of $\hbar\nu_i$ for any plane wave; that is, when its energy is measured, light behaves like a system of corpuscles of energy $h\nu_i$. In addition, the theory provides an infinite "zero point energy" $\sum h\nu_t/2$, which should give any cavity radiation an infinite mass and must be taken as an indication of certain limits which restrict the applicability of the laws of quantum mechanics (cf. Chapter 10).

Simultaneously K is the principal system of the field momentum, $\mathbf{G} = 1/4\pi c \int \mathbf{E} \times \mathbf{H} \, dv$, for we have

$$\mathbf{G} = -\frac{1}{4\pi c^2} \int \frac{d\mathbf{A}}{dt} \times \operatorname{curl} \mathbf{A} \, dv$$

$$= -\frac{1}{4\pi c^2} \sum_{it} \int \left(\frac{dq_i}{dt} u_i \times q_t \operatorname{curl} u_t \right) dv \qquad (319)$$

From the relation

$$u = \mathbf{e} \sqrt{\frac{4\pi c^2}{l^3}} \, e^{i\mathbf{k}\cdot\mathbf{r}}$$

it follows that

$$\operatorname{curl} u = i\mathbf{k} \times \mathbf{e} \sqrt{\frac{4\pi c^2}{l^3}} \, e^{i\mathbf{k}\cdot\mathbf{r}}$$

Because of the orthogonality of u in (319), all products vanish except those of the form $u_t u_t^*$, and, as $u_t \times \operatorname{curl} u_t^* = -i\mathbf{k}_t(4\pi c^2/l^3)$, we obtain

$$\mathbf{G} = i \sum_t \mathbf{k}_t \frac{dq_t}{dt} q_t^* = i \sum_t \mathbf{k}_t p_t^* q_t^*$$

Upon quantization, this expression becomes

$$\mathbf{G} = i \sum_t \mathbf{k}_t \tilde{P}_t \tilde{Q}_t = \sum_t \hbar \mathbf{k}_t \tfrac{1}{2} (\tilde{A}_t + B_t)(A_t - \tilde{B}_t)$$

$$= \sum \hbar \mathbf{k}_t \tfrac{1}{2} (\tilde{A}_t A_t + B_t A_t - \tilde{A}_t \tilde{B}_t - B_t \tilde{B}_t)$$

The two terms $B_t A_t$ and $\tilde{A}_t \tilde{B}_t$ in the above give zero, because, if $\sum_t$ means summation over all t and $\sum_{t>0}$ only over the positive t, then, since $\mathbf{k}_{-t} = -\mathbf{k}_t$, $A_{-t} = B_t$, and $B_{-t} = A_t$, we have

$$\sum_t \mathbf{k}_t B_t A_t = \sum_{t>0} \mathbf{k}_t (B_t A_t - B_{-t} A_{-t}) = \sum_{t>0} \mathbf{k}_t (B_t A_t - A_t B_t) = 0$$

Furthermore

$$\sum_t \mathbf{k}_t B_t \tilde{B}_t = -\sum_t \mathbf{k}_{-t} B_t \tilde{B}_t = -\sum_t \mathbf{k}_{-t} A_{-t} \tilde{A}_{-t} = -\sum_t \mathbf{k}_t A_t \tilde{A}_t$$

so that we obtain finally

$$\mathbf{G} = \sum_t \hbar \mathbf{k}_t \left(\tilde{A}_t A_t + \frac{E}{2} \right) \tag{320}$$

Thus energy and momentum permit a simultaneous exact measurement. The momentum of a wave propagated in the $\mathbf{k}$ direction, the frequency of which is ν, is always found to be $\hbar \mathbf{k} = \hbar \nu / c$ times the direction of $\mathbf{k}$.

Thus, in certain experiments, the transverse part of the electromagnetic field behaves like a system of particles that satisfy the Bose statistics. For the correctness of this corpuscular interpretation of light, it is essential that the quantities $\hbar \nu$ and $(\hbar \nu / c)\mathbf{e}$ (taken as energy and momentum respectively of a light quantum) transform like E and $\mathbf{p}$. Indeed, according to the theory of relativity, $E\mathbf{p}$ as well as $\hbar \nu$ and $(\hbar \nu / c)\mathbf{e}$, form a four-vector, so that the relations $E = \hbar \nu$ and $\mathbf{p} = (\hbar \nu / c)\mathbf{e}$ are relativistically invariant.

Nevertheless we must not overlook the truth that the concept of light particles explains the facts only within certain limits. All that we may infer from the preceding is that light, as far as energy and momentum are concerned, cannot be distinguished from a system of particles with energies $\hbar \nu$ and momenta $(\hbar \nu / c)\mathbf{e}$. In other respects there is no equivalence. For example, it proves to be impossible to coordinate a certain position to the light quantum, and generally we may state that the interpretation of the light quanta as real particles would lead to consequences that are positively wrong. For instance, we are not permitted to imagine that an atom, in order to absorb a light quantum, must literally be hit by it. The only claim of the theory is that always, in the interaction between light and matter, there is exchanged an energy quantity $\hbar \nu$, which must be understood in the sense that we are not able to analyze the process by which the exchange is effected, because any sharp measurement of the energy carried out on the radiation field excludes a simultaneous observation of the field quantities $\mathbf{E}$ and $\mathbf{H}$. This is evident at once because of the non-commutability of the matrix for $\mathbf{E}$ and the energy matrix (314). The matrix corresponding to

$$\mathbf{E} = -\frac{d\mathbf{A}/dt}{c} = -\frac{1}{c} \sum_i \frac{dq}{dt_i} u_i$$

is $-(1/c) \sum_i \bar{P}_i u_i$, and this is not diagonal in the principal system K

of the energy. Thus, when the vector representing the state has the direction of an axis of K, so that the energy has a distinct value, a measurement of $\mathbf{E}$ or $\mathbf{H}$ may furnish any value. This forms an essential condition for a consistent union of the particle and the wave picture. The coexistence of these two pictures is possible because any experiment in which light has the character of a wave motion makes the simultaneous observation of particles impossible and vice versa.

The field quantities $\mathbf{E}$ and $\mathbf{H}$, belonging to the same point of space, are also not simultaneously measurable because $\mathbf{E}$ and $\mathbf{H}$ are given in the matrix representation by $-(1/c) \sum_i \bar{P}_i u_i$ and $\sum_i Q_t$ curl u_t respectively, and, because of (315), these matrices are not commutative. The commutation relation which applies to $\mathbf{E}$ and $\mathbf{H}$ could be derived easily from (315), but we shall not go into that problem here.

Finally, note should be made of the point that the Hamiltonian $H = \sum_t \hbar \nu_t A_t \tilde{A}_t$ of the pure field contains the quantities A_t and $\tilde{A}_t$

only in the product. According to Section 43, this means that the number of light quanta does not change in a field that is not interacting with charged matter. In fact, light quanta can only be created or annihilated by processes in which the quanta are emitted or absorbed by charged particles.

57. Quantization of a System Consisting of Field and Particles. Now we must extend the quantization to the electrons contained in the cubic space considered. In the classical theory their Hamiltonian is given by

$$\sum_k c \sqrt{m^2 c^2 + \left(\mathbf{p}_k - \frac{e}{c} \mathbf{A}_t\right)^2} \qquad (321)$$

plus the Coulomb energy $\sum_{i>k} e^2/r_{ik}$, which is due to the longitudinal part of the field. In quantum mechanics all n particles form an antisymmetric system the state of which is described by a vector $\mathbf{X}$. This vector is referred to a coordinate system K the axes of which belong to a certain spatial configuration $x_1 y_1 z_1 x_2 y_2 z_2 \cdots , x_n y_n z_n$ or $P_1 P_2 \cdots P_n$ of the particles. It must be understood, however, that, because of the indistinguishability of the particles, there is no individual coordination of the P_i terms to the particles, but rather that a configuration $P_1 P_2 \cdots P_n$ only means that one of the particles is at P_1, another at P_2, and so on.   In addition to the P_i positions of the particles, the spin must be taken into account.   To fulfill this requirement we correlate to any axis of K certain values ρ_1, ρ_2, $\cdots$, ρ_n of the spin coordinates.   The meaning is that the quantity ρ (which can assume four values only) has the value ρ_1 for the particle at P_1, the value ρ_2 for that at P_2, and so on.   The total state of all the particles then can be represented by the function

$$\mathbf{X} = \psi(P_1 P_2 \cdots P_n \rho_1 \rho_2 \cdots \rho_n) \tag{322}$$

which, by the square of its magnitude, determines the probability that a particle with the spin state ρ_1 is found at P_1, that of state ρ_2 at P_2, and so on.   The function is antisymmetric in its indices, changing sign when two indices are interchanged.

According to Dirac (Section 45), in relativistic quantum mechanics the energy operator of a single particle for the case $\phi = 0$, $\mathbf{A} = \mathbf{A}_t$, is given by

$$H = c \sum_{i=1}^{3} \alpha_i \left[p_i - \frac{e}{c} A_i{}^{(t)}(P) \right] + mc^2 \beta$$

wherein α_i and β are the matrices defined by (232) and p_i is the operator $-(\hbar/i)(\partial/\partial x_i)$.   The matrices α_i and β operate on the spin coordinate ρ, whereas p_i is to act on the coordinates of the point P. On associating α_i to the vector $\vec{\alpha}$ and p_i to $\mathbf{p} = -(\hbar/i)$ grad, we can write

$$H = c \left[\vec{\alpha}, \mathbf{p} - \frac{e}{c} \mathbf{A}_t(P) \right] + mc^2 \beta \tag{323}$$

and so, for the energy operator which is to be applied to (322), that is, to the system of all the particles, considering also the Coulomb action we obtain

$$H = \sum_k \left\{ c \left[\vec{\alpha}^{(k)}, \mathbf{p}_k - \frac{e}{c} \mathbf{A}_t(P_k) \right] + mc^2 \beta^{(k)} \right\} + \sum_{i<k} \frac{e^2}{r_i{}^k} \tag{323'}$$

Finally we combine radiation and particles in a total system and refer its state $\mathbf{X}$ to a coordinate system K the axes of which, in addition to certain $P_1 P_2 \cdots P_n$ and $\rho_1 \rho_2 \cdots \rho_n$, are associated with certain numbers $n_1 n_2 \cdots$ of light quanta which make up the radiation. Then, instead of (322), we have

$$\mathbf{X} = \psi(P_1 P_2 \cdots P_n \rho_1 \rho_2 \cdots \rho_n n_1 n_2 \cdots) \tag{324}$$

and the energy operator becomes

$$H = \sum_t \hbar \nu_t \tilde{A}_t A_t$$

$$+ \sum_k \left\{ c \left[\alpha^{(k)}, \mathbf{p}_k - \frac{e}{c} \mathbf{A}_t(P_k) \right] + mc^2 \beta^{(k)} \right\} + \sum_{i>k} \frac{e^2}{r_{ik}} \quad (325)$$

We are particularly interested in that part of H corresponding to the interaction between radiation and the particles and expressed by

$$H' = - \sum_k e \, [\vec{\alpha}^{(k)}, \mathbf{A}_t(P_k)] = - \sum_{kt} e (\vec{\alpha}^{(k)}, Q_t u_t)$$

$$= -i \sum_{kt} e \sqrt{\frac{\hbar}{2\nu_t}} \, [\vec{\alpha}^{(k)} (\tilde{A}_t - B_t) u_t] \quad (326)$$

H' is of the first order in A_t and B_t, and this means that the interaction comes about by processes in which a photon is created or annihilated. Such processes are also responsible for the retarded interaction between the particles themselves. First, however, we shall show that the equation

$$\frac{\hbar}{i} \frac{d\mathbf{X}}{dt} = H\mathbf{X} \quad (327)$$

according to which the system changes with time, is identical with Maxwell's equations translated into the language of quantum mechanics. As we have seen in Section 33, equation (327) is equivalent to the statement that for any observable of the system the following equation holds:

$$\frac{\hbar}{i} \frac{dA}{dt} = AH - HA \quad (328)$$

We apply (328) to the field quantity $\mathbf{E} = -(1/c) \sum (dq_t/dt) u_t$, belonging to an arbitrarily given point P of the field. (The longitudinal part of $\mathbf{E}$ can be neglected since it cannot be quantized and, as a result, is commutative with H.)   If the matrix $-(1/c) \sum_t \tilde{P}_t u_t(P)$

which belongs to $\mathbf{E}(P)$ is denoted by $E(P)$, then, because

$$H = \tfrac{1}{2} \sum_t (\nu_t{}^2 \tilde{Q}_t Q_t + \tilde{P}_t P_t) - \sum_{kt} e[\vec{\alpha}^{(k)}, Q_t u_t(P_k)]$$

plus parts that commute with E, for $EH - HE$ we obtain

$$EH - HE = -\sum_{tt'} \frac{\nu_t^2}{2c} [\tilde{P}_t, \tilde{Q}_{t'}Q_{t'}]u_t + \sum_{ktt'} \frac{e}{c} \{\vec{\alpha}^{(k)}, [\tilde{P}_tQ_{t'}]u_t(P)u_{t'}(P_k)\}$$

For $t' = t$, $[\tilde{P}_t, \tilde{Q}_{t'}Q_{t'}]$ gives

$$\tilde{P}_t\tilde{Q}_tQ_t - \tilde{Q}_tQ_t\tilde{P}_t = (\tilde{P}_t\tilde{Q}_t - \tilde{Q}_t\tilde{P}_t)Q_t = -\frac{\hbar}{i}Q_t$$

For $t' = -t$, we get

$$\tilde{P}_tQ_t\tilde{Q}_t - Q_t\tilde{Q}_t\tilde{P}_t = Q_t(\tilde{P}_t\tilde{Q}_t - \tilde{Q}_t\tilde{P}_t) = -\frac{\hbar}{i}Q_t$$

Furthermore $[\tilde{P}_tQ_{t'}]$ differs from zero only for $t' = -t$, so that

$$\frac{dE}{dt} = \frac{1}{c}\sum_t \nu_t^2 Q_t u_t - \frac{e}{c}\sum [\vec{\alpha}^{(k)}, \sum_t u_t(P)u_t^*(P_k)] \qquad (329)$$

The first term on the right is identical with c curl H, where H denotes the matrix belonging to H; for, since curl curl $u_t = -\nabla^2 u_t = (\nu_t^2/c^2)u_t$,

$$\text{curl } H = \text{curl curl } A = \sum_t \frac{\nu_t^2}{c^2} Q_t u_t$$

In the second term on the right, we use the relation

$$\sum_t u_t(P)u_t^*(P_k) = 4\pi c^2 \, \delta(P - P_k)$$

so that (329) can be transformed into

$$\frac{dE}{dt} = c \text{ curl } H - 4\pi c \sum_k e\vec{\alpha}^{(k)} \, \delta(P - P_k) \qquad (330)$$

which corresponds to Maxwell's equation for point charges,

$$\text{curl } H = \frac{4\pi\rho\mathbf{v}}{c} + \frac{1}{c} \cdot \frac{d\mathbf{E}}{dt}$$

as the Dirac matrix vector $\vec{\alpha}$ replaces $\mathbf{v}/c$. Similarly we get

$$H = -c \text{ curl } E \qquad (331)$$

whereas, from $H = \sum_t Q_t$ curl u_t, it follows that

$$\text{div } H = 0 \qquad (332)$$

The description of the system is completed by the equation

$$\text{div } \boldsymbol{E} = 4\pi \sum_k e \, \delta(P - P_k) \qquad (333)$$

which takes the place of div $\boldsymbol{E} = 4\pi\rho$ and holds for the longitudinal part of the field $\boldsymbol{E}_l$. Since $\boldsymbol{E}_l$ is not a matrix but a quantity expressible by ordinary numbers, equation (333) is not adaptable to our plan but must be taken from somewhere else. $\boldsymbol{E}_l$ is a solenoidal field originating from the point charges. It produces the term $\sum_{i<k} (e^2/r_{ik})$ in H, and therefore it must fulfill equation (333).

The quantum-mechanical equations, (330) to (333), of electro-dynamics are in complete formal agreement with those of the classical theory, the only difference being that now the field quantities are inter-preted as matrices which satisfy certain commutation relations rather than as quantities which can be described by ordinary numbers. And so we arrive at equations which for any experiment supply infor-mation as to whether light will display undulating or corpuscular character. Often it has been maintained that quantum mechanics was unable actually to explain the ambiguous nature of light, having been able merely to bridge the chasm between the two pictures by a purely mathematical formalism. This is a misconception which under-estimates the performance of quantum mechanics. Any explanation involves the reduction of a phenomenon to certain laws. Quantum mechanics represents these laws in the equations which have been developed and therefore may claim to explain the facts as well as, let us say, ordinary mechanics explains the behavior of macro bodies. No theory can offer more than the description of physical facts with the aid of a mathematical scheme.

58. Interaction between Radiation and Matter. All inter-action processes between radiation and charged particles are accounted for by the part

$$H' = - \sum_k e[\vec{\alpha}^{(k)}, \, \mathbf{A}_t(P_k)]$$

of the Hamiltonian. The problem defined by (325), together with the commutation relations, cannot be solved exactly if this part of the Hamiltonian is to be taken into account. Therefore we must content ourselves with an approximation by considering H' a small perturba-tion and applying the methods of perturbation theory as developed in Chapter 4. Without H' the two parts of which the system is composed would be independent. Then the radiation would consist of light quanta $h\nu_t$, the numbers $n_1 n_2 \cdots$ of which remain constant. On the other hand, the stationary states of the particle system would be given by the solutions of the wave equation

$$\left\{ c \sum_k [(\vec{\alpha}^{(k)} \mathbf{p}_k) + mc^2 \beta^{(k)}] + \sum_{i<k} \frac{e^2}{r_{ik}} \right\} \psi(P_1 \cdots P_n \rho_1 \cdots \rho_n)$$

$$= E\psi(P_1 \cdots P_n \rho_1 \cdots \rho_n) \quad (334)$$

On the left-hand side, the expression in the braces is the energy operator, operating on the state represented by a function of the positions $P_1 P_2 \cdots P_n$ and the spin coordinates $\rho_1 \rho_2 \cdots \rho_n$. The square of the magnitude of this function determines the probability that, by measurement, a particle in the state ρ_1 will be found at P_1, another in state ρ_2 at P_2, and so on. On the right-hand side, E denotes an eigenvalue of the energy. In what follows we shall, for the sake of brevity, denote the solutions of (334) by ψ_a, ψ_b, $\cdots$ and the corresponding energies by E_a, E_b, $\cdots$. Then a certain state of the total system can be characterized by a number a indicating the state of the particle system, and the numbers $n_1 n_2 \cdots$ of the light quanta constituting the radiation. Owing to the interaction, the state does not persist, but after a given time t there is a certain probability of finding the system in another state b, $n_1' n_2' \cdots$, which has occurred in such a way that the particles have assumed another state, and, simultaneously, by emission and absorption processes, the numbers $n_1 n_2 \cdots$ of the light quanta have been changed to $n_1' n_2' \cdots$. According to (187), the probability of a transition from a, $n_1 n_2 \cdots$ to b, $n_1' n_2' \cdots$ is determined by the matrix element $H'_{a n_1 n_2 \dots, b n_1' n_2' \dots}$. This element refers to that coordinate system K of the Hilbert space the axes of which are correlated to the states $a, n_1 n_2 \cdots$. Because of (326), we have

$$H'_{a n_1 n_2 \cdots b n_1 n_2 \cdots}$$

$$= -i \sum_k \sum_t e \sqrt{\frac{\hbar}{2\nu_t}} (\vec{A}_t - B_t)_{n_1 n_2 \cdots n_1' n_2' \cdots} [\vec{\alpha}^{(k)} u_t(P_k)]_{ab} \quad (335)$$

On the right-hand side the matrices A_t and B_t have indices relative to the light quanta only, for A_t and B_t have nothing to do with the particles. On the other hand, $\vec{\alpha}^{(k)} u_t(P_k)$ operates only on the state of the particles by changing a function ψ of P_i and ρ_i into another function ψ' of the same variables. Referred to the system K, the operator becomes a matrix the elements of which are to be designated by the numbers of the particle states. To determine an element $(\overrightarrow{\alpha}^{(k)}u_t)_{ab}$, we assume an arbitrary state $\psi(P_1 \cdots P_n\rho_1 \cdots \rho_n)$ to be expanded in terms of ψ_a (which form an orthogonal system), that is,

$$\psi = \sum x_a\psi_a \tag{336}$$

The action of the operator $(\overrightarrow{\alpha}^{(k)}u_t)$ then transforms ψ into another vector ψ':

$$\psi' = [\overrightarrow{\alpha}^{(k)}u_t(P_k)]\psi = \sum_a x_a{}'\psi_a \tag{337}$$

the relation between x_a and $x_a{}'$ being given by

$$x_a{}' = \sum_b (\overrightarrow{\alpha}^{(k)}u_t)_{ab}x_b \tag{338}$$

We now normalize the ψ_a terms by means of $\int \psi_a{}^*\psi_b = \delta_{ab}$. The integral is to be understood in the sense that we must integrate over the coordinate space of *all* the particles and consider $\psi_a{}^*\psi_b$ an abbreviation for the sum of all the products, $\psi_a{}^*(\rho_1 \cdots \rho_n)\psi_b(\rho_1 \cdots \rho_n)$ with $\rho_i = 1, 2, 3, 4$. From (337) it then follows that

$$x_a{}' = \int \psi_a{}^*[\overrightarrow{\alpha}^{(k)}u_t(P_k)]\psi$$

or, if we substitute (336) for ψ,

$$x_a{}' = \sum_b x_b \int \psi_a{}^*[\overrightarrow{\alpha}^{(k)}u_t(P_k)]\psi_b$$

On comparison with (338), we find that

$$[\overrightarrow{\alpha}^{(k)}u_t(P_k)]_{ab} = \int \psi_a{}^*[\overrightarrow{\alpha}^{(k)}u_t(P_k)]\psi_b \tag{339}$$

$\overrightarrow{\alpha}^{(k)}u_t$ is to be understood as the scalar product of the vector $\overrightarrow{\alpha}^{(k)}$ and the vector u_t. The components of u_t are ordinary numbers, but those of $\overrightarrow{\alpha}^{(k)}$ are matrices. The product $(\overrightarrow{\alpha}^{(k)}u_t)$ is, therefore, caused to act on ψ_b by transforming the four quantities $\psi_b(\rho)$, $(\rho = 1, 2, 3, 4)$, with the help of $(\overrightarrow{\alpha}^{(k)}u_t)$ into four other quantities $\psi_b{}'(\rho)$.

The same considerations apply to the matrices $\tilde{A}_t$ and B_t which occur in (335) as applied to X in Section 43. Thus only those elements of

$\tilde{A}_t$ and B_t are different from zero for which $n_t' = n_t \pm 1$, whereas all the other n_i' terms equal the n_i terms.   We have

$$(A_t)_{n_t, n_t+1} = (B_t)_{n_t, n_t+1} = \sqrt{n_t + 1}$$
$$(\tilde{A}_t)_{n_t, n_t-1} = (\tilde{B}_t)_{n_t, n_t-1} = \sqrt{n_t}$$

(340)

In these equations $(A_t)_{n_t, n_t+1}$ means an element

$$(A_t)_{n_1 n_2 \cdots n_t \cdots, n_1 n_2 \cdots n_t+1 \cdots}$$

with arbitrary whole numbers $n_1 n_2 \cdot \cdot \cdot$, the other elements to be taken in a similar sense.   Then it follows from (335) that the transition probability is different from zero only for the passages a, $n_1 n_2 \cdot \cdot \cdot$ to b, $n_1' n_2' \cdot \cdot \cdot$ in which one of the numbers n_i increases or decreases by unity, that is, $n_i' = n_i \pm 1$, all other n_i' equaling the n_i, since for any other transition the elements of A and B vanish.   A transition $n_t = n_t + 1$ corresponds to the emission of a light quantum and is due to B_t, the elements of which, according to (340), differ from zero only for the case $n_t \to n_t + 1$.   On the other hand, $\tilde{A}_t$ is responsible for absorption processes $n_t \to n_t - 1$.   Therefore the probability of emission or absorption is determined by the elements

$$H'_{an_t, bn_t+1} = ie \sqrt{\frac{\hbar}{2\nu_t}} \sqrt{n_t + 1} \sum_k \int \psi_a{}^* [\vec{\alpha}^{(k)} u_t(P_k)] \psi_b$$

(341)

$$H'_{an_t, bn_t-1} = -ie \sqrt{\frac{\hbar}{2\nu_t}} \sqrt{n_t} \sum_k \int \psi_a{}^* [\vec{\alpha}^{(k)} u_t(P_k)] \psi_b$$

The elements are of the first order in the charge e and correspond to transitions in which only one of the quantum numbers $n_1 n_2 \cdot \cdot \cdot$ is changed.   They are, therefore, the fundamental quantities in the theory of all those processes in which a single photon is created or annihilated, a condition which is fulfilled, for example, if an atom emits or absorbs a photon.   For the most part, however, in the processes that are due to the interaction between radiation and matter, two or more light quanta are involved.   For instance, a scattering process changes the radiation in such a way that a light quantum vanishes to make room for another one that is created.   For the treatment of such processes the perturbation theory of the first order does not suffice, as all the matrix elements of H' which correspond to the transitions vanish.   Then we must resort to the second or higher approximations by effecting the transition, according to Section 37, through one or more *intermediate states*. The probability for a transition, for example, of the kind $an_i n_k \rightarrow bn_i + 1,\ n_k - 1$ is then [cf. (186)], determined by the quantity

$$\sum_c \frac{H'_{an_i n_k, c n_i + 1, n_k}\, H'_{c n_i + 1, n_k, b n_i + 1, n_k - 1}}{E_{an_i n_k} - E_{c, n_i + 1, n_k}}$$

that is, by a matrix element of the second order in e. Thus we may classify the processes resulting from the interaction between radiation and matter, according to the number of light quanta involved, into processes of the first and second order and so on, and characterize them by the corresponding power of e.

According to Section 37 the transition probability has a finite value only for transitions in which the energy of the system is conserved; this holds for processes of any order. It should be noticed, however, that the energy of the virtual intermediate states may have any value. The momentum is conserved if the particle on which the radiation is acting is free. For then the function ψ in (341) is given by $\psi = a(\rho)e^{i\mathbf{p}\cdot\mathbf{r}/\hbar}$. With $u = \mathbf{e}_i\sqrt{4\pi c^2/l^3}\, e^{i\mathbf{k}_i\cdot\mathbf{r}}$ for a single particle, if we designate the product $(\vec{\alpha}\mathbf{e}_i)$ by α_e, we obtain

$$H'_{an_i, bn_i + 1} = ie\sqrt{\frac{\hbar}{2\nu_t}}\sqrt{\frac{4\pi c^2}{l^3}}\sqrt{n_i + 1}\,(a_a,\ \alpha_e a_b)\int e^{i(-\mathbf{p}_a + \mathbf{k}_i\hbar + \mathbf{p}_b)/\hbar}$$

and a corresponding expression for $H'_{an_i, bn_i - 1}$. The integral has a value different from zero only for $\mathbf{p}_a - \mathbf{p}_b = \hbar\mathbf{k}_i$, so that the only transitions possible are those in which the momentum of the absorbed or emitted photon is equal to the change in the momentum of the particle. It must be emphasized, however, that the emission and absorption of a light quantum by a free particle is possible only for the transition into a virtual intermediate state. The transition into the final state would require the conservation not only of the momentum but also of the final energy, and this condition cannot be fulfilled in a consistent way. In the case of an emission, this is seen at once when we refer the particle to that coordinate system in which it is at rest. The emission of a quantum would then demand that the energy of the particle diminish by $\hbar\nu$, which, without a loss of mass, is not possible. On the other hand, an absorption process would require that the energy increase by $mc^2(1/\sqrt{1 - \beta^2}) = \hbar\nu$ and that the momentum increase by $mv/\sqrt{1 - \beta^2} = \hbar\nu/c$, and these two conditions are incompatible with each other. But an electron can emit or absorb a photon by passing into an intermediate state, because then the energy need not be conserved. Of course, an electron that is bound to an atom can emit or absorb a light quantum just as well, since it can transfer part of its momentum to the atom.

59. Emission and Absorption of a Light Quantum by an Atom. We take as an example of a process of the first order, the emission or absorption of a light quantum by an atom, assuming, for the sake of simplicity, an atom with only one electron. In the calculation, without a noticeable error, we shall be satisfied with a non-relativistic approximation by substituting $\mathbf{v}/c$ for $\overrightarrow{\alpha}$ in the expression for the interaction H', so that

$$H' = -\frac{e}{c}(\mathbf{v}\mathbf{A}_t) = -\frac{ie}{c}\sum_t \sqrt{\frac{\hbar}{2\nu_t}}(\tilde{A}_t - B_t)(vu_t)$$

where $\mathbf{v}$ is the velocity of the electron and the u terms are the vector functions $\mathbf{e}_t \sqrt{4\pi c^2/l^3}\, e^{i\mathbf{k}\cdot\mathbf{r}}$. Then, for the matrix element H'_{an_t,bn_t+1}, we obtain

$$H'_{an_t,bn_t+1} = \frac{ie}{c}\sqrt{\frac{\hbar}{2\nu_t}}\sqrt{n_t + 1}\,(vu_t)_{ab} \tag{342}$$

and thus

$$\left|H'_{an_t,bn_t+1}\right|^2 = \frac{e^2}{c^2}\frac{\hbar}{2\nu_t}(n_t + 1)\left|(vu_t)_{ab}\right|^2 \tag{342'}$$

where n_t is the number of light quanta contained in the space. In order to evaluate we must, according to (339), form the expression $\int \psi_a{}^*(vu_t)\psi_b$, in which ψ_a and ψ_b denote the wave function of the atom in the states a and b. (vu_t) is the operator $(\mathbf{v}\cdot\mathbf{e}_t)\sqrt{4\pi c^2/l^3}\, e^{i\mathbf{k}\cdot\mathbf{r}}$. The wavelength $2\pi/|\mathbf{k}|$ of the light which is emitted or absorbed by the atom is always greater than the extension of the atom, so that $e^{i\mathbf{k}\cdot\mathbf{r}}$ may be considered constant within the domain in which ψ_a and ψ_b are noticeably different from zero: in $|H'|^2$, $e^{i\mathbf{k}\cdot\mathbf{r}}$ and $e^{-i\mathbf{k}\cdot\mathbf{r}}$ therefore give 1. Thus, if θ denotes the angle between $\mathbf{v}$ and the direction $\mathbf{e}_t$ of propagation, we have

$$\left|(vu_t)_{ab}\right|^2 = \left|v_{ab}\right|^2 \cos^2\theta\,\frac{4\pi c^2}{l^3}$$

In the transition $a \to b$, the energy of the atom decreases by $E_a - E_b$, and a light quantum $h\nu_t$ is created simultaneously. The conservation of energy demands therefore that $E_a - E_b = h\nu_t$. Now if the matrix

$X = \|x_{ik}\|$ of an observable is referred to the principal system of the energy, then, according to (164),

$$\frac{dx_{ab}}{dt} = \frac{i}{\hbar}(E_b - E_a)x_{ab}$$

Then, when we apply this relation to the xyz coordinates of the electron, since $dx/dt = v_x$ we get

$$(v_x)_{ab} = \frac{i}{\hbar}(E_b - E_a)x_{ab} = i\nu_t x_{ab}$$

and hence

$$|\mathbf{v}_{ab}|^2 = \nu_t^2\{|x_{ab}|^2 + |y_{ab}|^2 + |z_{ab}|^2\}$$

so that $|H'|^2$ is given by

$$|H'_{an_t,bn_t+1}|^2 = \frac{e^2}{c^2}\frac{\hbar}{2\nu_t}(n_t + 1)\nu_t^2\frac{4\pi c^2}{l^3}\cos^2\theta\{|x_{ab}|^2 + |y_{ab}|^2 + |z_{ab}|^2\}$$

Now the characteristic frequencies ν_t of a cavity radiation correspond to a very dense line spectrum, and thus the considerations of Section 37 apply. We have seen that, in this case, it is not important to evaluate the probability with which the creation of a light quantum of definite frequency ν_t is to be expected, but that it would be better to consider all quanta with an energy between E and $E + dE$ and a direction of propagation that lies within an angle $d\Omega$. According to (188), a light quantum that satisfies these conditions is created in unit time with the probability

$$dW = \overline{|H'|}^2\frac{2\pi}{\hbar}\rho\,d\Omega$$

in which $\rho\,d\Omega\,dE$ denotes the number of the radiation oscillators with a frequency between $E/\hbar$ and $(E + dE)/\hbar$ and a direction within $d\Omega$. To determine this number, we use the relation (300), according to which

$$\nu = \frac{2\pi c}{l}\sqrt{n_1^2 + n_2^2 + n_3^2}$$

If we imagine that in a three-dimensional space all the points P are marked, the coordinates of which are integer numbers $n_1 n_2 n_3$, then any P corresponds to a frequency $\nu = 2\pi cr/l$, where r denotes the distance of P from the origin of coordinates. The number to be determined is, therefore, given by the number of the points P within the distance $r = (l/2\pi c)\nu$ and $r + dr = (l/2\pi c)(\nu + d\nu)$ lying within the cone $d\Omega$. r and $r + dr$ define a spherical shell of volume $4\pi r^2\,dr$, and therefore the volume enclosed by $d\Omega$ is $4\pi r^2\,dr(d\Omega/4\pi)$. This element of volume is identical with the number of the enclosed points which have integer coordinates, so that $\rho\,d\Omega\,dE$ is given by

$$\rho\,d\Omega\,dE = 2\left(\frac{l}{2\pi c}\right)^3 \nu^2\,d\nu\,d\Omega \qquad \text{or} \qquad \rho\,d\Omega = 2\left(\frac{l}{2\pi c}\right)^3 \frac{\nu^2}{\hbar}\,d\Omega \quad (343)$$

The factor 2 is necessary because, for any ν_t, there are two directions of polarization. For dW we now obtain

$$
\begin{aligned}
dW &= \frac{2\pi}{\hbar}\,2\left(\frac{l}{2\pi c}\right)^3 \frac{\nu_t^2}{\hbar}\,d\Omega\,\frac{e^2}{c^2}\frac{\hbar}{2\nu_t}\,(\bar{n}_t+1)\nu_t^2\,\frac{4\pi c^2}{l^3}\,\overline{\cos^2\theta}\{|x_{ab}|^2 \\
&\qquad\qquad\qquad\qquad\qquad\qquad\qquad\qquad\qquad + |y_{ab}|^2 + |z_{ab}|^2\} \\
&= \frac{e^2}{\hbar\pi c^3}\,\nu_t^3\,d\Omega(\bar{n}_t+1)\,\overline{\cos^2\theta}\{|x_{ab}|^2 + |y_{ab}|^2 + |z_{ab}|^2\} \quad (344)
\end{aligned}
$$

where $\bar{n}_t$ is the average number of light quanta per frequency and direction of polarization. dW is composed of two parts: one part is proportional to $\bar{n}_t$ and corresponds to an emission induced by the radiation; the other part, which is independent of $\bar{n}_t$, represents a *spontaneous* emission. The total spontaneous emission is found from (344) by integrating over $d\Omega$. For this purpose we substitute the angle θ' between $\mathbf{v}$ and $\mathbf{k}$ for the angle θ between $\mathbf{v}$ and $\mathbf{e}$. It is verified readily with the help of a figure that $\overline{\cos^2\theta} = \tfrac{1}{2}\sin^2\theta'$, so that we finally obtain for the probability of a spontaneous emission

$$
\begin{aligned}
W &= \frac{e^2}{\hbar\pi c^3}\frac{\nu_t^3}{2}\,\{|x_{ab}|^2 + |y_{ab}|^2 + |z_{ab}|^2\}\int\int \sin^3\theta'\,d\theta'\,d\phi \\
&= \frac{4e^2}{3\hbar c^3}\,\nu_t^3\{|x_{ab}|^2 + |y_{ab}|^2 + |z_{ab}|^2\}
\end{aligned}
$$

If we take into account the fact that the notation ν now represents the frequency times 2π, this is in agreement with (105).

In order to evaluate the probability of an absorption we must start from the matrix element

$$H'_{an_t,bn_t-1} = -\frac{ie}{c}\sqrt{\frac{\hbar}{2\nu_t}}\,\sqrt{n_t}\,(\mathbf{v}u_t)_{ab}$$

which differs from (342) in that it contains $\sqrt{n_t}$ instead of $\sqrt{n_t+1}$. This means that there is no spontaneous but only an induced absorption, a fact that agrees with experience.

60. The Divergences Occurring in the Higher Approximations. Here we are to consider the influence the interaction term

H' has on the energy levels of the system consisting of radiation and particles. Without H', these levels would be given by $E = E_0 + \sum_t n_t \hbar \nu_t$, where E_0 denotes the energy belonging to a stationary state of the particle system. Because of H', E is to be corrected by additive terms $E^1, E^2, \cdots$ which are to be calculated according to the method of Section 35. As shown there, the correction term E^1 of the first order for the kth level is given by the diagonal term H_{kk}' of the perturbation matrix, which in our case is $H'_{an_1n_2 \cdots an_1n_2} \cdots$. As is seen from (326), this term is zero since all the diagonal elements of $\tilde{A}_t$ and B_t vanish. The interaction of the first order leaves the energy levels unchanged. The term E^2, on the contrary, according to (177) is given by

$$E^2 = \sum_{m \neq k} \frac{H_{km}' H_{mk}'}{E_k - E_m} = \sum_{bn_1'n_2' \cdots} \frac{H'_{an_1n_2 \cdots bn_1'n_2'} \cdots H'_{bn_1'n_2' \cdots an_1n_2} \cdots}{E - E'}$$

(345)

and is not zero. E^2 can be evaluated on the basis of certain simplifying assumptions. We consider the case of one electron only and assume that all the numbers n_i of the light quanta are zero. The particle may be at rest, and therefore its energy is mc^2. Then in the summation only such of the elements $H'_{an_1n_2 \cdots bn_1'n_2'} \cdots$ appear for which one of the n' has the value unity, all the other n_i', and the n_i as well, being zero. The ground state of the particle is signified by a, and in what follows the subscript 0 refers to that state. Some other state of positive or negative energy is denoted by b. Making use of (341), and because $n_i = 0$, we have, for E^2,

$$E^2 = \frac{e^2\hbar}{2} \sum_t \frac{\frac{1}{\nu_t} \int \psi_0{}^*(\vec{\alpha}u_t)\psi_b \int \psi_b{}^*(\vec{\alpha}u_t)\psi_0}{mc^2 - (E_b + \hbar\nu_t)}$$

(346)

The denominator accounts for the fact that the total energy of the system in the initial state is the rest energy mc^2 of the electron, whereas the final energy is made up of the energy E_b of the particle plus that of the light quantum $\hbar\nu_t$. As the evaluation of the sum is somewhat troublesome,† we shall be content to give the result

$$E^2 = \frac{e^2\hbar\pi}{ml^3} \sum_t \frac{1}{\nu_t}$$

† W. Heitler, *Theory of Radiation*, Oxford University Press, 1948.

in which the summation extends over all the eigenfrequencies of the radiation.   As the number of frequencies between ν and $\nu + d\nu$ is, according to (343), given by

$$8\pi \left(\frac{l}{2\pi c}\right)^3 \nu^2 \, d\nu$$

then E^2 can also be written in the form

$$E^2 = \frac{e^2 \hbar}{mc^2 \pi} \int^{\infty} \nu \, d\nu \tag{347}$$

The integral being divergent, the particle, in its interaction with the light quanta, undergoes an infinite displacement of its energy level, the consequence being that, besides an infinite Coulomb energy due to the longitudinal field, it would possess an infinite transverse self-energy as well.   Because $\hbar$ occurs in (347), we see that the transverse self-energy is a quantum effect which diverges not only in the second but in all higher approximations as well.   Evidently this divergence is due to the *short* waves contained in the radiation.   Generally the application of the quantum-mechanical perturbation theory may be expected to furnish infinite correction terms of the energy provided, that there is an infinity of states n for which the elements H_{mn}' of the perturbation matrix differ from zero, thus making possible transitions from m into all these states.   The transverse self-energy of the electron being considered here is only a typical example of divergences of this kind.   Another example is the infinite self-energy of a light quantum caused by the interaction of the quantum with electrons of negative energy.   In this example the divergence results from the infinity of intermediate states into which the system of light quantum and electrons can pass by the creation of pairs.

In summary we may say that the application of quantum mechanics to the electromagnetic field leads to a theory that basically is, without doubt, correct, inasmuch as it embraces a great part of the experimental facts.   There are certain consequences, however, which contradict experience in that some quantities which are unquestionably finite (such as the self-energy of the electron) assume infinite values.   Not all these troublesome divergences, which among other things make a consistent relativistic solution of the many-body problem impossible, originate in quantum mechanics.   The infinite Coulomb self-energy of a point charge is present in the classical theory, which attempts to overcome the difficulty by assigning to the electron an extension of the order of magnitude $r_0 = e^2/mc^2$.   This assumption cannot, however, be reconciled with the principle of relativity.   According to this theory any extended body can be deformed, so that an extended electron had to be pictured as a thing consisting of parts that move relative to each other, an idea evidently incompatible with the concept of an elementary particle. On principle, therefore, it is impossible to devise a relativistic theory in which the particle is treated as an extended body without thereby losing the character of an elementary particle. The result of such an attempt would invariably be a continuum theory in which the concept of an indivisible particle has no meaning. Already, for this reason, the classical theory was forced to consider the electron a point charge, with the consequence that an infinite self-energy had to be accepted in the bargain. Since, however, this energy originates from the longitudinal field which cannot be quantized, quantum mechanics could not avoid taking over this divergence as it stood. But quantum mechanics presents added divergences which are not, at least not immediately, connected with the point character of the particles but arise from the necessity of taking into account wavelengths of any shortness, that is, of considering fields with an infinite number of degrees of freedom. It is because of this circumstance that the theory has to attribute to a cavity radiation an infinite zero point energy caused by the short wavelengths. We have seen also that the evaluation of the transverse self-energy of a charged particle provides infinite correction terms of the second and higher orders. This situation suggests the conclusion that there must be a certain limit to the applicability of quantum mechanics by which the effectiveness of the short waves is restricted. The limitation must be due to the efficiency of a fundamental constant which has been disregarded up to now and the theory of which will be developed in Chapter 10.

PROBLEMS

1. From (315) derive the commutation relations for **E** and **H**.

2. Describe the manner in which the ambiguous nature of light has to be understood according to quantum mechanics.

3. Why is it impossible to quantize the Coulomb energy?

4. From what arguments can it be inferred that the rest mass of the photon is zero? Compare the equations of Maxwell with those of Proca. In what way would light have to behave if the rest mass of the photon differed from zero?

5. Discuss the origin of the divergences occurring in quantum electrodynamics.

9

WAVE FIELDS

AND NUCLEAR MATTER

The meson is the most important particle with which modern physics is concerned. It may be taken for granted that in the cosmic radiation there are positive and negative particles with a mass about two hundred times that of the electron mass. However, more recent investigations make it probable that there are mesons of different masses which seem to be transmuted into one another by some sort of radioactive decay. From experimental evidence, the normal meson possesses only a very short mean lifetime, after which it disintegrates into an electron and a neutrino. One of the reasons why such great importance is attached to this particle is that it seems to mediate the forces the protons and neutrons of an atomic nucleus exert on one another. The generally accepted view is that these forces are brought into play by an interchange of mesons between the nuclear particles. In a manner similar to that in which the electrons act on one another by a field, the nuclear particles are assumed to be connected by a field which satisfies a second-order wave equation. The field originates from the nuclear particles and manifests itself in the appearance of mesons which, when the field is quantized, appear also in the mathematical formalism. In this way the interaction between two nuclear particles appears in the particle picture as an exchange of mesons. Let us suppose, for example, that a proton is face to face with a neutron. The proton may emit a positive meson which is subsequently absorbed by the neutron, and as a result the proton is changed into a neutron and vice versa. This means that momentum is transferred from one particle to the other and therefore a force is acting between the two particles.

Up to the present, attempts to develop this idea into a consistent theory have failed, being handicapped by divergences which cannot be removed satisfactorily without a supplementary principle. Therefore, in what follows, we shall be concerned only with the foundations of the theory, investigating the possibilities given for the interaction of the wave fields considered in the two preceding chapters, and nuclear matter. Such far-reaching restrictions are imposed on these possibilities by the theory of relativity that, in seeking the interaction terms, we cannot go astray. On the other hand, the application of the theory to the problems of nuclear forces and cosmic radiation has as yet produced no definite results. We shall, therefore, merely outline these problems without going into details.

61. The Lagrangian of the Interaction.† The fields with which we have dealt in the preceding chapters do not exist in vacuo but issue from material particles on which they are reacting, so that the fields and the corresponding particles form closed systems. We base the following considerations on the assumption that it is the protons and neutrons of an atomic nucleus which, because of a certain "charge," are able to radiate and absorb the field. (The concept "charge" is used here in a general sense and has nothing to do with an electric charge.) It is convenient to describe this property by means of the Lagrangian which corresponds to the system of field and particles, and which must contain a term representing the interaction between field and matter. By its nature, the Lagrangian is an invariant scalar function, and therefore, in determining the interaction, we are confronted with the problem of forming an invariant out of the field quantities ψ and χ, introduced in Chapter 7, and at the same time from the wave function Φ of a nuclear particle. As the spin of the nuclear particles is $\frac{1}{2}$, we have to apply the Dirac equation to them. Consequently Φ is identical with the quantity consisting of four components introduced in Section 45 in order to treat particles having the spin $\frac{1}{2}$. It can be shown that with the help of the matrices defined by (232):

$$\alpha_i = \begin{bmatrix} 0 & \gamma_i \\ \gamma_i & 0 \end{bmatrix} \qquad \beta = \begin{bmatrix} 1 & 0 \\ 0 & -1 \end{bmatrix}$$

where

$$\gamma_1 = \begin{bmatrix} 0 & 1 \\ 1 & 0 \end{bmatrix} \qquad \gamma_2 = \begin{bmatrix} 0 & i \\ -i & 0 \end{bmatrix} \qquad \gamma_3 = \begin{bmatrix} 1 & 0 \\ 0 & -1 \end{bmatrix} \qquad 1 = \begin{bmatrix} 1 & 0 \\ 0 & 1 \end{bmatrix}$$

The following tensor functions can be formed from Φ:

Scalar: $w_0 = \Phi^* \beta \Phi$

Four-vector: $w_i = \Phi^* \alpha_i \Phi \qquad w_4 = i\Phi^* \Phi$

Antisymmetric tensor of second order: (348)

$$w_{ik} = \Phi^* \beta \alpha_i \alpha_k \Phi \qquad w_{4k} = i\Phi^* \beta \alpha_k \Phi$$

† Cf. N. Kemmer, *Proc. Roy. Soc. London*, **A166**, 127 (1938).

Pseudovector: $w_{4ik} = \Phi^*\alpha_i\alpha_k\Phi$ $w_{123} = -i\Phi^*\alpha_1\alpha_2\alpha_3\Phi$

Pseudoscalar: $w_{1234} = \Phi^*\beta\alpha_1\alpha_2\alpha_3\Phi$

The reader is reminded that the x_4 is defined as ict and that the components of the tensors must be understood in accordance with this definition, the consequence being that there is no difference between a covariant and contravariant tensor. In the products above, Φ is to be treated as a matrix with its components in the first vertical column, and Φ^* contains the components in the first horizontal row (cf. Section 23). When the coordinate system is changed, the products transform according to their notation. All the quantities in (348) are, of course, to be considered as functions of x, y, z, and t.

Let us now, on the other hand, consider the fields at our disposal. Each of them can be described by two functions, each of the functions representing a scalar, vector, or antisymmetric tensor. Throughout Chapter 7 we denoted the tensor of the lower order by ψ and the other by χ according to the following scheme:

Scalar field: Scalar ψ and four-vector χ_α (Section 47)

Vector field: Four-vector ψ_α and tensor $\chi_{\alpha\beta}$ (Section 49)

Pseudovector field: (349)

Tensor $\psi_{\alpha\beta}$ and four-vector $\chi_{\alpha\beta\gamma}$ (Section 50)

Pseudoscalar field:

Pseudovector $\psi_{\alpha\beta\gamma}$ and pseudoscalar $\chi_{\alpha\beta\gamma\delta}$ (Section 48)

The problem now is to unite the quantities of (348) and (349) in such a way as to form invariants. If we make the assumption that the interaction depends only on the functions ψ and χ *but not on their derivatives*, the combination can be effected in this way only. This is the simplest and therefore the most plausible assumption on which the theory can be founded. Then the invariance can be achieved only by multiplying every quantity of (349) by the corresponding quantity of (348). For example, we must multiply $\psi_{\alpha\beta}$ by $w_{\alpha\beta}^*$ and summate over all the products $\psi_{\alpha\beta}w_{\alpha\beta}^*$. If we provide the products with factors, the interaction is described by

Scalar field: $-\kappa(g_1 w_0\psi^* + f_1 w_\alpha\chi_\alpha^*)$ + conjugate complex

Vector field:

$-\kappa(g_2 w_\alpha\psi_\alpha^* + f_2 \tfrac{1}{2}w_{\alpha\beta}\chi_{\alpha\beta}^*)$ + conjugate complex

Pseudovector field: $\hspace{8.5cm}$ (350)

$$-\kappa(g_3\ \tfrac{1}{2}w_{\alpha\beta}\psi_{\alpha\beta}{}^* + f_3\ \tfrac{1}{6}w_{\alpha\beta\gamma}\chi_{\alpha\beta\gamma}{}^*) + \text{conjugate complex}$$

Pseudoscalar field:

$$-\kappa(g_4\ \tfrac{1}{6}w_{\alpha\beta\gamma}\psi_{\alpha\beta\gamma}{}^* + f_4\ \tfrac{1}{24}w_{\alpha\beta\gamma\delta}\chi_{\alpha\beta\gamma\delta}{}^*) + \text{conjugate complex}$$

According to our convention, the expressions are to be summed up from 1 to 4 over any index that occurs twice. The factors $\tfrac{1}{2}$, $\tfrac{1}{6}$, and $\tfrac{1}{24}$ are inserted because the index convention sometimes provides the same product several times. As an example of this, from $w_{\alpha\beta\gamma}\psi_{\alpha\beta\gamma}{}^*$ we obtain the product $w_{123}\psi_{123}{}^*$ 3! times. The factors mentioned above remove this abundance, so that the products appear in the expressions only once. The factor $-\kappa$ is chosen for reasons of convenience. The numbers g_i and f_i express the strength of the interaction. For the present we shall treat them as ordinary numbers, but it will turn out that for charged mesons they have the character of two-row matrices.

The expressions of (350) refer to the case where there is only one nuclear particle. If the field interacts with several particles, we have to coordinate a wave function Φ^k to each one of them and substitute the sums $w_0 = \sum\limits_k \Phi^{k*}\beta^k\Phi^k$, $w_1 = \sum\limits_k \Phi^{k*}\alpha_i{}^k\Phi^k$, and so on for $w_0, w_1, \cdots$.

62. Scalar and Pseudoscalar Fields. First we shall apply the theory to a scalar field which is in interaction with one nuclear particle. According to (250) and (350), the Lagrangian is then given by

$$\bar{L} = -\kappa(\psi^*\psi + \chi_\alpha{}^*\chi_\alpha)$$
$$- \kappa(gw_0\psi^* + fw_\alpha\chi_\alpha{}^*) + \text{conjugate complex} \quad (351)$$

In order to obtain from this the Hamiltonian $\bar{H}$ which is required for the evaluation of the transition probabilities, we must evaluate first the momenta $\pi = \partial\bar{L}/\partial\ (d\psi/dt)$ and $\pi^* = \partial\bar{L}/\partial\ (d\psi^*/dt)$ associated with ψ and ψ^*. Since $d\psi/dt = i\kappa c\chi_4$, we find that

$$\pi = \frac{1}{i\kappa c}\frac{\partial\bar{L}}{\partial\chi_4} = -\frac{1}{ic}\chi_4{}^* - \frac{1}{ic}f^*w_4{}^*$$

$$\pi^* = -\frac{1}{ic}\chi_4 - \frac{1}{ic}fw_4$$

$\hspace{9cm}$ (351')

Hence

$$\frac{d\psi}{dt} = i\kappa c\chi_4 = \kappa c^2\left(\pi^* + \frac{1}{ic}fw_4\right)$$

and thus for $\bar{H} = (d\psi/dt)\pi + (d\psi^*/dt)\pi^* - \bar{L}$ we obtain

$$\bar{H} = \kappa c^2 \left(\pi^* + \frac{1}{ic} f w_4\right)\pi + \kappa c^2 \left(\pi + \frac{1}{ic} f^* w_4^*\right)\pi^* + \kappa\psi^*\psi + \kappa\chi_i^*\chi_i$$

$$- \kappa c^2 \left(\pi + \frac{1}{ic} f^* w_4^*\right)\left(\pi^* + \frac{1}{ic} f w_4\right) + \kappa g w_0 \psi^* + \kappa f w_i \chi_i^*$$

$$- \kappa f i c w_4 \left(\pi + \frac{1}{ic} f^* w_4^*\right) + \text{conjugate complex}$$

Where an index i occurs twice in this expression it means a summation from 1 to 3 only, and the added conjugate complex applies only to the last three terms. The expression reduces to

$$\bar{H} = \kappa(c^2\pi^*\pi + \psi^*\psi + \chi_i^*\chi_i)$$
$$+ \kappa(g w_0 \psi^* + f w_i \chi_i^* - i c f w_4 \pi) + \text{conjugate complex} \quad (352)$$

and represents the energy density of the field. The first terms in parentheses belong to the pure field, whereas the remaining ones give the energy due to the interaction of the field with nuclear matter. If we take into account that $\chi = 1/\kappa$ grad ψ, then, because of (348), the interaction energy H' becomes

$$H' = \kappa \int dv \, \Phi^* \left\{ g\beta\psi^* + f\left[c\pi + \frac{1}{\kappa}(\vec{\alpha} \text{ grad } \psi^*) \right] \right\} \Phi$$
$$+ \text{conjugate complex} \quad (353)$$

The reader is advised to keep carefully in mind how a product of the kind $\Phi^*[\,\cdot\cdot\cdot\cdot\cdot\cdot\,]\Phi$ is to be read. The bracket contains a four-row matrix (the term $fc\pi$ is to be thought of as multiplied by the unit matrix) which operates on the vector Φ, after which the new vector is to be multiplied by Φ^*. The operators $\vec{\alpha}$ and β belong to the nuclear particles. If the velocity $\mathbf{v}$ of this particle is small compared to c, we may substitute $\mathbf{v}$ for $c\vec{\alpha}$ so that, for a particle at rest, the operator $\vec{\alpha}$ grad ψ^* drops out. Furthermore we may set $\beta = 1$ for a particle at rest, so that, on the assumption $f = 0$, (353) becomes

$$H' = \kappa \int dv \, \Phi^*[g\psi^* + g^*\psi]\Phi = \kappa[g\psi^*(P) + g^*\psi(P)] \quad (354)$$

where $\psi(P)$ denotes the value of the function ψ at the point P occupied by the particle. For the transformation, attention is given to the fact that the probability density $\Phi^*\Phi$ differs from zero only in the immediate neighborhood of P, so that $\Phi^*\Phi$ may be set equal to $\delta(P' - P)$.

In the particle picture the interaction is looked upon as the emission or absorption of a scalar meson by the nuclear particle, this being analogous to the emission or absorption of a photon by an electron. To formalize this conception it is necessary to quantize the field by expanding ψ into

$$\psi = \frac{1}{\sqrt{l^3}} \sum q_i e^{i\mathbf{k}_i \cdot \mathbf{r}}$$

and transcribing the q_i coefficients into the matrices of (280). This gives

$$H' =$$

$$i\kappa \sqrt{\frac{c\hbar}{2l^3}} \sum_i \frac{1}{\sqrt[4]{1 + k_i^2/\kappa^2}} [g(\tilde{A}_i - B_i)e^{-i\mathbf{k}_i \cdot \mathbf{r}} - g^*(A_i - \tilde{B}_i)e^{i\mathbf{k}_i \cdot \mathbf{r}}] \quad (355)$$

H' is again referred to the coordinate system K which was defined in Section 52, wherein the products $\tilde{A}_i A_i$ and $\tilde{B}_i B_i$ are diagonal. In the case where ψ is complex, that is, for a charged field, the axes of K are to be designated by two sequences of numbers $n_1^+ n_2^+ \cdots$ $n_1^- n_2^- \cdots$ so that we have

$$A^{(i)}{}_{n_i^+, n_i^+ +1} = \sqrt{n_i^+ + 1} \qquad \tilde{A}^{(i)}{}_{n_i^+, n_i^+ -1} = \sqrt{n_i^+}$$

$$B^{(i)}{}_{n_i^-, n_i^- +1} = \sqrt{n_i^- + 1} \qquad \tilde{B}^{(i)}{}_{n_i^-, n_i^- -1} = \sqrt{n_i^-} \tag{356}$$

all other elements being zero. In these expressions it is to be understood that all the indices n_i^+ and n_i^- which are not included have arbitrary values. However, any n_i' is equal to n_i, and this means that for H' only the elements

$$H'{}_{\substack{n_1^+ n_2^+ \cdots \\ n_1^- n_2^- \cdots}} {}_{\left|\substack{n_1^{+\prime} n_2^{+\prime} \cdots \\ n_1^{-\prime} n_2^{-\prime} \cdots}\right.}$$

differ from zero, for which all except one of the $n_i^{+\prime}$ or $n_i^{-\prime}$ differs from n_i^+ or n_i^- by ± 1. A transition $n_i \to n_i + 1$, which, according to (356), can be effected only by one of the A_i or B_i, means the emission of a meson, whereas the transition $n_i \to n_i - 1$ due to $\tilde{A}_i$ or $\tilde{B}_i$ indicates absorption. Therefore, of the matrices in (355), A_i and B_i are responsible for the emission and $\tilde{A}_i$ and $\tilde{B}_i$ for the absorption of a positive or negative meson. In the case of a real field, the mesons are neutral, and then, according to (284), we have to substitute A_{-i} and $\tilde{A}_{-i}$ for B_i and B_{-i}, making it unnecessary to distinguish between n_i^+ and n_i^-.

According to (184), the elements H_{nm}' of H' determine the probability of a transition $n \to m$. The emission of a positive meson having the energy $\epsilon_i = c \sqrt{m_0{}^2 c^2 + k_i{}^2 \hbar^2}$ has a probability which must be evaluated from

$$H'_{n_i{}^+, n_i{}^+ +1} = -ig^* \kappa \sqrt{\frac{c\hbar}{2l^3}} \frac{1}{\sqrt[4]{1 + k_i{}^2/\kappa^2}} A^{(i)}{}_{n_i{}^+, n_i{}^+ +1} e^{i\mathbf{k}_i \cdot \mathbf{r}_0}$$

$$= -ig^* \hbar \sqrt{\frac{c\kappa^3}{2l^3 \epsilon_i}} \sqrt{n_i{}^+ + 1}\; e^{i\mathbf{k}_i \cdot \mathbf{r}_0}$$

In this expression $\mathbf{r}_0$ denotes the radius vector from the origin to the position of the nuclear particle. Similarly the elements of the other possible processes are given by

$$H'_{n_i{}^-, n_i{}^- +1} = -ig\hbar \sqrt{\frac{c\kappa^3}{2l^3 \epsilon_i}} \sqrt{n_i{}^- + 1}\; e^{-i\mathbf{k}_i \cdot \mathbf{r}_0}$$

$$H'_{n_i{}^+, n_i{}^+ -1} = ig\hbar \sqrt{\frac{c\kappa^3}{2l^3 \epsilon_i}} \sqrt{n_i{}^+}\; e^{-i\mathbf{k}_i \cdot \mathbf{r}_0} \qquad (357)$$

$$H'_{n_i{}^-, n_i{}^- -1} = ig^* \hbar \sqrt{\frac{c\kappa^3}{2l^3 \epsilon_i}} \sqrt{n_i{}^-}\; e^{i\mathbf{k}_i \cdot \mathbf{r}_0}$$

In the case of neutral mesons, (355) must be multiplied by $1/\sqrt{2}$ (cf. Section 52), and, since $A_{-i} = B_i$ and $A_i = B_{-i}$, the sum reduces to

$$H' = i\kappa \sqrt{\frac{c\hbar}{l^3}} \frac{1}{2} \sum_i \frac{1}{\sqrt[4]{1 + k_i{}^2/\kappa^2}} (g + g^*)(\tilde{A}_i - A_{-i}) e^{-i\mathbf{k}_i \cdot \mathbf{r}}$$

and for H'_{n_i, n_i+1} and H'_{n_i, n_i-1} we obtain

$$H'_{n_i, n_i+1} = -i \frac{g + g^*}{2} \sqrt{\frac{c\kappa^3}{l^3}} \sqrt{n_i + 1}\; e^{i\mathbf{k}_i \cdot \mathbf{r}_0}$$

$$H'_{n_i, n_i-1} = i \frac{g + g^*}{2} \sqrt{\frac{c\kappa^3}{l^3}} \sqrt{n_i}\; e^{-i\mathbf{k}_i \cdot \mathbf{r}_0}$$

The theory just developed, according to which the interaction between a nuclear particle and a meson field can be interpreted in terms of emission and absorption processes, depends on an essential condition when the meson field is charged. The processes considered are possible only if the protons and neutrons are capable of transmuting themselves into each other. This is essential since a proton, on emitting a positive meson, loses its charge and becomes a neutron and, conversely, a neutron, on emitting a negative meson, becomes a proton. Thus we are forced to consider *proton and neutron as two transmutable modifications of the same particle, the nucleon.* Therefore, in order to characterize the state of a nucleon, we require, in addition to xyz and the spin coordinate ρ, a fifth quantity τ which by arbitrary convention has the value zero for the neutron and unity for the proton. This means a corresponding extension of the coordinate system K of the Hilbert space. For a description of a system of one nucleon and the field, K would be sufficient without τ provided that the axes were specified by: (i) two sequences of numbers $n_1{}^+n_2{}^+ \cdots n_1{}^-n_2{}^- \cdots$ which refer to the field and indicate a state in which, for any i, there are $n_i{}^+$ positive and $n_i{}^-$ negative mesons of energy ϵ_i; (ii) x, y, z, and ρ values which define the position and spin state of the particle. Because of τ any of these axes must be taken twice, value $\tau = 0$ being assigned to one of them and $\tau = 1$ to the other. If the vector $\mathbf{X}$, which represents the state, has the direction of an axis $\tau = 0$, the particle is a neutron; in the other case it is a proton. This means that, for the interaction, H' must contain a matrix which intermediates between the axes $\tau = 0$ and $\tau = 1$. This matrix is associated with the factor g by setting

$$g = g \begin{bmatrix} 0 & 1 \\ 0 & 0 \end{bmatrix} \qquad g^* = g^* \begin{bmatrix} 0 & 0 \\ 1 & 0 \end{bmatrix} \tag{358}$$

wherein g and g^* on the right-hand sides now denote ordinary numbers. The matrices operate on τ only, and it is to be understood that the first row is for $\tau = 0$ and the second row for $\tau = 1$. The matrix g has only one element g_{01}, which differs from zero and permits a transition, neutron $\rightarrow$ proton, whereas all the other transitions, $P \rightarrow P$, $P \rightarrow N$, $N \rightarrow N$, are blocked by g. In a corresponding way g^* permits the transition $P \rightarrow N$, all others being blocked. The expression (357) for H' can now be given the following interpretation: $H'_{n_i{}^+, n_i{}^++1}$, which is associated with the emission of a positive meson, contains g^*; this means that the emission is possible only when there is a simultaneous transmutation of a proton into a neutron. On the other hand, $H'_{n_i{}^-, n_i{}^-+1}$ corresponds to the emission of a negative meson and contains g, thereby requiring the transmutation of a neutron into a proton.

The matrices of (358) can be represented formally by using the Dirac matrices γ_1 and γ_2 as defined by (231), namely,

$$\gamma_1 = \begin{pmatrix} 0 & 1 \\ 1 & 0 \end{pmatrix} \qquad \gamma_2 = \begin{pmatrix} 0 & i \\ -i & 0 \end{pmatrix} \tag{358'}$$

It follows from this that

$$\begin{bmatrix} 0 & 1 \\ 0 & 0 \end{bmatrix} = \tfrac{1}{2}(\gamma_1 - i\gamma_2) \qquad \begin{bmatrix} 0 & 0 \\ 1 & 0 \end{bmatrix} = \tfrac{1}{2}(\gamma_1 + i\gamma_2)$$

and thus g and g^* take the forms

$$g\tfrac{1}{2}(\gamma_1 - i\gamma_2) \qquad g^*\tfrac{1}{2}(\gamma_1 + i\gamma_2)$$

When γ_1 and γ_2 are applied in this sense, they have nothing to do with the spin of the nucleon but operate only on the charge coordinate τ which, because of its analogy to the spin, is often called "isotopic spin."

According to (350), in the case of a pseudoscalar field the interaction is given by

$$\bar{L}' = -\kappa(g\tfrac{1}{6}w_{\alpha\beta\gamma}\psi_{\alpha\beta\gamma}{}^* + f\tfrac{1}{24}w_{\alpha\beta\gamma\delta}\chi_{\alpha\beta\gamma\delta}{}^*) + \text{conjugate complex}$$

If we denote the pseudovectors $w_{\alpha\beta\gamma}$ and $\psi_{\alpha\beta\gamma}$ by w_α' and χ_α' respectively and the pseudoscalars $w_{\alpha\beta\gamma\delta}$ and $\chi_{\alpha\beta\gamma\delta}$ by w_0' and ψ', then

$$\bar{L}' = -\kappa(gw_\alpha'\chi_\alpha'{}^* + fw_0'\psi'{}^*) + \text{conjugate complex}$$

A comparison with (351) shows that all we must do is to substitute the pseudoscalar ψ_0' and ψ' for w_0 and ψ, and the pseudovectors w_α' and $\chi_\alpha' = (1/\kappa)(\partial\psi'/\partial x_\alpha)$ for the vectors w_α and χ_α. Then for H' we obtain

$$\bar{H}' = \kappa(fw_0'\psi'{}^* + gw_i'\chi_i'{}^* - icgw_4'\pi') + \text{conjugate complex}$$

wherein, according to (351'),

$$\pi' = \frac{1}{i\kappa c}\frac{\partial\bar{L}}{\partial\chi_4'} = -\frac{1}{ic}\chi_4' - \frac{1}{ic}g^*w_4'{}^*$$

Taking into account that

$$w_0' = \Phi^*\beta\alpha_1\alpha_2\alpha_3\Phi \qquad w_i' = \Phi^*\alpha_i\alpha_k\Phi \qquad w_4' = -i\Phi^*\alpha_1\alpha_2\alpha_3\Phi$$

and since $i\alpha_2\alpha_3 = \sigma_1$, etc., we obtain for H'

$$H' = \kappa \int dv\, \Phi^* \left\{ f\beta\alpha_1\alpha_2\alpha_3\psi'{}^* - g\left[c\alpha_1\alpha_2\alpha_3\pi' + \frac{i}{\kappa}(\vec{\sigma}\,\text{grad}\,\psi'{}^*) \right] \right\} \Phi$$

$$+ \text{conjugate complex} \quad (359)$$

The terms with the factor $\alpha_1\alpha_2\alpha_3$ may be set equal to zero in the case of a particle at rest, reducing the above to

$$H' = -i \int dv\, \Phi^*[g(\vec{\sigma}\,\text{grad}\,\psi'{}^*) + g^*(\vec{\sigma}\,\text{grad}\,\psi')]\Phi$$

$$= -ig(\vec{\sigma}\,\text{grad}\,\psi'{}^*)_0 - ig^*(\vec{\sigma}\,\text{grad}\,\psi')_0$$

$$(360)$$

The index 0 signifies that the gradient is to be taken at the point occupied by the particle.

On comparing (360) with (354), we see that the scalar and pseudo-scalar fields, which cannot be distinguished in vacuo, undergo quite different interactions with nucleons. Whereas H' depends only on the density of the nuclear matter in the case of a scalar field, there is the added dependence on the spin $\vec{\sigma}$ in the case of the pseudoscalar field. This is due to the fact that, in order to arrive at an invariant Lagrangian, we have to combine the field with different Φ terms.

63. Vector and Pseudovector Fields. If only the part dealing with the particles is disregarded, the Lagrangian for a vector field is, according to (263) and (350), given by

$$\bar{L} = -\kappa(\psi_\alpha^*\psi_\alpha + \tfrac{1}{2}\chi_{\alpha\beta}^*\chi_{\alpha\beta})$$
$$- \kappa(gw_\alpha\psi_\alpha^* + \tfrac{1}{2}fw_{\alpha\beta}\chi_{\alpha\beta}^*) + \text{conjugate complex}$$

where $\chi_{\alpha\beta}$ is defined by $\dfrac{1}{\kappa}\left(\dfrac{\partial\psi_\beta}{\partial x_\alpha} - \dfrac{\partial\psi_\alpha}{\partial x_\beta}\right)$. From $\bar{L}$ we get for π_i

$$\pi_i = \frac{1}{i\kappa c}\frac{\partial\bar{L}}{\partial\chi_{4i}} = -\frac{1}{ic}(\chi_{4i}^* + f^*w_{4i}^*) \tag{361}$$

$$\pi_i^* = -\frac{1}{ic}(\chi_{4i} + fw_{4i}) \qquad \pi_4 = \pi_4^* = 0$$

Because of the relation

$$\chi_{4i} = \frac{1}{ic\kappa}\frac{d\psi_i}{dt} - \frac{1}{\kappa}\frac{\partial\psi_4}{\partial x_i}$$

we have

$$\frac{d\psi_i}{dt} = ic\kappa\chi_{4i} + ic\frac{\partial\psi_4}{\partial x_i}$$

so that the relation

$$\bar{H} = \frac{d\psi_i}{dt}\pi_i + \frac{d\psi_i^*}{dt}\pi_i^* - \bar{L}$$

becomes

$$\bar{H} = ic\kappa(\chi_{4i}\pi_i + \chi_{4i}^*\pi_i^*) + ic\left(\frac{\partial\psi_4}{\partial x_i}\pi_i + \frac{\partial\psi_4^*}{\partial x_i}\pi_i^*\right) - \bar{L}$$

In the expression $H = \int \bar{H}\,dv$ the terms with $(\partial\psi_4/\partial x_i)\pi_i$ and $(\partial\psi_4^*/\partial x_i)\pi_i^*$ may be replaced by $-\psi_4(\partial\pi_i/\partial x_i)$ and $-\psi_i^*(\partial\pi_i^*/\partial x_i)$, a

change which occurs when we integrate by parts. We then obtain
for $\bar{H}$

$$\bar{H} = ic\kappa(\chi_{4i}\pi_i + \chi_{4i}{}^*\pi_i{}^*) - ic(\psi_4 \operatorname{div}\vec{\pi} + \psi_4{}^* \operatorname{div}\vec{\pi}{}^*)$$

$$+ \kappa\psi_i{}^*\psi_i + \kappa\psi_4{}^*\psi_4 + \frac{\kappa}{2}\chi_{ik}{}^*\chi_{ik} + \kappa\chi_{4i}{}^*\chi_{4i}$$

$$+ \kappa g w_i \psi_i{}^* + \kappa g w_4 \psi_4{}^* + \frac{\kappa}{2} f w_{ik}\chi_{ik}{}^*$$

$$+ \kappa f w_{4i}\chi_{4i}{}^* + \text{conjugate complex} \quad (362)$$

The summation over i and k is from 1 to 3 only.

In (362), ψ_4 but not π_4 occurs. If the Hamiltonian contains a
coordinate q_k the momentum p_k of which is zero, we may, by way of
definition, substitute for q_k an arbitrary function $f(q_i)$ of the other q_i
whereby H is changed into an expression from which q_k is eliminated.
All the q_i coordinates are then given by the canonical equations as
functions of time, and by this the coordinate q_k is also determined in its
dependence on time. In our case we have ψ_4 instead of q_k, and it can
be defined now as an extension of (258) by

$$\psi_4 = \frac{1}{\kappa}\frac{\partial\chi_{4i}}{\partial x_i} - g w_4 \quad (363)$$

If we substitute this value of ψ_4 in the equation for $\bar{H}$, the equation
becomes one containing only ψ_1, ψ_2, $\psi_3 = \vec{\psi}$ together with the corresponding momenta π_1, π_2, $\pi_3 = \vec{\pi}$.

In order to arrive at the interaction, we must now select from (362)
those terms which contain the factor g or f. At the same time we use
(363) instead of ψ_4 and put for χ_{4i} the quantity $-ic\pi_i{}^* - f w_{4i}$. We
then have

$$\bar{H}' = -ic\kappa(f w_{4i}\pi_i + f^* w_{4i}{}^*\pi_i{}^*) + ic(g w_4 \operatorname{div}\vec{\pi} + g^* w_4{}^* \operatorname{div}\vec{\pi}{}^*)$$

$$+ ic(g w_4 \operatorname{div}\vec{\pi} + g^* w_4{}^* \operatorname{div}\vec{\pi}{}^*) + \kappa ic(f w_{4i}\pi_i + f^* w_{4i}{}^*\pi_i{}^*)$$

$$+ \kappa g w_i \psi_i{}^* - icg w_4 \operatorname{div}\vec{\pi} + \frac{\kappa}{2} f w_{ik}\chi_{ik}{}^* - \kappa icf w_{4i}\pi_i$$

$$+ \text{conjugate complex}$$

$$= icg w_4 \operatorname{div}\vec{\pi} + \kappa g w_i \psi_i{}^* + \frac{\kappa}{2} f w_{ik}\chi_{ik}{}^* - \kappa icf w_{4i}\pi_i$$

$$+ \text{conjugate complex}$$

and, since $H' = \int \bar{H}' \, dv$, and taking the expressions of (348) for w_i and w_{i4}, we get for H'

$$H' = \int dv \, \Phi^* \left\{ g[\kappa(\overrightarrow{\alpha\psi}^*) - c \operatorname{div} \overrightarrow{\pi}] \right.$$
$$\left. + f\kappa\beta \left[-\frac{i}{\kappa} (\overrightarrow{\sigma} \operatorname{curl} \overrightarrow{\psi}^*) + c(\overrightarrow{\alpha\pi}) \right] \right\} \Phi + \text{conjugate complex}$$

For a nucleon at rest the above equation reduces to

$$H' = - \int dv \, \Phi^*[gc \operatorname{div} \overrightarrow{\pi} + fi\kappa\beta(\overrightarrow{\sigma} \operatorname{curl} \overrightarrow{\psi}^*)] + \text{conjugate complex}$$

$$= -gc(\operatorname{div} \overrightarrow{\pi})_0 - fi(\overrightarrow{\sigma} \operatorname{curl} \overrightarrow{\psi}^*)_0 + \text{conjugate complex} \qquad (364)$$

The first part determines the interaction due to longitudinal mesons, and the second part is caused by transverse mesons. The index 0 again indicates that $\operatorname{div} \overrightarrow{\pi}$ and $\operatorname{curl} \overrightarrow{\psi}^*$ must be taken at the point occupied by the nucleon. In the same manner as in the preceding section, the probabilities of an emission or absorption of a meson can be evaluated from H'. To do so we expand $\overrightarrow{\psi}$ and $\overrightarrow{\pi}$ into

$$\overrightarrow{\psi} = \frac{1}{\sqrt{l^3}} \sum_{ij} q_{ij} \mathbf{e}_{ij} e^{i\mathbf{k}_i \cdot \mathbf{r}} \qquad \overrightarrow{\pi} = \frac{1}{\sqrt{l^3}} \sum_{ij} p_{ij} \mathbf{e}_{ij} e^{-i\mathbf{k}_i \cdot \mathbf{r}}$$

and transcribe q_{ij} and p_{ij} into matrices Q_{ij} and P_{ij} which, according to (291), we define by

$$Q_{ij} = -i \sqrt{\frac{\hbar}{2}} \sqrt[4]{\frac{c^2 \left(\kappa + \frac{k_i^2}{\kappa} \delta_{j1} \right)}{\kappa + \frac{k_i^2}{\kappa} (1 - \delta_{j1})}} (A_{ij} - \tilde{B}_{ij})$$

$$P_{ij} = \sqrt{\frac{\hbar}{2}} \sqrt[4]{\frac{\kappa + \frac{k_i^2}{\kappa} (1 - \delta_{j1})}{\left(\kappa + \frac{k_i^2}{\kappa} \delta_{j1} \right) c^2}} (\tilde{A}_{ij} + B_{ij})$$

The A_{ij} and B_{ij} terms are required in order to satisfy the relations of (356) (a suitable coordinate system K having been chosen). Then the A_{ij} and B_{ij} pertain to emission and the $\tilde{A}_{ij}$ and $\tilde{B}_{ij}$ to absorption, so that, for example, the element $H'_{n_{i1}{}^+, n_{i1}{}^+ + 1}$ which determines the probability of the emission of a positive meson ($j = 1$) is, with the help of (364), given by

$$H'_{n_{i1}{}^+, n_{i1}{}^+ + 1} = -g^* c \sqrt{\frac{\hbar}{2l^3}} \sqrt[4]{\frac{\kappa}{c^2 \left(\kappa + \frac{k_i{}^2}{\kappa} \right)}} \sqrt{n_{i1}{}^+ + 1} \operatorname{div} (\mathbf{e}_{i1} e^{-i\mathbf{k}_i \cdot \mathbf{r}})_0$$

Since, for a longitudinal meson, $\mathbf{e}_{i1}$ has the direction of $\mathbf{k}_i$, we have

$$\operatorname{div} (\mathbf{e}_{i1} e^{-i\mathbf{k}_i \cdot \mathbf{r}}) = -i(e_x k_{ix} + \cdots) e^{-i\mathbf{k}_i \cdot \mathbf{r}} = -i k_i e^{-i\mathbf{k}_i \cdot \mathbf{r}}$$

and therefore

$$H_{n_{i1}{}^+, n_{i1}{}^+ + 1} = ig^* \sqrt{\frac{\hbar^2 c \kappa}{2l^3}} \frac{1}{\sqrt{\epsilon_i}} \sqrt{n_{i1}{}^+ + 1} \, k_i e^{-i\mathbf{k}_i \cdot \mathbf{r}_0} \qquad (365)$$

ϵ_i is the energy of the emitted meson, and $\mathbf{r}_0$ denotes the radius vector to the position of the particle. The element is associated with that g^* which permits the transition $P \to N$ only.

The emission of a negative longitudinal meson is made possible by the matrix B_{i1} which furnishes the element

$$H'_{n_{i1}{}^-, n_{i1}{}^- + 1} = -ig \sqrt{\frac{\hbar^2 c \kappa}{2l^3}} \frac{1}{\sqrt{\epsilon_i}} \sqrt{n_{i1}{}^- + 1} \, k_i e^{i\mathbf{k}_i \cdot \mathbf{r}_0} \qquad (365')$$

The absorption element can be evaluated by the rule $H'_{n_i+1, n_i} = H'^*_{n_i, n_i+1}$.

The emission of a transverse meson is due to curl ψ or curl ψ^*. For example, in the case of a positive meson, $H'_{n_{ij}{}^+, n_{ij}{}^+ + 1}$ is given by

$$H'_{n_{ij}{}^+, n_{ij}{}^+ + 1} = -f^* \sqrt{\frac{\hbar}{2l^3}} \sqrt[4]{\frac{c^2 \kappa}{\kappa + k_i{}^2/\kappa}} \sqrt{n_{ij}{}^+ + 1} \, [\vec{\sigma} \operatorname{curl} (\mathbf{e}_{ij} e^{i\mathbf{k}_i \cdot \mathbf{r}})_0]$$

For curl $(\mathbf{e}_{ij} e^{i\mathbf{k}_i \cdot \mathbf{r}})$ we find

$$\operatorname{curl}_x (\mathbf{e}_{ij} e^{i\mathbf{k}_i \cdot \mathbf{r}}) = \frac{\partial}{\partial y} (e_z e^{i\mathbf{k}_i \cdot \mathbf{r}}) - \frac{\partial}{\partial z} (e_y e^{i\mathbf{k}_i \cdot \mathbf{r}}) = i[\mathbf{k}_i \times \mathbf{e}_{ij}]_x e^{i\mathbf{k}_i \cdot \mathbf{r}}$$

hence

$$H'_{n_{ij}{}^+, n_{ij}{}^+ + 1} = if^* \sqrt{\frac{\hbar^2 \kappa c}{2l^3}} \frac{1}{\sqrt{\epsilon_i}} \sqrt{n_{ij}{}^+ + 1} \, (\vec{\sigma} \cdot \mathbf{e}_{ij} \times \mathbf{k}_i) e^{i\mathbf{k}_i \cdot \mathbf{r}_0}$$

Similarly we obtain

$$H'_{n_{ij}{}^-, n_{ij}{}^- + 1} = if \sqrt{\frac{\hbar^2 \kappa c}{2l^3}} \frac{1}{\sqrt{\epsilon_i}} \sqrt{n_{ij}{}^- + 1} \, (\vec{\sigma} \cdot \mathbf{e}_{ij} \times \mathbf{k}_i) e^{-i\mathbf{k}_i \cdot \mathbf{r}_0} \qquad (366)$$

And for neutral mesons we find

$$H'_{ni1,ni1+1} = i\frac{g+g^*}{2}\sqrt{\frac{\hbar^2\kappa c}{l^3}}\frac{1}{\sqrt{\epsilon_i}}\sqrt{n_{i1}+1}\,k_i e^{i\mathbf{k}_i \cdot \mathbf{r}_0}$$

$$H'_{nij,nij+1} = -i\frac{f+f^*}{2}\sqrt{\frac{\hbar^2\kappa c}{l^3}}\frac{1}{\sqrt{\epsilon_i}}\sqrt{n_{ij}+1}\,(\vec{\sigma}\cdot\mathbf{e}_{ij}\times\mathbf{k}_i)e^{i\mathbf{k}_i\cdot\mathbf{r}_0}$$

(367)

From the formulas for a vector field we can easily derive those for a *pseudovector* field. According to (350), the interaction terms for the two fields are given by

$$-\kappa(g_2 w_\alpha \psi_\alpha{}^* + \tfrac{1}{2}f_2 w_{\alpha\beta}\chi_{\alpha\beta}{}^*) + \text{conjugate complex}$$

$$-\kappa(\tfrac{1}{6}f_3 w_{\alpha\beta\gamma}\chi_{\alpha\beta\gamma}{}^* + \tfrac{1}{2}g_3 w_{\alpha\beta}\psi_{\alpha\beta}{}^*) + \text{conjugate complex}$$

According to Section 48, the $\chi_{\alpha\beta\gamma}$ form a pseudovector having the components

$$\chi_1{}' = \chi_{234} \qquad \chi_2{}' = \chi_{314} \qquad \chi_3{}' = \chi_{124} \qquad \chi_4{}' = -\chi_{123}$$

Therefore we have

$$\tfrac{1}{6}w_{\alpha\beta\gamma}\chi_{\alpha\beta\gamma}{}^* = w_{234}\chi_1{}'^* + w_{314}\chi_2{}'^* + w_{124}\chi_3{}'^* - w_{123}\chi_4{}'^*$$

That is, the ψ_α are to be replaced by the $\chi_\alpha{}'$ and the w_α by w_{ik4} and $-w_{123}$. Furthermore we saw in Section 50 that the tensor components $\chi_{\alpha\beta}$ of the vector field, in the case of the pseudovector field, are to be replaced *not by* $\psi_{\alpha\beta}$, but by the six-vector $\psi_{\alpha\beta}{}'$, which is dual to $\psi_{\alpha\beta}$ in the sense that $\psi_{12}{}' = \psi_{43}$, and so on. Thus $\tfrac{1}{2}w_{\alpha\beta}\chi_{\alpha\beta}{}^*$ is to be replaced by

$$\tfrac{1}{2}w_{\alpha\beta}\psi_{\alpha\beta}{}'^*$$
$$= w_{23}\psi_{41}{}^* + w_{31}\psi_{42}{}^* + w_{12}\psi_{43}{}^* + w_{41}\psi_{23}{}^* + w_{42}\psi_{31}{}^* + w_{43}\psi_{12}{}^*$$

With this new Lagrangian the calculation is to be carried out in the same way as for a vector field. Now, instead of π_i, we have $\pi_i{}' = \partial\bar{L}/\partial(d\chi_i{}'/dt)$, which is found to be $-(1/ic)\psi_{4i}{}'^*$. For the Hamiltonian of the interaction we obtain

$$H' = \int dv\,\Phi^*\{f[-\kappa i(\vec{\sigma}\vec{\chi}'^*) + c\alpha_1\alpha_2\alpha_3\,\mathrm{div}\,\vec{\pi}'] + g\beta[i(\vec{\alpha}\,\mathrm{curl}\,\vec{\chi}'^*)$$
$$- \kappa c(\vec{\sigma}\vec{\pi}')]\}\Phi + \text{conjugate complex} \quad (368)$$

For a particle at rest the expression reduces to

$$H' = -f i\kappa(\vec{\sigma}\vec{\chi}'^*)_0 - g\kappa c(\vec{\sigma}\vec{\pi}')_0 + \text{conjugate complex} \quad (368')$$

64. The Potential of the Nuclear Forces.   With the help of the theory developed in the two preceding sections it should be possible to solve certain problems with which modern physics is particularly concerned.   One of these problems is the question of the forces with which the protons and neutrons of an atomic nucleus act on one another.   The idea suggests itself of explaining these forces by assuming an exchange of mesons between the nuclear particles, an idea which, as we shall see, provides a potential that is in conformity with at least the most characteristic properties of nuclear forces, for example, in accounting for their extraordinarily small range.   However, with decreasing separation of the nuclear particles, the potential becomes infinite as $1/r^3$, and such a strong divergence would exclude the existence of a lowest stationary state.   Therefore we are compelled to accept the theoretical potential $V(r)$ only for the region outside a certain "cut-off" radius r_0, whereas for $r < r_0$ it is assumed that $V(r)$ is either zero or $V(r_0)$.   It is clear that this procedure of cutting off the potential at $r = r_0$, which is rather arbitrary and, in addition, not relativistically invariant, excludes the validity of the theory for just that region within which the effectiveness of the nuclear forces is primarily limited.   In addition to this fundamental difficulty, other problems arise.   Are the forces mediated by charged or uncharged mesons, or are both kinds in action?   There is experimental evidence (Tuve, Heydenburg, and Hafstad) that between two protons there is exactly the same attraction as between a proton and a neutron.   This fact would suggest the assumption that the forces are due exclusively to neutral mesons (Bethe's neutral theory).   On the other hand, however, the radioactive decay can be understood only on the assumption that nuclear particles also emit charged mesons, and for this reason Kemmer proposed his "symmetric theory" in which both charged and uncharged mesons are assumed to be effective.   This theory, however, runs into the difficulty that the quadripole moment of the deuteron appears with the wrong sign.   Again there is the question as to which of the four possible meson fields should be applied to the theory.   It has become impossible to explain all experimental facts on the basis of one kind of mesons only, and therefore Möller and Rosenfeld suggested as a solution a resort to a combination of vector and pseudoscalar mesons.   The cosmic radiation is assumed to contain such a combination also, a radiation which, because of the different lifetimes of the two kinds of mesons, in the lower layers of the atmosphere should consist of pseudoscalar mesons only.

Thus at the present stage the theory of nuclear forces still has a very provisional character, the more so since the transmutation processes of the mesons seem to take place in such a way as to influence the mechanism. Nevertheless it may be of use to the reader to study at least the method of the theory, since he gets an insight into the difficulties that occur and at the same time becomes familiar with the concept of an "exchange force" which plays such an important part in modern physics. We may confine our investigation of the forces brought about by vector mesons; however, we must treat the cases of charged and uncharged mesons separately.

(a) *The Forces Mediated by Neutral Mesons.* As neutral mesons can be exchanged between like particles as well as between unlike ones, the forces caused by them are independent of the nature of the nuclear particles. In order to evaluate these forces we consider two particles which are in interaction with a neutral meson field. Without the interaction H', the system, which consists of the particles and the field, would, in a stationary state, possess an energy E_0 composed of the energies of the particles and the field. By the interaction, which we consider a small perturbation, the energy is changed by correction terms which, according to Section 35, in the first, second, and higher orders are given by

$$E^1 = H_{oo}' \qquad E^2 = \sum_n \frac{H_{on}' H_{no}'}{E_o - E_n}, \quad \text{etc.} \qquad (369)$$

The index o indicates the state of the system to which the correction terms belong and may be supposed to correspond to a field containing no mesons (all $n_{ij} = 0$), whereas the index n denotes an intermediate state into which a transition from the state o is possible so that $H' \neq 0$. Since the correction terms are due to H', they give the energy called forth by the interaction, that is, both the energy with which the particles act on one another by means of the field and the energy corresponding to the forces exerted by the particles on themselves.

According to (364), H' is a linear function of $\vec{\psi}$ and $\vec{\pi}$ and is, therefore, also a linear function of the matrices Q_{ij} and P_{ij}. As all the diagonal elements of these matrices are zero, the correction term $H_{oo}' = E^1$ of the first order vanishes. The term E^2, however, differs from zero. In the expression for E^2, H_{on}' corresponds to the transition of the system to a possible intermediate state. According to (356) the system is capable only of transitions from the state o (all $n_{ij} = 0$) into those states in which the field contains only one meson of an arbitrary kind ij, whereas the nuclear particles remain unchanged (actually, they undergo a reaction which, however, may be disregarded). Let us first suppose that the created meson is emitted by particle 1. The system then returns to the initial state (the factor H_{no}' in E^2), whereby the possibilities arise that the meson is absorbed by either 1 or 2. The E^2 that comes about in the first way occasions a self-energy of particle 1, whereas the interaction energy is effected by the second process. The latter energy, which will depend on the positions $\mathbf{r}_1$ and $\mathbf{r}_2$ of the two particles, may be denoted by V. V is composed of two parts, V_{I} and V_{II}, which are due to longitudinal and transverse mesons respectively. To evaluate V_{I} and V_{II} we have to make use of the expressions (367). The denominator in (369) is the difference between the energies of the system in the states o and n and thus equal to the negative energy of the exchanged meson. If we set g equal to g^* and f equal to f^* in (369), we obtain

$$V_{\mathrm{I}} = -2 \frac{g^2 \hbar^2 c \kappa}{l^3} \sum_i \frac{k_i^2 e^{i\mathbf{k}_i \cdot (\mathbf{r}_1 - \mathbf{r}_2)}}{\epsilon_i^2} \tag{370}$$

$$V_{\mathrm{II}} = -2 \frac{f^2 \hbar^2 c \kappa}{l^3} \sum_{ij} \frac{(\vec{\sigma}_1 \cdot \mathbf{e}_{ij} \times \mathbf{k}_i)(\vec{\sigma}_2 \cdot \mathbf{e}_{ij} \times \mathbf{k}_i)}{\epsilon_i^2} e^{i\mathbf{k}_i \cdot (\mathbf{r}_1 - \mathbf{r}_2)} \tag{371}$$

The factor 2 is necessary since for any exchange there is an inverse one that furnishes the same contribution.

We shall first use the expressions (370) and (371) to make clear the nature of an *exchange force*. A force of this kind must always occur if two particles have the possibility of exchanging a particle, regardless of the kind, and in this way transfer momentum to each other. However, it must not be understood that the force comes about by a real exchange in a kind of ball playing; for it is only the *potentiality* of an exchange that matters, just as the potential energy of a lifted stone is due to the potentiality of its falling down. In the case of the stone, the energy is given by the product of the weight and altitude. In our case, in place of this product the perturbation theory provides the expression

$$\frac{H_{on}' H_{no}'}{E_o - E_n}$$

where n denotes an intermediate state created by the emission of a meson. In this expression, however, only one potentiality of an exchange is taken into account since it refers to a meson of a given momentum.   To obtain the total energy we must consider all possible momenta $\hbar k_i$, in this way arriving at the sums in (370) and (371).

This corpuscular interpretation, however, is not adaptable to a certain circumstance which is of essential importance for an exchange force and becomes conspicuous only in the wave picture.   In this picture a wave $e^{ik_i \cdot r}$ of the wavelength $\lambda_i = 2\pi/k_i$ corresponds to any exchange, and the potential energy is the result of the interferences of all these possible waves.   It is because of this interference that the energy V depends on the distance of the two particles, an inconceivable fact in the corpuscle picture.

To evaluate the sums in (370) and (371), in which $\vec{\sigma}_1$ and $\vec{\sigma}_2$ denote the spins of the two nucleons, we replace the sums by integrals by using (343) for the number of the propagation vectors k_i with a direction within the angle $d\Omega$ and a k_i between k and $k + dk$.   According to (343), this number is given by

$$ \frac{d\Omega l^3}{(2\pi c)^3} \, \nu^2 \, d\nu = \frac{d\Omega l^3}{(2\pi)^3} \, k^2 \, dk $$

(without the factor 2, which had to be used in Section 59, for there were two directions of polarization for any k_i).   Because of the relation $\epsilon_i = \hbar c \sqrt{\kappa^2 + k_i^2}$, (370) and (371), with $r_1 - r_2 = r$, become

$$ V_{\mathrm{I}} = -2 \, \frac{g^2 \kappa}{(2\pi)^3 c} \int d\Omega \int dk \, \frac{k^4}{\kappa^2 + k^2} \, e^{ik \cdot r} \qquad (372) $$

$$ V_{\mathrm{II}} = -2 \, \frac{f^2 \kappa}{(2\pi)^3 c} \sum \int d\Omega \int dk \, \frac{k^2}{\kappa^2 + k^2} \, (\vec{\sigma}_1 \cdot e_j \times k)(\vec{\sigma}_2 \cdot e_j \times k) e^{ik \cdot r} $$

$$ (373) $$

The integral in (372) can be transformed if k^4 is replaced by $k^2(k^2 + \kappa^2 - \kappa^2)$, thus becoming

$$ \int d\Omega \int dk \, k^2 e^{ik \cdot r} - \kappa^2 \int d\Omega \int dk \, \frac{k^2}{\kappa^2 + k^2} \, e^{ik \cdot r} $$

The first integral represents the sum of all $e^{ik \cdot r}$, which, by a well-known theorem that is valid for orthogonal functions, is given by

$$ \sum e^{ik \cdot r} = \sum e^{ik_i \cdot (r_1 - r_2)} = \delta(r_1 - r_2) = \delta(r) $$

Thus the sum vanishes for any distance $r \neq 0$ and consequently may be omitted. We then have for V_{I}

$$V_{\mathrm{I}} = \frac{2g^2\kappa^3}{(2\pi)^3 c} \int d\Omega \int dk \, \frac{k^2}{\kappa^2 + k^2} e^{i\mathbf{k}\cdot\mathbf{r}}$$

The integral is a function of $r = |\mathbf{r}|$. If we assume that particle 2 is at the origin of the coordinate system ($\mathbf{r}_2 = 0$), by differentiating $f(r)$ relative to the coordinates xyz of particle 1, we get

$$\Delta f(r) = -\int d\Omega \int dk \, \frac{k^4}{\kappa^2 + k^2} e^{i\mathbf{k}\cdot\mathbf{r}}$$

$$= \kappa^2 \int d\Omega \int dk \, \frac{k^2}{\kappa^2 + k^2} e^{i\mathbf{k}\cdot\mathbf{r}} = \kappa^2 f(r) \qquad (374)$$

The solution of this differential equation is $f(r) = Ce^{-\kappa r}/r$, where C is a constant. To determine this constant we evaluate $f(r)$ for $\kappa = 0$, and we find that

$$f_0(r) = \int d\Omega \int dk e^{i\mathbf{k}\cdot\mathbf{r}}$$

$$= 2\pi \int_0^\pi \sin\theta \, d\theta \int_0^\infty dk e^{ikr\cos\theta} = 4\pi \int_0^\infty dk \, \frac{\sin kr}{kr} = \frac{2\pi^2}{r}$$

Thus the constant is $2\pi^2$, and we have

$$V_{\mathrm{I}} = \frac{1}{2} \frac{g^2\kappa^3}{\pi c} e^{-\kappa r/r} \qquad (375)$$

To evaluate V_{II} due to the transverse mesons ($j = 2, 3$), we carry out the summation over j first. Since $\mathbf{e}_{i2} \times \mathbf{k}_i = \pm k_i \mathbf{e}_{i3}$ and $\mathbf{e}_{i3} \times \mathbf{k}_i = \pm k_i \mathbf{e}_{i2}$, we find

$$\sum_j (\vec{\sigma}_1 \cdot \mathbf{e}_{ij} \times \mathbf{k}_i)(\vec{\sigma}_2 \cdot \mathbf{e}_{ij} \times \mathbf{k}_i) = k_i^2 |\vec{\sigma}_1||\vec{\sigma}_2| \{\cos(\vec{\sigma}_1 \mathbf{e}_{i2}) \cos(\vec{\sigma}_2 \mathbf{e}_{i2})$$

$$+ \cos(\vec{\sigma}_1 \mathbf{e}_{i3}) \cos(\vec{\sigma}_2 \mathbf{e}_{i3})\}$$

If in the braces we add and subtract $\cos(\vec{\sigma}_1 \mathbf{e}_{i1}) \cos(\vec{\sigma}_2 \mathbf{e}_{i1})$, the first three terms together with $k_i^2 |\vec{\sigma}_1||\vec{\sigma}_2|$ give $k_i^2 (\vec{\sigma}_1 \vec{\sigma}_2)$, whereas the last term gives $(\sigma_1 \vec{\mathbf{k}}_i)(\sigma_2 \vec{\mathbf{k}}_i)$, since $\mathbf{e}_{i1}$ has the direction of $\mathbf{k}_i$. Thus we obtain

$$V_{\mathrm{II}} = -\frac{2f^2\kappa}{(2\pi)^3 c} \int d\Omega \int dk \, \frac{k^4}{\kappa^2 + k^2} \left((\vec{\sigma}_1 \vec{\sigma}_2) - \frac{(\vec{\sigma}_1\mathbf{k})(\vec{\sigma}_2\mathbf{k})}{k^2} \right) e^{i\mathbf{k}\cdot\mathbf{r}}$$

That part of the integral containing $(\vec{\sigma_1}\vec{\sigma_2})$ can be transformed into

$$\int d\Omega \int dk \, \frac{k^4}{\kappa^2 + k^2} \, e^{i\mathbf{k}\cdot\mathbf{r}} \, (\vec{\sigma_1}\vec{\sigma_2}) = -(\vec{\sigma_1}\vec{\sigma_2})\kappa^2 \int d\Omega \int dk \, \frac{k^2}{\kappa^2 + k^2} \, e^{i\mathbf{k}\cdot\mathbf{r}}$$

$$= -(\vec{\sigma_1}\vec{\sigma_2})\kappa^2 2\pi^2 \frac{e^{-\kappa r}}{r}$$

If in addition we take the direction of $\mathbf{r} = \mathbf{r}_1 - \mathbf{r}_2$ as the z axis and denote the angle $(\mathbf{k}z)$ by θ, we have

$$\int d\Omega \int dk \, \frac{k^2}{\kappa^2 + k^2} \, e^{i\mathbf{k}\cdot\mathbf{r}} \, (\vec{\sigma_1}\mathbf{k})(\vec{\sigma_2}\mathbf{k})$$

$$= \int \int \sin\theta \, d\theta \, d\phi \int dk \, \frac{k^2}{\kappa^2 + k^2} (\sigma_{1x}k_x + \cdots)(\sigma_{2x}k_x \cdots)$$

Since $k_x{}^2 = k^2 \sin^2\theta \cos^2\phi$, the product $\sigma_{1x}\sigma_{2x}$ gives the contribution

$$\sigma_{1x}\sigma_{2x} \int dk \, \frac{k^4}{\kappa^2 + k^2} \int \sin^3\theta \, d\theta \int d\phi \cos^2\phi e^{ikr\cos\theta}$$

The integration over $\cos^2\phi$ gives π. By resolving $\sin^3\theta$ into $\sin\theta(1 - \cos^2\theta)$ and making use of (374), we obtain

$$\sigma_{1x}\sigma_{2x}\pi \left\{ -\kappa^2\pi \frac{e^{-\kappa r}}{r} - \int dk \, \frac{k^4}{\kappa^2 + k^2} \int d\theta \sin\theta \cos^2\theta e^{ikr\cos\theta} \right\}$$

To evaluate the last integral we differentiate the equation

$$\int dk \, \frac{k^4}{\kappa^2 + k^2} \int d\theta \sin\theta e^{ikr\cos\theta} = \pi \frac{e^{-\kappa r}}{r}$$

twice with respect to r, and we obtain

$$-\int dk \, \frac{k^4}{\kappa^2 + k^2} \int d\theta \sin\theta \cos^2\theta e^{ikr\cos\theta} = \pi\kappa^2 e^{-\kappa r} \left(\frac{1}{r} + \frac{2}{\kappa r^2} + \frac{2}{\kappa^2 r^3} \right)$$

Therefore the contribution of $\sigma_{1x}\sigma_{2x}$ is

$$\sigma_{1x}\sigma_{2x}\pi^2\kappa^2 e^{-\kappa r} \left(\frac{2}{\kappa r^2} + \frac{2}{\kappa^2 r^3} \right)$$

An exactly corresponding contribution is due to $\sigma_{1y}\sigma_{2y}$. On the other hand, from $\sigma_{1z}\sigma_{2z}$ we obtain

$$\sigma_{1z}\sigma_{2z} 2\pi \int dk \, \frac{k^4}{\kappa^2 + k^2} \int d\theta \sin\theta \cos^2\theta e^{ikr\cos\theta}$$

$$= -\sigma_{1z}\sigma_{2z}2\pi^2\kappa^2 e^{-\kappa r} \left(\frac{1}{r} + \frac{2}{\kappa r^2} + \frac{2}{\kappa^2 r^3} \right)$$

The contributions of $\sigma_{1x}\sigma_{2y}$ and so on vanish. So, since $\sigma_z = (\vec{\sigma}\mathbf{r})r$, we obtain

$$V_{\mathrm{II}} = \frac{f^2\kappa^3}{2\pi c}\frac{e^{-\kappa r}}{r}\left[(\vec{\sigma}_1\vec{\sigma}_2)\left(1 + \frac{1}{\kappa r} + \frac{1}{\kappa^2 r^2}\right)\right.$$
$$\left. - \frac{(\vec{\sigma}_1\mathbf{r})(\vec{\sigma}_2\mathbf{r})}{r^2}\left(1 + \frac{3}{\kappa r} + \frac{3}{\kappa^2 r^2}\right)\right] \quad (376)$$

The potentials V_{I} and V_{II} are quite different. V_{I}, which arises from the longitudinal mesons, is independent of the spins, whereas V_{II} depends on the spins $\vec{\sigma}_1$ and $\vec{\sigma}_2$ of the two particles. V_{II} is composed of two parts. The first part is spherically symmetric, that is, it corresponds to a central force, and is proportional to $(\vec{\sigma}_1\vec{\sigma}_2)$, thus it is positive for parallel spins and negative for antiparallel spins. The second part is proportional to $(\vec{\sigma}_1\mathbf{r})(\vec{\sigma}_2\mathbf{r})$, that is, it depends not only on the magnitude but also on the direction of the distance r, so that the eigenfunction of the system consisting of the two particles loses its spatial symmetry, and the same holds for the charge distribution. Indeed, in the case of a deuteron, the existence of such an asymmetry was shown by Kellog, Rabi, Ramsey, and Zacharias.

(b) *The Forces Mediated by Charged Mesons.* In the case of the second approximation as considered here, charged mesons can act only between unlike particles because an exchange of charged mesons between like particles is impossible. The exchange is necessarily connected with a change of the charges of the particles, the proton being bound to transmute itself into a neutron, and vice versa. Therefore we cannot calculate the interaction energy of the second order E^2 in the same way as for neutral mesons. For them we imagined that the system is brought from its initial state A into an intermediate state Z by the emission of a meson by particle 1, whereupon the meson is absorbed by the other particle 2. In this way the initial state is restored. But if we apply the same procedure to a charged meson, we get a final state E which differs from A since the two particles have interchanged the charge coordinates τ. Therefore the quantity

$$\epsilon_{AE} = \sum_Z \frac{H_{AZ}{}'H_{ZE}{}'}{E_A - E_Z}$$

has not the meaning of an energy correction but rather determines the probability of a transition of the system from the state A into the state E. As we shall see, we can, however, form a matrix from the

ϵ_{AE} and determine the energy corrections by bringing this matrix into diagonal form. For this purpose, proton and neutron are considered two modifications of the same particle, the ability to appear as a proton or as a neutron being described by a "charge coordinate" τ. The proton state may be denoted by $\tau = 1$, and that of the neutron by $\tau = 0$. We must then coordinate in the Hilbert space two axes, $\tau = 0$ and $\tau = 1$, to a nucleon. If the vector representing the state lies in the direction of one of these axes, the particle is with certainty a neutron or a proton, but otherwise there is only a certain probability of finding a neutron or proton by a measurement of the charge. Since we are now dealing with a system consisting of two nucleons, we need four axes, each of which belongs to a value of τ_1 and τ_2 so that the axes are to be marked by two indices. If we simply write a, b, c, d for 00, 01, 10, 11, a vector in the direction a means that both the first and second particles are neutrons; b indicates the state wherein 1 is a neutron, 2 a proton, and so on.

We now consider the transitions between the states a, b, c, d and correlate an ϵ_{AE} to each of them. A transition between two of the states is only possible if either of the particles 1 or 2 emits a meson which thereupon is absorbed by 2 or 1. The meson may be positive or negative, longitudinal or transverse, so that, according to these possibilities,

$$\epsilon_{AE} = \sum_Z \frac{H_{AZ}' H_{ZE}'}{E_A - E_Z}$$

can be resolved into four partial sums. For the H_{AZ}' and H_{ZE}' quantities, the expressions of (366) must be substituted in which a factor g or f occurs. According to (358) these factors are matrices by which only certain transitions are permitted. In what follows we shall denote the factors belonging to particles 1 and 2 by $g_1 f_1$ and $g_2 f_2$ respectively. If $A \rightarrow Z$ means that a positive longitudinal meson is emitted by 1, and $Z \rightarrow E$ that it is absorbed by 2, the factor of the product $H_{AZ}' H_{ZE}'$ is $g_1^* g_2$. For a negative meson the factor is $g_1 g_2^*$. The contribution of a longitudinal meson to ϵ_{AZ} therefore carries the factor $g_1^* g_2 + g_1 g_2^*$, which must be taken twice, since the meson may as well be emitted by 2 and absorbed by 1. We shall now denote the "isotopic spin matrices" γ_1 and γ_2, defined by (358'), by $\tau^{(1)}$ and $\tau^{(2)}$ in order to indicate that they are now used with reference to the charge coordinate and not to the spin. Then, denoting by g' an ordinary number, we have

$$g = g' \tfrac{1}{2}(\tau^{(1)} - i\tau^{(2)}) \qquad g^* = g'^* \tfrac{1}{2}(\tau^{(1)} + i\tau^{(2)})$$

$$\therefore g_1^* g_2 + g_1 g_2^* = |g'|^2 \, \tfrac{1}{2}(\tau_1^{(1)}\tau_2^{(1)} + \tau_1^{(2)}\tau_2^{(2)})$$

The factors $g_1{}^*g_2$ and $g_1g_2{}^*$ are not to be read as products of matrices in the sense of (120); they represent four-row matrices operating in the space scaffolded by the axes $a = 00$, $b = 01$, $c = 10$, $d = 11$. g_1 operates on the first, g_2 on the second, so that, for example, $(g_1g_2{}^*)_{ab}$ is to be understood as $(g_1)_{00}(g_2{}^*)_{01}$. Since only g_{01} and $g_{10}{}^*$ differ from zero, $g_1{}^*g_2 + g_1g_2{}^*$ represents the matrix

$$g_1{}^*g_2 + g_1g_2{}^* = |g'|^2 \tfrac{1}{2}(\tau_1{}^{(1)}\tau_2{}^{(1)} + \tau_1{}^{(2)}\tau_2{}^{(2)}) = |g'|^2 \begin{bmatrix} 0 & 0 & 0 & 0 \\ 0 & 0 & 1 & 0 \\ 0 & 1 & 0 & 0 \\ 0 & 0 & 0 & 0 \end{bmatrix} \quad (377)$$

The meaning of this matrix factor is that charged mesons can cause transitions only between the states b and c (for ϵ_{AE} determines the probability of the transition $A \rightarrow E$), that is, one particle must be a proton, the other a neutron. Aside from this "exchange factor," the evaluation of ϵ_{AE} is the same as that of the expression (369) for E^2 with which ϵ_{AE} conforms if we disregard the charge. Thus we obtain for ϵ_{aa}, ϵ_{ab} and so on the matrix

$$\epsilon_{AE} = \frac{1}{2}\left(\frac{|g'|^2}{g^2} V_{\mathrm{I}} + \frac{|f'|^2}{f^2} V_{\mathrm{II}}\right) \begin{bmatrix} 0 & 0 & 0 & 0 \\ 0 & 0 & 1 & 0 \\ 0 & 1 & 0 & 0 \\ 0 & 0 & 0 & 0 \end{bmatrix} \quad (378)$$

V_{I} and V_{II} being defined by (375) and (376). The factor $\tfrac{1}{2}$ is necessary because, according to (366), the elements of H' for charged mesons are $1/\sqrt{2}$ times smaller than those for neutral ones. The distinction of g', f', and g, f means that these factors may be different for charged and neutral mesons.

The ϵ_{AE} defined by (378) cannot as yet be interpreted as energy corrections, since the initial and final states are not identical. But by a rotation of the coordinate system, that is, a passage to other axes a', b', c', d', we can make the matrix in (378) diagonal. Then we obtain four quantities $\epsilon_{a'a'}$, $\epsilon_{b'b'}$, $\epsilon_{c'c'}$, $\epsilon_{d'd'}$ which may be considered energy corrections of the states a', b', c', and d'.

To carry out the plan we determine first the eigenvalues of the matrix in (378) by solving the equation

$$\begin{vmatrix} -\alpha & 0 & 0 & 0 \\ 0 & -\alpha & 1 & 0 \\ 0 & 1 & -\alpha & 0 \\ 0 & 0 & 0 & -\alpha \end{vmatrix} = \alpha^2(\alpha^2 - 1) = 0$$

The solutions are $\alpha = 0$, which occurs twice, and $\alpha = \pm 1$. These eigenvalues belong to four orthogonal directions a', b', c', d'. If

$\mathbf{e}_i$ $(i = 1, 2, 3, 4)$ denotes four unit vectors in these directions, and $x_k^{(i)}$ $(k = a, b, c, d)$ their components relative to the axes a, b, c, d, the $\mathbf{e}_i$, as eigenvectors of the matrix

$$M = \begin{bmatrix} 0 & 0 & 0 & 0 \\ 0 & 0 & 1 & 0 \\ 0 & 1 & 0 & 0 \\ 0 & 0 & 0 & 0 \end{bmatrix}$$

must satisfy the equations $M\mathbf{e}_i = \alpha_i \mathbf{e}_i$. For $\alpha = 0$ it follows from these equations (the two corresponding eigenvectors $\mathbf{e}_1$ and $\mathbf{e}_4$ may belong to the directions a' and d')

$$x_c^{(1)} = 0 \qquad x_b^{(1)} = 0 \qquad x_c^{(4)} = 0 \qquad x_b^{(4)} = 0$$

That is, the directions a' and d' lie in the a-d plane and may be chosen so as to coincide with a and d. Thus if a vector has one of these two directions, both particles are either protons or neutrons. The corresponding $\epsilon_{a'a'}$ and $\epsilon_{d'd'}$ are zero, in accordance with the fact that there is no interaction between two like particles. For $\alpha = 1$, belonging to $\mathbf{e}_2 = b'$, however, we obtain from $M\mathbf{e}_2 = \mathbf{e}_2$

$$x_c^{(2)} = x_b^{(2)} \qquad x_a^{(2)} = x_d^{(2)} = 0$$

Thus b' lies in the b-c plane and has equal components relative to the b and c axes. Therefore a vector with the direction of b' represents a state which is symmetric in the charge coordinates τ_1 and τ_2. The probability amplitudes for the statements 1 = proton, 2 = neutron, and vice versa, are equal.

Finally for the eigenvalue $\alpha = -1$ $(\mathbf{e}_3 = c')$ we obtain, from $M\mathbf{e}_3 = -\mathbf{e}_3$,

$$x_b^{(3)} = -x_c^{(3)} \qquad x_a^{(3)} = x_d^{(3)} = 0$$

corresponding to a state which is antisymmetric in τ_1 and τ_2.

Thus the interaction between two nucleons, brought about by charged mesons, can be described by the eigenvalues of the matrix

$$V = \frac{1}{2}\left(\frac{|g'|^2}{g^2} V_{\mathrm{I}} + \frac{|f'|^2}{f^2} V_{\mathrm{II}}\right) \frac{1}{2} \left(\tau_1^{(1)}\tau_2^{(1)} + \tau_1^{(2)}\tau_2^{(2)}\right) \qquad (379)$$

Two of these eigenvalues are zero, and the other two are given by

$$\pm \frac{1}{2}\left(\frac{|g'|^2}{g^2} V_{\mathrm{I}} + \frac{|f'|^2}{f^2} V_{\mathrm{II}}\right)$$

in which the positive sign is to be taken for a state which is symmetric as to charge, and the negative one for the antisymmetric state.

(c) *Comparison with Experience.* We wish here to draw a brief comparison between the results at which we have arrived and the formulations reached when experimental facts are included in a purely phenomenological theory. From the facts we learn, at least to a certain approximation, that between two nucleons a central force of very small range must be acting, the potential of which can be represented by $e^{-\kappa r}/r$. Furthermore it seems probable that the interaction is due to an exchange force, that is, it comes about by a mechanism in which the charges or spins of the two particles are interchanged. Formally, this is to be expressed in a way that the potential, when it acts as an operator on the state, interchanges the values of one or both of the observables mentioned above. An example of an operator of this kind is the matrix $\frac{1}{2}(\tau_1^{(1)}\tau_2^{(1)} + \tau_1^{(2)}\tau_2^{(2)})$, which has the property of multiplying a symmetric or antisymmetric function describing a state by 1 or -1 respectively; this means that the effect of the operator must consist of an interchange of the charges. The effect of $\frac{1}{2}(\tau_1^{(1)}\tau_2^{(1)} + \tau_1^{(2)}\tau_2^{(2)})$ on the symmetric states $a = 00$ and $d = 11$ is zero, from which it must be inferred that a potential of the sort (379) holds only for unlike particles. If the potential is required to include the forces between like particles as well, the exchange factor must be changed to

$$\tfrac{1}{2}(1 + \tau_1^{(1)}\tau_2^{(1)} + \tau_1^{(2)}\tau_2^{(2)} + \tau_1^{(3)}\tau_2^{(3)}) = \tfrac{1}{2}(1 + (\vec{\tau_1}\vec{\tau_2}))$$

is $\tau^{(3)}$ denotes the isotopic spin matrix

$$\tau^{(3)} = \gamma_3 = \begin{bmatrix} 1 & 0 \\ 0 & -1 \end{bmatrix}$$

$\tau_1^{(3)}\tau_2^{(3)}$ is a diagonal matrix with the elements $1, -1, -1, 1$ which, added to $\tau_1^{(1)}\tau_2^{(1)} + \tau_1^{(2)}\tau_2^{(2)}$, furnishes a matrix with the eigenvalues, $1, 1, -3, 1$. Therefore an exchange force with the factor $(1 + (\vec{\tau_1}\vec{\tau_2})/2$ works also in the state $a = 00$ and $d = 11$ and is used in Kemmer's symmetric theory.

In the same way as $(1 + (\vec{\tau_1}\vec{\tau_2}))/2$ acts on the charges, $(1 + (\vec{\sigma_1}\vec{\sigma_2}))/2$ operates on the spins of the two particles. This operator multiplies the three states which are spin symmetric by 1, and the antisymmetric state by -1. According to (241) the $\sigma^{(i)}$ are defined as four-row matrices each of which is built up in two equal steps:

$$\sigma^{(1)} = \begin{bmatrix} \tau^{(1)} & 0 \\ 0 & \tau^{(1)} \end{bmatrix} \qquad \sigma^{(2)} = \begin{bmatrix} \tau^{(2)} & 0 \\ 0 & \tau^{(2)} \end{bmatrix} \qquad \sigma^{(3)} = \begin{bmatrix} \tau^{(3)} & 0 \\ 0 & \tau^{(3)} \end{bmatrix}$$

The two steps correspond to the states of positive and negative energy.

As we are dealing only with the spin here, we may simply take $\vec{\tau}$ for $\vec{\sigma}$.

Thus there are the following three possibilities for an exchange force with the potential $e^{-\kappa r}/r$:

$$a\,\frac{e^{-\kappa r}}{r}\,[1 + (\vec{\sigma_1}\vec{\sigma_2})]_{\text{(Bartlett)}}$$

$$b\,\frac{e^{-\kappa r}}{r}\,[1 + (\vec{\tau_1}\vec{\tau_2})]_{\text{(Heisenberg)}}$$

$$c\,\frac{e^{-\kappa r}}{r}\,[1 + (\vec{\tau_1}\vec{\tau_2})][1 + (\vec{\sigma_1}\vec{\sigma_2})]_{\text{(Majorana)}}$$

If we take as a fourth possibility a force without exchange, all four types can be combined in the general formula

$$V = \frac{e^{-\kappa r}}{r}\,[a + b(\vec{\sigma_1}\vec{\sigma_2}) + c(\vec{\tau_1}\vec{\tau_2}) + d(\vec{\sigma_1}\vec{\sigma_2})(\vec{\tau_1}\vec{\tau_2})] \qquad (380)$$

wherein the constants a, b, c, d can be chosen in such a way as to arrive at the best possible agreement with experience.

Now the theory of the meson does indeed furnish a potential the range of which is limited to $r \sim 1/\kappa$ by the factor $e^{-\kappa r}$. κ can be calculated from the mass m_0 of the meson with which it is connected by the relation $m_0 = \hbar\kappa/c$. For an m_0 of nearly 200 electron masses, a value of 2×10^{-13} cm is found for $1/\kappa$ which is in good agreement with experiment. In addition it is seen that the potential (379), when, according to Kemmer's symmetric theory, $(\vec{\tau_1}\vec{\tau_2})$ is substituted for $\tau_1^{(1)}\tau_2^{(1)} + \tau_1^{(2)}\tau_2^{(2)}$, takes on a form that to a certain extent is in conformity with (380) provided we set $a = b = 0$. It consists essentially of a Heisenberg and a Majorana force in which the first one, by means of $(\vec{\tau_1}\vec{\tau_2})$, exchanges only the charges and the second one, by means of $(\vec{\sigma_1}\vec{\sigma_2})(\vec{\tau_1}\vec{\tau_2})$, exchanges the spins as well. There is, however, in (379) a further term with the factor $(\vec{\sigma_1}\mathbf{r})(\vec{\sigma_2}\mathbf{r})$ which represents a tensor force that is dependent on the spins and is not foreseen in the phenomenological theory. This term is important for the explanation of the quadripole moment of the deuteron. As is seen from (376), its expression contains a term that depends on r like $1/r^3$, and this divergence makes the theory a failure, for it can be shown easily that, in the case of an attraction with a divergence greater than $1/r^2$, no stationary state of lowest energy exists. In order to prove this we imagine that one of the two nucleons is fixed in space. Let r be the radius of the orbit belonging to the stationary state, that is, the radius of the region within which the wave function of the movable particle differs noticeably from zero. According to the uncertainty relations the momentum would then be of the order of magnitude $\hbar/r$, and from this it can be inferred that the kinetic energy has to be of the order of $1/r^2$. This means that, if r is decreased, the decrease of the potential energy would outweigh the increase of kinetic energy, the effect being that the total energy would diminish. Thus for any r a transition to a smaller r has to be possible, that is, an atomic nucleus of finite radius could not exist, in obvious contradiction to the experimental facts.

By combining a vector and a pseudoscalar field and by choosing the constants in a suitable way, we could make the term with $1/r^3$ vanish, but in this case the effect would be that the tensor force required for the explanation of the quadripole moment would vanish as well. Thus the solution of the nuclear problem is impossible as long as the divergences of the potential cannot be removed in a relativistically invariant way (cf. Chapter 10).

65. Nuclear Scattering of Mesons. Mesons are deviated from their straight paths when passing through matter. These deviations, like those of photons which are caused by electrons, come about in a way that a nucleon absorbs a meson of given momentum $\hbar\mathbf{k}$ and in return emits another of momentum $\hbar\mathbf{k}'$. In the following we shall treat the process of *elastic* scattering only, for which the momenta $\hbar\mathbf{k}$ and $\hbar\mathbf{k}'$ of the absorbed and emitted meson are of equal amount. For this purpose we suppose that the nuclear particle is infinitely heavy so that it does not undergo a noticeable change in energy by the absorption and emission of a meson.

For the treatment of scattering processes, according to (186), we must begin with the evaluation of the quantity

$$H' = \sum_Z \frac{H_{AZ}' H_{ZE}'}{E_A - E_Z}$$

which determines the probability of a transition $A \rightarrow E$ through an intermediate state Z. We consider an initial state A in which, besides the nuclear particle, only one vector meson of momentum $\hbar\mathbf{k}$ is present; in the final state this meson is assumed to have disappeared, making room for another of momentum $\hbar\mathbf{k}'$. The transition is effected in such a way that the nucleon absorbs the first meson and emits the second one. If first we consider the case of a neutral meson, there are two possibilities:

(i) The meson $\hbar\mathbf{k}$ is absorbed first, and then the meson $\hbar\mathbf{k}'$ is emitted. The system then uses an intermediate state Z_1 in which no meson is present.

(ii) The above processes occur in the reverse order. In this case both of the mesons are present in the intermediate state Z_2.

The matrix elements of (367) are to be substituted for H_{AZ}' and H_{ZE}'. If we consider a longitudinal meson and make the extension l of the cubic space equal to unity, we shall have

$$H_{AZ_1}' = H_{Z_2E}' = ig\sqrt{\frac{\hbar^2\kappa c}{\epsilon}}\,k e^{i\mathbf{k}\cdot\mathbf{r}}$$

$$H_{Z_1E}' = H_{AZ_2}' = -ig\sqrt{\frac{\hbar^2\kappa c}{\epsilon'}}\,k' e^{-i\mathbf{k}'\cdot\mathbf{r}}$$

Furthermore, if ϵ and ϵ' denote the energies associated with the momenta $\hbar\mathbf{k}$ and $\hbar\mathbf{k}'$,

$$E_A - E_{Z_1} = \epsilon \qquad E_A - E_{Z_2} = -\epsilon'$$

For an elastic process we have $k = k'$ and $\epsilon = \epsilon'$, so that we obtain

$$H' = \frac{H_{AZ_1}'H_{Z_1E}'}{\epsilon} - \frac{H_{AZ_2}'H_{Z_2E}'}{\epsilon} = 0$$

That is, the probability of an elastic scattering process for neutral mesons is zero, because the contributions of Z_1 and Z_2 cancel each other.

On the other hand, for *charged* mesons the cross section turns out to be different from zero. If, for example, we take a proton and a positive (longitudinal) meson, then, since the proton is not able to absorb the meson, the scattering process can take place only through the intermediate Z_2 state, and according to (365) we obtain

$$H' = -\frac{H_{AZ_2}'H_{Z_2E}'}{\epsilon} = g^2\frac{\hbar^2 c\kappa}{\epsilon^2}\,k^2 e^{i(\mathbf{k}-\mathbf{k}')\cdot\mathbf{r}}$$

Apart from the sign, the same value holds for a negative meson which can be scattered by a proton only through an intermediate state Z_1, since the proton cannot emit a negative meson. The probability dW of a meson being scattered in unit time so that the momentum $\hbar\mathbf{k}'$ of the scattered particle lies within a certain angle $d\Omega$, according to (188), is given by

$$dW = \frac{2\pi}{\hbar}\,|H'|^2\rho\,d\Omega$$

where ρ denotes the density which, when multiplied by dE, gives the number of final states which have an energy between E and $E + dE$. The number of meson states having a momentum of amount lying between k and $k + dk$ and of direction within $d\Omega$, for $l = 1$, according to (343) is given by

$$\frac{d\Omega}{(2\pi)^3} k^2 \, dk$$

Thus we have

$$\rho \, dE = \frac{1}{(2\pi)^3} k^2 \, dk$$

Since $\epsilon = E = c\hbar \sqrt{\kappa^2 + k^2}$, then

$$dE = \frac{c\hbar k \, dk}{\sqrt{\kappa^2 + k^2}} = \frac{c^2 \hbar^2 k \, dk}{\epsilon}$$

Thus ρ becomes

$$\rho = \frac{\epsilon k}{(2\pi)^3 c^2 \hbar^2}$$

For dW we obtain

$$dW = \frac{2\pi}{\hbar} g^4 \frac{\hbar^4 c^2 \kappa^2}{\epsilon^4} k^4 \frac{1}{(2\pi)^3} \frac{\epsilon k}{c^2 \hbar^2} d\Omega$$

In order to find the cross section dq we set $dW = J \, dq$, J denoting the intensity of the meson radiation, that is, the number of mesons passing per unit time through unit surface perpendicular to the radiation. As the space with $l = 1$ is assumed to contain only one meson, J is identical with the velocity v of the meson. From the relation $m_0 v / \sqrt{1 - v^2/c^2} = \hbar k$ we obtain for this velocity

$$v = \frac{\hbar k c^2}{\epsilon}$$

so that for dq we obtain

$$dq = \frac{1}{(2\pi)^2 c^2} g^4 \kappa^2 \frac{k^4}{\epsilon^2} d\Omega \qquad (381)$$

Thus the cross section for charged vector mesons should increase infinitely with increasing energy. However, in this case we arrive at values which, compared with the measured values† for energy above

† F. L. Code, *Phys. Rev.*, **50**, 229 (1941), and R. P. Shu, *Phys. Rev.*, **61**, 6 (1942).

10^8 ev, turn out to be far too high. According to measurements by Code, the cross section for mesons with an energy of 0.8×10^9 ev is about 0.6×10^{-27} cm^2, whereas the theory gives one of 0.6×10^{-23} cm^2. A better agreement with experiment is had on the assumption of scalar or pseudoscalar mesons. Then the factor k^4 in the numerator drops out, so that the cross section should diminish rapidly with increasing energy. Whether this is true can be decided only by further measurements.

66. Magnetic Moment of Proton and Neutron. Since both the proton and neutron have the spin $\frac{1}{2}$, then, according to Dirac's theory, it should be expected that the magnetic moment of the proton is a nuclear magneton $e\hbar/2Mc$, where M is the mass of the proton. On the other hand, the moment of the uncharged neutron should be zero. Actually, however, measurement furnishes 2.785 magnetons for the proton and -1.935 for the neutron. The explanation of these unexpected values must be sought in the transmutability of the two particles. Let us suppose that a proton is brought into a weak magnetic field. The spin will then take an orientation parallel to the field, thus giving rise to a magnetic moment of the same direction and magnitude of a magneton, but the moment will change when the proton transmutes itself into a neutron by the emission of a positive meson. By an investigation of the transition probabilities† it can be shown that a proton in a magnetic field can only emit a meson the spin of which has the direction of the field. By the emission, therefore, the particle takes on a spin $-\frac{1}{2}$ which, since the particle is no longer charged, is not able to produce a moment. Instead of the particle, the emitted meson has a moment which by measurement is ascribed to the proton. From the probability with which per unit time a proton is transmuted into a neutron by the emission of a meson, the fraction α of the time during which the particle is a neutron can be evaluated, whereas in the remaining time, $1 - \alpha$, it is a proton. Then in the time $1 - \alpha$ the moment, expressed in nuclear magnetons, is unity. In the time α, however, it will be M/m_0, so that the measurement will give a moment of the magnitude $1 - \alpha + \alpha(M/m_0)$. The possibility that the transmutation is due to the emission of a scalar or pseudoscalar meson can still be considered. The moment of the meson then is zero, and for the moment of the proton we obtain $\mu_P = 1 - \alpha - \beta + \alpha(M/m_0)$ if β represents that part of the time during which the nucleon exists as a neutron plus a scalar meson. If we let μ_P

† For this purpose, we have to expand the emitted field in terms of spherical waves. Cf. H. Fröhlich, W. Heitler, and N. Kemmer, *Proc. Roy. Soc. London*, **166**, 154 (1938).

equal $1 - \alpha + \alpha((M/m_0) - (\beta/\alpha))$, at any rate we shall have $\beta/\alpha \ll M/m_0$ and $\alpha \ll \alpha(M/m_0)$, so that we obtain $\mu_P \sim 1 + \alpha(M/m_0)$.

The probability of a transmutation of a neutron into a proton by the emission of a negative meson is the same as that for the inverse transmutation of a proton. Hence, during the time α, the neutron will be a proton. In this case the spin is $-\frac{1}{2}$ and the total moment of particle and meson is $-1 - M/m_0$, so that $\mu_N = -\alpha - \alpha(M/m_0) \sim -\alpha(M/m_0)$. From this simple consideration it is readily seen that by the transmutation of the nucleons the proton obtains a moment $\mu_P > 1$, and the neutron a moment $\mu_N < 0$. We should expect $\mu_P + \mu_N \sim 1$, a relation that, at least approximately, is actually confirmed.

In the rigorous theory we have to evaluate the self-energy of a nucleon which arises from the interaction with the corresponding meson field when a weak magnetic field H is acting on the nucleon. According to (369) this energy is given by

$$E^2 = \sum \frac{H_{on}{}' H_{no}{}'}{E_o - E_n}$$

In the transition $o \to n$, a nucleon at rest emits a meson the spin of which has the direction of H and which in the transition $n \to o$ is reabsorbed. Therefore $E_o - E_n$ is essentially equal to the energy of the emitted meson consisting of the part $\hbar c \sqrt{\kappa^2 + k^2}$ and the energy $-(e\hbar/2m_0 c)H$ which is due to the magnetic moment $e\hbar/2m_0 c$. Strictly speaking, we should take into account also the magnetic energy of the proton, which energy disappears in the transition $o \to n$, but we may neglect this since we are considering only the effect of the emitted meson. Accordingly we must substitute in the denominator of the expression for E^2 the quantity $-[\hbar c \sqrt{\kappa^2 + k^2} - (e\hbar/2m_0 c)H]$. By expanding in terms of the field strength H, assumed small, we get a series $W_0 - \mu' H + \cdots$ which by means of the factor μ' of H gives the desired supplementary moment, since the energy due to H is given by the product of field and moment. In order to evaluate μ' we must take the expressions (366) for $H_{on}{}'$ and $H_{no}{}'$ and, as in Section 64, replace the sum by an integral. In this calculation we have to keep in mind the fact that in the presence of a magnetic field only mesons with spin in the direction of H can be emitted. We then get

$$E^2 = -\frac{|f|^2 \kappa}{3\pi^2 c} \int dk \, \frac{k^4}{(\sqrt{\kappa^2 + k^2} - eH/2m_0 c^2)^2}$$

If we neglect the terms with H^2, the denominator in the integral term can be written

$$\kappa^2 + k^2 - \frac{eH}{m_0 c^2} \sqrt{\kappa^2 + k^2} \sim \kappa^2 + k^2 - \frac{eH}{\hbar c}$$

wherein $\sqrt{\kappa^2 + k^2}$ is put equal to $\kappa = m_0 c/\hbar$. On multiplying numerator and denominator by $\kappa^2 + k^2 + eH/\hbar c$ we obtain

$$E^2 = C - \frac{|f|^2 \kappa}{3\pi^2 c} \frac{eH}{\hbar c} \int dk \frac{k^4}{(\kappa^2 + k^2)^2}$$

and thus the supplementary moment sought after is

$$\mu_P' = \frac{|f|^2 \kappa e}{3\pi^2 c^2 \hbar} \int dk \frac{k^4}{(\kappa^2 + k^2)^2} \tag{382}$$

A similar calculation is to be carried out for the neutron, the only difference being that the neutron emits a negative meson the magnetic energy of which is $+ (e\hbar/2m_0 c)H$, so that we get the relation $\mu_N' = -\mu_P'$.

The integration in (382) is from $k = 0$ to $k = \infty$, which leads to an infinite value of μ'. As we have seen in Section 60, this result is inevitable, according to the perturbation theory, when a quantity is calculated to which any wavelength of the field furnishes a contribution. As long as quantum mechanics is not amended by a principle that limits the wavelengths in a relativistically invariant way, equation (382) can be made convergent only by means of a "cutting-off" process wherein the upper limit of the integral k_0 is of the order of magnitude κ. One then obtains for μ_P' a value the order of magnitude of which corresponds to experiment. A method which provides the same result without any arbitrariness is to be discussed in Chapter 10.

67. Mesons in an Electromagnetic Field. Mesons play an important role in cosmic radiation, the hard component of this radiation, with good reason, being supposed to consist of them. When passing through the atmosphere, the mesons undergo different processes, those in which an electromagnetic field is acting being of particular importance. Thus we have to investigate the behavior of mesons in an electromagnetic field with special consideration for the case of a light wave. Equivalently, the question concerns the way in which the wave equation of the meson must be changed when an electromagnetic field described by the four-potential $\Phi(\Phi_1 \Phi_2 \Phi_3 = \mathbf{A}, \Phi_4 = i\phi)$ is present. According to Section 49, in this case the operators $\partial/\partial x_\alpha$, with $x_4 = ict$, are to be replaced by $\partial/\partial x_\alpha + (ie/\hbar c)\Phi_\alpha$ and $\partial/\partial x_\alpha - (ie/\hbar c)\Phi_\alpha$ respectively. Taking a vector meson field as an example, instead of (257), we obtain the equations

$$\left(\frac{\partial}{\partial x_\alpha} + \frac{ie}{\hbar c}\Phi_\alpha\right)\psi_\beta - \left(\frac{\partial}{\partial x_\beta} + \frac{ie}{\hbar c}\Phi_\beta\right)\psi_\alpha = \kappa\chi_{\alpha\beta}$$

$$\left(\frac{\partial}{\partial x_\alpha} - \frac{ie}{\hbar c}\Phi_\alpha\right)\psi_\beta{}^* - \left(\frac{\partial}{\partial x_\beta} - \frac{ie}{\hbar c}\Phi_\beta\right)\psi_\alpha{}^* = \kappa\chi_{\alpha\beta}{}^* \tag{383}$$

and, instead of (258),

$$\left(\frac{\partial}{\partial x_\alpha} + \frac{ie}{\hbar c}\Phi_\alpha\right)\chi_{\alpha\beta} = \kappa\psi_\beta$$

$$\left(\frac{\partial}{\partial x_\alpha} - \frac{ie}{\hbar c}\Phi_\alpha\right)\chi_{\alpha\beta}{}^* = \kappa\psi_\beta{}^* \tag{384}$$

The latter equations, in which $\chi_{\alpha\beta}$ are defined by (383), can be derived from the Lagrangian $L = \int dv\,\bar{L}$ with

$$\bar{L} = -\frac{\kappa}{2}\chi_{\alpha\beta}{}^*\chi_{\alpha\beta} - \kappa\psi_\alpha{}^*\psi_\alpha \tag{385}$$

$\bar{L}$ being understood as a function of the independent variables ψ_α and $\psi_\alpha{}^*$, for by varying one of the variables $\psi_\beta{}^*$ into $\psi_\beta{}^* + \delta\psi_\beta{}^*$, we obtain

$$\int dt \int dv\,\delta\bar{L} = -\int dt \int dv\left(\sum_\alpha \kappa\chi_{\alpha\beta}\,\delta\chi_{\alpha\beta}{}^* + \kappa\psi_\beta\,\delta\psi_\beta{}^*\right)$$

$$= -\int dt \int dv\left[\sum_\alpha \chi_{\alpha\beta}\left(\frac{\partial}{\partial x_\alpha} - \frac{ie}{\hbar c}\Phi_\alpha\right)\delta\psi_\beta{}^* + \kappa\psi_\beta\,\delta\psi_\beta{}^*\right]$$

$$= -\int dt \int dv\left(\sum_\alpha -\frac{\partial\chi_{\alpha\beta}}{\partial x_\alpha} - \frac{ie}{\hbar c}\Phi_\alpha\chi_{\alpha\beta} + \kappa\psi_\beta\right)\delta\psi_\beta{}^*$$

The summation is not to be extended over β, which now has a definite value, and thus in the term with $\chi_{\alpha\beta}\,\delta\chi_{\alpha\beta}{}^*$ the factor $\frac{1}{2}$ drops out. On setting the expression equal to zero, we obtain (384).

The momenta π_k and $\pi_k{}^*$, conjugate to ψ_k and $\psi_k{}^*$, can be determined from (385). Then we obtain

$$\pi_k = \frac{\partial\bar{L}}{\partial\,(d\psi_k/dt)} = -\frac{1}{ic}\chi_{4k}{}^* \qquad \pi_k{}^* = -\frac{1}{ic}\chi_{4k} \qquad \pi_4 = \pi_4{}^* = 0 \tag{386}$$

And for the Hamiltonian we obtain

$$\bar{H} = \sum_{k=1}^{3} \left[\frac{d\psi_k}{dt}\pi_k + \frac{d\psi_k{}^*}{dt}\pi_k{}^* \right] - \bar{L}$$

$$= \sum_{k=1}^{3} \pi_k \left[c^2 \kappa \pi_k{}^* + \frac{e}{\hbar}(\Phi_4 \psi_k - \Phi_k \psi_4) + ic\frac{\partial \psi_4}{\partial x_k} \right]$$

$$+ \pi_k{}^* \left[c^2 \kappa \pi_k - \frac{e}{\hbar}(\Phi_4 \psi_k{}^* - \Phi_k \psi_4{}^*) + ic\frac{\partial \psi_k{}^*}{\partial x_k} \right] - \sum_{k=1}^{3} c^2 \pi_k{}^* \pi_k$$

$$+ \frac{\kappa}{2}\sum_{i,k=1}^{3}\left[\left(\frac{\partial}{\partial x_i} - \frac{ie}{\hbar c}\Phi_i\right)\psi_k{}^* - \left(\frac{\partial}{\partial x_k} - \frac{ie}{\hbar c}\Phi_k\right)\psi_i{}^*\right]$$

$$\left[\left(\frac{\partial}{\partial x_i} + \frac{ie}{\hbar c}\Phi_i\right)\psi_k - \left(\frac{\partial}{\partial x_k} + \frac{ie}{\hbar c}\Phi_k\right)\psi_i\right] + \kappa\psi_\alpha{}^*\psi_\alpha \quad (387)$$

The quantities Φ_i describing the electromagnetic field are here considered as given space-time functions, that is, we disregard the reaction of the mesons on the field. If, according to (384) and (385), ψ_4 and $\psi_4{}^*$ are replaced by

$$\psi_4 = -\frac{ic}{\kappa}\sum_{k=1}^{3}\left(\frac{\partial}{\partial x_k} + \frac{ie}{\hbar c}\Phi_k\right)\pi_k{}^* \qquad \psi_4{}^* = -\frac{ic}{\kappa}\sum_{k=1}^{3}\left(\frac{\partial}{\partial x_k} - \frac{ie}{\hbar c}\Phi_k\right)\pi_k$$

then (387) represents a function of ψ_1, ψ_2, ψ_3 and π_1, π_2, π_3 together with the conjugate complex quantities. In the interaction between the mesons and the electromagnetic field, only those terms are of consequence which contain the potential Φ. The totality of these is given by

$$H' = \frac{e}{\hbar}\Phi_4[(\vec{\pi}\vec{\psi}) - (\vec{\pi}^*\vec{\psi}^*)] - \frac{e}{\hbar}[\psi_4(\vec{\pi}\vec{\Phi}) - \psi_4{}^*(\vec{\pi}^*\vec{\Phi})]$$

$$- \frac{ie}{\hbar c}\kappa[(\vec{\Phi}\times\vec{\psi}^* \cdot \operatorname{curl}\vec{\psi}) - (\vec{\Phi}\times\vec{\psi}\cdot\operatorname{curl}\vec{\psi}^*)]$$

$$+ \frac{e^2\kappa}{\hbar^2 c^2}(\vec{\Phi}\times\vec{\psi}\cdot\vec{\Phi}\times\vec{\psi}^*) = \frac{e}{\hbar}\Phi_4[(\vec{\pi}\vec{\psi}) - (\vec{\pi}^*\vec{\psi}^*)]$$

$$+ \frac{eic}{\hbar\kappa}[(\vec{\pi}\vec{\Phi})\operatorname{div}\vec{\pi}^* - (\vec{\pi}^*\vec{\Phi})\operatorname{div}\vec{\pi}] - \frac{2e^2}{\kappa\hbar^2}(\vec{\pi}\vec{\Phi})(\vec{\pi}^*\vec{\Phi})$$

$$- \frac{ie\kappa}{\hbar c}[(\vec{\Phi}\times\vec{\psi}^*\cdot\operatorname{curl}\vec{\psi}) - (\vec{\Phi}\times\vec{\psi}\cdot\operatorname{curl}\vec{\psi}^*)]$$

$$+ \frac{e^2\kappa}{\hbar^2 c^2}(\vec{\Phi}\times\vec{\psi}\cdot\vec{\Phi}\times\vec{\psi}^*) \qquad (388)$$

The meaning of this expression becomes immediately clear if both the electromagnetic field Φ and the meson field ψ are quantized. According to (302) and (316), we must in this case substitute for Φ

$$\vec{\Phi} = \sum_{ij} C e_{ij}(\tilde{X}_{ij}e^{i\mathbf{k}_i\cdot\mathbf{r}} - X_{ij}e^{-i\mathbf{k}_i\cdot\mathbf{r}}) \tag{389}$$

(In this we use the notation X_{ij} instead of A_t and take into account the fact that $B_t = A_{-t}$.) In the summation relative to j, it is from 2 to 3. The time field component Φ_4 which may be considered an external force does not enter into the quantization. On the other hand, according to (288) and (291), we have

$$\vec{\psi} = \sum_{ij} C_i{}' \mathbf{e}_{ij}(A_{ij} - \tilde{B}_{ij})e^{i\mathbf{k}_i\cdot\mathbf{r}} \qquad \vec{\pi} = \sum_{ij} C_i{}'' \mathbf{e}_{ij}(\tilde{A}_{ij} + B_{ij})e^{-i\mathbf{k}_i\cdot\mathbf{r}} \tag{390}$$

If in (388) we substitute these expressions, for H' we obtain a matrix that represents a sum of matrix products. It is sufficient to consider the products that arise from one of the terms of (388), for example, from $(\vec{\pi}\vec{\Phi})$ div $\vec{\pi}^*$. According to (389) and (390) we have

$$\int dv \, (\vec{\pi}\vec{\Phi}) \text{ div } \vec{\pi}^* = \int dv \, C_{ilm}(\mathbf{e}_{ij}\mathbf{e}_{ij'})(\tilde{X}_{ij}e^{i\mathbf{k}_i\cdot\mathbf{r}} - X_{ij}e^{-i\mathbf{k}_i\cdot\mathbf{r}})$$
$$\times (\tilde{A}_{lj} + B_{lj'})e^{-i\mathbf{k}_l\cdot\mathbf{r}}(A_{m1} + \tilde{B}_{m1})e^{i\mathbf{k}_m\cdot\mathbf{r}} \tag{391}$$

C_{ilm} denoting a factor that depends on i, l, m. To comprehend the significance of the matrix we must consider that, because of X_{ij}, A_{ij}, B_{ij} together with the conjugate complex matrices, only the following transitions are permitted:

X_{ij}:   Creation of a photon of the kind ij
$\tilde{X}_{ij}$:   Annihilation of a photon of the above kind
A_{ij}:   Creation of a positive ij meson
$\tilde{A}_{ij}$:   Annihilation of a positive ij meson
B_{ij}:   Creation of a negative ij meson
$\tilde{B}_{ij}$:   Annihilation of a negative ij meson

The meaning of the products in (391) is immediately clear. For example, the term with the product $\tilde{X}_{ij}\tilde{A}_{lj'}A_{m1}$ determines the probability of a process by which an ij photon together with a positive ij meson disappears and in return a longitudinal positive meson is created. The term $\tilde{X}_{ij}B_{lj'}A_{m1}$ belongs to a process in which a disappearing photon makes room for a positive and negative meson, and so on.

With any product occurring in (391), a power of e belongs as a factor. For example, in the product $\tilde{X}_{ij}\tilde{A}_{lj'}B_{m1}$, the factor is

$$e^{-i(\mathbf{k}_i+\mathbf{k}_l-\mathbf{k}_m\cdot\mathbf{r})}$$

the integral of which differs from zero only if $\mathbf{k}_i + \mathbf{k}_l = \mathbf{k}_m$, that is, if the momentum of the two disappearing particles is equal to the momentum of the created meson. Thus the only transitions which are possible are those in which momentum is conserved.

PROBLEMS

1. Calculate the products w_0, w_1, etc., defined by (347).
2. Calculate the invariants (349), making use of the results of Problem 1.
3. According to (373) and (374), the potential of the nuclear forces comes about by the interference of waves. How must the spectrum of the waves be limited in order that the potential become approximately constant between $r = 0$ and $r = r_0$?
4. Discuss the various terms arising from the evaluation of (391).

10

INTRODUCTION OF

A FUNDAMENTAL LENGTH

68. The Idea of a Fundamental Length. In the preceding chapters we saw that, when we attempt to apply the principles of quantum mechanics to the electromagnetic field or some other wave field, we are faced with the difficulty that certain definitely finite quantities such as the self-energy of the electron or the energy of a cavity radiation become infinite. Some divergences, for example the infinite Coulomb self-energy of a point charge, are not associated with the idea of quantum mechanics but originate in the point character of the particles and hence have already appeared in the literature of classical physics. In what follows we shall not refer to this sort of divergence but will confine ourselves to those due to quantum mechanics. These arise in such a way that the theory is forced to admit waves of any small wavelength and so account for a field with an infinite number of degrees of freedom. A typical example of this kind, although of little moment, is the infinite energy which, according to the theory, should correspond to a cavity radiation. Consider the radiation enclosed in a cubic box. Here, in evaluating the zero-point energy, the theory must consider any stationary wave which is adaptable to the dimensions of the box, its realization, therefore, being possible. But this condition is fulfilled for an infinity of waves with infinitely decreasing wavelengths. Therefore a zero-point energy $h\nu/2$ must be assigned to any of these waves (cf. Section 56), and as a result the summation gives an infinite value for the whole energy. All the divergences that occur in quantum mechanics, in so far as they are not due to the point character of the particles, are of this kind, as can be seen, for example, upon evaluating the transverse self-energy of the electron (cf. Section 60), or that of the magnetic moment of the proton or neutron (Section 66). There can be no doubt that the only remedy for these divergences is the introduction of a principle that limits the number of waves by removing the effectiveness of those waves with a frequency exceeding a certain limit. However, this principle must satisfy the condition for relativistic invariance. For example, we must not simply decide that waves with frequencies above a certain limit are ineffective, since we can increase or decrease a given frequency by any amount by transferring to another coordinate system, the consequence being that the limit would be dependent on the choice of a reference system. For this reason we must try to attain our end in such a way that we start from the theory, as developed in the preceding chapters, which we know satisfies the requirements of relativity, and modify this theory by means of an invariant correction which has the effect of rendering ineffective waves of extremely small wavelengths.

Before proceeding with this plan, let us explain first the physical meaning of the method to be followed in settling this problem of divergences. Evidently such a procedure must be based on the introduction of a universal constant which, in a manner similar to Planck's constant h or to the velocity of light constant c, limits the possibility of observation. The present situation in quantum mechanics is somewhat similar to that which existed in physics prior to the development of the theories of relativity and quantum mechanics. In both of these cases the old theory turned out to be a failure because it was based on an incorrect estimate of the possibilities of measurement. Pre-relativistic theory held the view that the simultaneousness of events, occurring at different places, may be defined by means of signals transmitted from one place to another with an infinite velocity, whereas this velocity actually is limited by the constant c. On the other hand, classical mechanics considered it possible to measure the values of two conjugate observables simultaneously with any desired degree of accuracy. Relativity theory and quantum mechanics originated from the rectification of these prejudices. And so we may presume that it is again an incorrect estimate of the possibilities of observation which introduces intrinsic difficulties into quantum mechanics. The question that arises this time is whether it is possible to ascertain the position of a particle as accurately as we wish or whether the accuracy is limited by a universal constant. As a matter of fact, we shall see that the alteration of the mathematical formalism suggested in what follows corresponds to the thesis: *It is, on principle, impossible to invent an experiment of any kind that will permit a distinction between the positions of two particles at rest the distance of which is below a certain limit l_0.* In other words, we cannot ascertain the position of a particle at rest with a greater accuracy than with a possible error l_0. It should be noticed that this theorem applies to particles at rest, that is, the particles must be known to be at rest before the

measurement is made.   The constant l_0 has the dimension of a length
and is, as we shall see, of the same order of magnitude as that of the
radius of the classical electron, with which, however, l_0 is not identical.
In the following we shall call l_0 the fundamental length and consider it
a constant of first order which, like Planck's constant h and the light
velocity constant c, limits the possibilities of observation.

69. Introduction of l_0 into the Interaction Terms.   The problem to be solved is the introduction of l_0 into the theory in such a way
that the divergences caused by the quantum-mechanical formalism
disappear without, at the same time, destroying the invariance of the
theory.   For this purpose we consider a system consisting of a field
of some kind and particles.   The field may be described by a scalar
or tensor function of the coordinates and the time, that is, by one of
the ψ functions (with one or more components) discussed in Chapter
7.   As for the particles, we are concerned solely with electrons and
nucleons, that is, with particles of spin $\frac{1}{2}$ which can be represented
by a Dirac function Φ with four components.   The physical nature of
the system can then be described by a Hamiltonian composed of three
parts, one referring to the field, another to the particles, and the third,
denoted by H', corresponding to the interaction between the field
and the particles.   We are concerned only with the latter part since
all the divergences here are due to H'.   With a few exceptions H'
depends on ψ linearly.   Interaction terms which do not agree with this
condition may be disregarded at first; they will be discussed later.
As examples we may consider the interaction (326) of an electromagnetic field $\psi = \mathbf{A}_t$ upon an electron:

$$H' = -e(\vec{\alpha}\mathbf{A}_t) \tag{326}$$

or that of a pseudoscalar field ψ upon a nucleon:

$$H' = -ig(\vec{\sigma}\,\mathrm{grad}\,\psi^*) - ig^*(\vec{\sigma}\,\mathrm{grad}\,\psi) \tag{360}$$

In these expressions $\mathbf{A}_t$ and ψ are meant as representations of wave
fields.   In order to take into account the corpuscular character of the
field also, which is manifested by the appearance of photons and
mesons, we have to quantize the field by expanding $\mathbf{A}_t$ and ψ into
series $\sum q_i e^{i\mathbf{k}_i \cdot \mathbf{r}}$ and transcribing the coefficients q_i into matrices
Q_i.   As we have seen, the field then changes into a system of oscil-
lators the behavior of which permits a very simple description using
the matrices A_i and B_i, introduced in Chapter 7.   Associated with the
unperturbed system of field and particles is a principal system K in

the Hilbert space the axes of which have the following meaning. When the vector $\mathbf{x}$, which represents the state of the system (for which H' is assumed to be zero), has the direction of an axis of K, the field consists of n_1 particles (photons or mesons) of the sort 1, n_2 particles of the sort 2, and so on, whereas the material system (for simplicity, one electron or one nucleon only) is in one of its stationary states. This means that any axis of K can be characterized by a sequence $n_1 n_2 \cdots$ of numbers which define the state of the field and a number a which determines the state of the material particle. To simplify the notation we shall write n instead of $n_1 n_2 \cdots$, in this way distinguishing the different states of the field by numbers n, each one of which represents a certain sequence $n_1 n_2 \cdots$. Then the axes of K can be characterized by $1a$, or $2b$, and so on, $1a$ meaning that the field is in the state $n_1 n_2 \cdots$ that corresponds to $n = 1$ and the particle is in the state a.

Now let us take into account the interaction H'. Whereas the other two terms of the Hamiltonian H are diagonal in K (defined as the principal system belonging to the energy of the unperturbed system), H', by the quantization of ψ, transforms into a matrix which is a linear function of A_i and B_i and is *not* diagonal in K but consists of elements connecting a field state n with another state n' which differs from n in that it contains one photon or meson of some kind more or less than n. That this is so can be seen at once from the expressions of (222) for the matrices A_i and B_i. For example, if the states $1a$ and $2b$ satisfy this condition, an element is contained in H' which mediates a transition by means of which the particle changes its state from a to b, simultaneously emitting or absorbing a photon or meson. Therefore a certain wave vector $\mathbf{k}$ belongs to any element of H' which, by $\hbar\mathbf{k}$, determines the momentum of the particular photon or meson with which the element is concerned.

Here arises the question of how the expression for the interaction H' is to be altered in order that the divergences that occur in the traditional theory may disappear. This alteration, aside from the purpose for which it is designed, must fulfill two conditions:

(i) It must be relativistically invariant, that is, H' as a part of the Hamiltonian possesses certain transformation properties, which properties must remain unchanged. This requirement is satisfied if H' is changed in such a way that it does not depend on the choice of the coordinate system.

(ii) H' must remain Hermitean; otherwise it would lose its physical interpretability.

We comply with these requirements by multiplying every element of H' by an invariant factor determined in the following way. We consider some element of H' which may connect the states na and $n'b$, that is, the element $H'_{na,n'b}$. The space-time coordinate system used may be denoted by K, and the wave vector of the photon or meson emitted or absorbed in the transition $n \rightarrow n'$, when referred to K, may be denoted by $\mathbf{k}$. The reference system K is now exchanged for that other system K' in which the state a of the electron or nucleon is transformed into a state of rest. The meaning of this is clear if the particle is free; for an electron or nucleon bound to an atom or nucleus, the meaning is that the center of gravity of the atom or nucleus is at rest relative to K'. The vector $\mathbf{k}$ is then transformed into a certain vector $\mathbf{k}'$. Around the particle in the system K' we construct a sphere of diameter l_0 and evaluate the expression

$$\kappa_1 = \frac{\left| \int dv \, e^{i\mathbf{k}' \cdot \mathbf{r}} \right|}{v \left| e^{i\mathbf{k}' \cdot \mathbf{r}} \right|}$$

in which the integration is to be extended over the volume v of the sphere. In the denominator the value of $e^{i\mathbf{k}' \cdot \mathbf{r}}$ at the center of the sphere must be taken. The value of κ_1 is evidently unity for $|\mathbf{k}'| = 2\pi/\lambda' \ll 2\pi/l_0$ and zero for $|\mathbf{k}'| \gg 2\pi/l_0$. In a second transformation we pass from K to that system K'' wherein the state b becomes a state of rest and evaluate the expression

$$\kappa_2 = \frac{\left| \int dv \, e^{i\mathbf{k}'' \cdot \mathbf{r}} \right|}{v \left| e^{i\mathbf{k}'' \cdot \mathbf{r}} \right|}$$

Finally we combine κ_1 and κ_2 and get

$$\kappa = \frac{1}{2} \left(\frac{\left| \int dv \, e^{i\mathbf{k}' \cdot \mathbf{r}} \right|}{v \left| e^{i\mathbf{k}' \cdot \mathbf{r}} \right|} + \frac{\left| \int dv \, e^{i\mathbf{k}'' \cdot \mathbf{r}} \right|}{v \left| e^{i\mathbf{k}'' \cdot \mathbf{r}} \right|} \right) = \frac{1}{2} (\kappa_1 + \kappa_2) \qquad (392)$$

This is an invariant factor the value of which does not depend on the coordinate system K, since we have to pass from any system K to the same systems K' and K''. The value of κ lies between 0 and 1; it is zero if the wave vectors $\mathbf{k}'$ and $\mathbf{k}''$ correspond to wavelengths λ' and λ'', both of which are $\ll l_0$, and it is equal to unity if λ' and λ'' are $\gg l_0$. But κ may have any value between these two limits; for example, it has the value $\frac{1}{2}$ if one $\lambda \gg l_0$ and the other $\lambda \ll l_0$.

The theory now is that any element of the interaction matrix H' must be multiplied by the corresponding κ. By this procedure we change H' in such a way that the invariance of the theory is not destroyed, since the new H' matrix differs from the original only in an invariant pattern imprinted on it. This pattern consists of the κ factors and remains unchanged upon transformation to another coordinate system, the effect being that H' retains its transformation properties. It is clear at once that the correction is gauge invariant also, since the vectors $\mathbf{k}'$ and $\mathbf{k}''$ from which κ is evaluated are independent of the choice of the potentials ϕ and $\mathbf{A}$. It is seen furthermore that the Hermitean character of H' is conserved since the correction factor κ for two elements of H' which are symmetric relative to the diagonal of H' is the same. To achieve this we had to choose a correction factor κ which takes account of both the initial and final states in the same way.

The pattern of the κ which is imprinted upon H' evidently limits the effectiveness of extremely small wavelengths so that the transitions that have to be admitted by the present theory can occur no longer. This effect is due to the universal length l_0, which plays the role of a limiting constant. The integrals by which the κ factors are defined are not to be understood in the sense that by them we would ascribe an extension in the ordinary sense of the word, that is, a space filled with matter to the particle. We have made it clear already that such an interpretation could not be reconciled with the view of relativity (Section 60). For this reason the concept "extension of an elementary particle" must be given a new definition, and we do this by means of the κ factors. We forego any interpretation of these factors, being content with the proof that the altered formalism gives a correct description of the experimental facts.

70. Application to Electrodynamics. In order that the suggested scheme be useful it is essential that it leave unchanged those results of the present theory which have proved to be correct, or at least change them to so small a degree that it escapes detection. On the other hand, it must involve drastic alterations where the theory openly contradicts the facts. For example, the theory would be disproved if the length l_0, which is of the order of magnitude 10^{-13} cm, should prevent photons of a wavelength less than l_0 (of an energy above 10^8 ev) from interacting with electrons, for, actually, the phenomenon of cascade showers can be understood only on the assumption that photons of at least 10^{11} ev must still be effective. On the other hand, a limiting wavelength of the order of magnitude of 10^{-13} cm really seems to exist for mesons, for there is experimental evidence that mesons with a de Broglie wavelength very much smaller than l_0 are neither emitted nor absorbed by nuclear particles. It is most essential that the theory account for these seemingly inconsistent facts.

First let us consider the interaction of a photon with a free electron. According to (341) the probability of the absorption of a photon is determined by the matrix element

$$H'_{an_t, bn_t-1} = -ie \sqrt{\frac{\hbar}{2\nu_t}} \sqrt{n_t} \int \psi_a{}^* (\vec{\alpha u_t}) \psi_b \qquad (341)$$

In this, ψ_a and ψ_b signify the states of the electron before and after the absorption and can be represented in the form

$$\psi_a = a_a(\rho) e^{i \mathbf{p}_a \cdot \mathbf{r}/\hbar} \qquad \psi_b = a_b(\rho) e^{i \mathbf{p}_b \cdot \mathbf{r}/\hbar}$$

$a_a(\rho)$ and $a_b(\rho)$ being functions of the spin coordinate ρ, and $\mathbf{p}_a$ and $\mathbf{p}_b$ the momenta of the electron in the states a and b. In addition (cf. Section 54), we have

$$u = \sqrt{\frac{4\pi c^2}{l^3}} \, \mathbf{e} e^{i \mathbf{k} \cdot \mathbf{r}}$$

where $\mathbf{e}$ denotes a unit vector which determines the direction of polarization and $\mathbf{k}$ the wave vector of the photon. Expression (341) then becomes

$$H'_{an_t, bn_t-1} = -ie \sqrt{\frac{\hbar}{2\nu_t}} \sqrt{\frac{4\pi c^2}{l^3}} \sqrt{n_t} \, a^*(\vec{\alpha e}) a_b \int e^{i(-\mathbf{p}_a + \mathbf{p}_b - \mathbf{k}\hbar)/\hbar}$$

The integral differs from zero only if $\mathbf{p}_b - \mathbf{p}_a = \mathbf{k}\hbar$; this means that only those transitions are possible in which momentum is conserved. There is, however, no limit to $|\mathbf{k}| = 2\pi/\lambda$, and thus it should be expected that any light, however small its wavelength may be, can be absorbed. We now determine the correction factor κ by which H'_{an_t, bn_t-1} is to be multiplied. For the sake of simplicity it can be assumed that the electron is originally at rest so that $\mathbf{p}_a$ is zero. As the system K' is then identical with K, we have

$$\kappa_1 = \frac{\left| \int dv \, e^{i \mathbf{k} \cdot \mathbf{r}} \right|}{v \left| e^{i \mathbf{k} \cdot \mathbf{r}} \right|}$$

For light with a wavelength very much less than l_0 this fraction is zero. On the other hand, the factor κ_2 does not vanish for any wavelength, for in order to evaluate κ_2 we have to pass to the K'' coordinate system in which the electron which is moving with a momentum $\mathbf{p}_b$ relative to K is at rest. If we choose the direction of $\mathbf{p}_b$ as the x axis, K'' moves along the x axis with a velocity v defined by

$$p_b = \frac{mv}{\sqrt{1 - v^2/c^2}} = \hbar k = \frac{h}{\lambda}$$

and thus

$$\frac{v}{c} = \frac{h}{mc\sqrt{\lambda^2 + h^2/m^2c^2}} \qquad 1 - \frac{v^2}{c^2} = \frac{1}{1 + h^2/m^2c^2\lambda^2}$$

According to a well-known formula of relativity theory, the wavelength λ is changed by the passage $K \to K''$ into

$$\lambda'' = \lambda \frac{1 + \beta \cos \theta'}{\sqrt{1 - \beta^2}} \qquad (393)$$

where θ' is the angle between the direction in which the light is propagated and the x axis, the measurement being made in the system K''. Since in our case $\theta' = 0$, we get

$$\lambda'' = \lambda \frac{2}{\sqrt{1 - \beta^2}} = 2\lambda \sqrt{1 + \frac{h^2}{c^2m^2\lambda^2}} = 2\sqrt{\lambda^2 + \frac{h^2}{m^2c^2}}$$

h/mc is of the order of magnitude 10^{-10} cm. Therefore λ'' is very much greater than l_0, so that in any case κ_2 has the value unity. Thus the effect of l_0 on the absorption of a photon by an electron which is initially at rest is that the corresponding matrix element for $\lambda \gg l_0$ remains unchanged, but for $\lambda \ll l_0$ it is reduced to one-half the classical value.

On emission, the effect is different. Here, again, the matrix element remains the same for $\lambda \gg l_0$, whereas for $\lambda \ll l_0$ both κ_1 and κ_2 vanish, for, through the emission, the electron gets a recoil in the opposite direction, in consequence of which λ'' becomes smaller than λ since now $\lambda'' = \lambda(1 - \beta/\sqrt{1 - \beta^2}) < \lambda$. According to our theory an electron at rest should, therefore, be incapable of the virtual emission of a light quantum with a wavelength very much smaller than l_0. As we shall see, this secures a finite value to the transverse self-energy of an electron.

As an application of the theory, it may be sufficient to consider the Compton effect. This effect concerns the scattering of a light wave by a free electron; the electron absorbs a wave of frequency ν and in return emits another of frequency ν' which in general differs from ν. According to quantum mechanics this process is accomplished in two steps: the electron first changes from its initial state A into an intermediate state Z_1 by absorbing the light quantum $h\nu$, whereupon it passes to the final state F by emitting the quantum $h\nu'$. But the transition $A \rightarrow F$ can as well take place so that $h\nu'$ is first emitted (intermediate state Z_2) and then $h\nu$ absorbed. As in all transitions, momentum is conserved and, besides, the final energy must equal the initial:

$$\frac{h\nu}{c} \mathbf{e} = \frac{h\nu'}{c} \mathbf{e}' + \mathbf{p} \tag{394}$$

$$h\nu + mc^2 = h\nu' + c\sqrt{m^2c^2 + p^2} \tag{395}$$

$\mathbf{e}$ and $\mathbf{e}'$ are two unit vectors indicating the directions of the absorbed and emitted photons respectively, and it further is assumed that the electron is at rest initially, moving afterward with the momentum $\mathbf{p}$. If we denote the angle between $\mathbf{e}$ and $\mathbf{e}'$ by θ, from (394) it follows that

$$p^2 = \frac{h^2}{c^2} (\nu^2 + \nu'^2 - 2\nu\nu' \cos\theta)$$

By introducing this expression into (395) we get the equation

$$\nu' = \nu \frac{mc^2}{mc^2 + h\nu(1 - \cos\theta)} = \nu \frac{1}{1 + \dfrac{h\nu}{mc^2} 2\sin^2\dfrac{\theta}{2}} \tag{396}$$

from which, for a given ν and θ, the frequency ν' of the scattered light wave can be computed.

It can be seen from (396) that the change $\nu-\nu'$ increases with increasing θ. If the primary radiation is of an extremely short wavelength in the sense that $h\nu \gg mc^2(= \frac{1}{2}$ mev), two regions of θ have to be distinguished. For $\sin^2\theta/2 \ll mc^2/h\nu$, that is, for a very small angle of deflection, ν' is equal to ν. However, for a finite θ, $(h\nu/mc^2)2\sin^2\theta/2 \gg 1$, and therefore $\nu' = mc^2/(2h\sin^2\theta/2)$, that is, the wavelength of the scattered light then becomes of the order of magnitude h/mc, the Compton wavelength, $\lambda_0 = 0.4 \times 10^{-10}$ cm.

These relations are, of course, not changed by the κ correction factors since they do not influence the process of scattering as such but only the probability of its occurring, which is determined by the elements of the H' matrix. According to Section 37 this probability is given by

$$dW = \frac{2\pi}{h} \rho(E_A)\left|H'\right|^2 d\Omega$$

where

$$H' = \sum_{Z_1} \frac{H_{AZ_1}'H_{Z_1F}'}{\epsilon_A - \epsilon_{Z_1} + h\nu} + \sum \frac{H_{AZ_2}'H_{Z_2F}'}{\epsilon_A - \epsilon_{Z_2} - h\nu'} \tag{397}$$

Here dW means the probability that in unit time a photon $h\nu$ is scattered in such a way that the direction of the scattered photon lies within a solid angle $d\Omega$. ϵ_A, ϵ_{Z_1} and ϵ_{Z_2} are the energies of the electron in states A, Z_1, and Z_2 respectively. The summation is to be extended over all the states having the same $\mathbf{p}'$ and $\mathbf{p}''$; there are four such states for each momentum, differing in the direction of spin and the sign of the energy. By evaluating (397)† we obtain the differential cross section, which is given by the Klein-Nishina formula

$$dq = \frac{1}{4} r_0{}^2 \, d\Omega \left(\frac{\nu'}{\nu}\right)^2 \left(\frac{\nu}{\nu'} + \frac{\nu'}{\nu} - 2 + 4\cos^2\theta\right)$$

For $\lambda \gg l_0$, this formula is not changed by l_0. When $\lambda \ll l_0$, however, H'_{AZ_1} is diminished to half the value, for, according to our considerations regarding the absorption of a light wave, $\kappa_1 = 0$ and $\kappa_2 = 1$. For the transition $Z_1 \to F$ we must distinguish the regions $\theta \sim 0$ and $\theta \neq 0$. In both cases the electron in the state Z_1 moves with the velocity acquired in the transition $A \to Z_1$ by the absorption of a primary photon and therefore is given by $mv/\sqrt{1 - \beta^2} = h\nu/c$, from which, since $v \sim c$, it follows that $\sqrt{1 - \beta^2} = mc^2/h\nu = \lambda/\lambda_0$, where λ_0 denotes the Compton wavelength and λ that of the primary radiation. The K' system moves together with the electron, and therefore the wavelength λ' measured in K' is given by $\lambda' = \lambda_1(1 + \beta \cos\theta')/\sqrt{1 - \beta^2}$, where by λ_1 we denote the wavelength of the scattered photon as measured in K'. θ' is the angle of deflection in K' which, according to a formula of relativity theory, is related to the angle θ measured in K by

$$\cos\theta' = \frac{\cos\theta - \beta}{1 - \beta\cos\theta} \tag{398}$$

Since the denominator is positive, this fraction provides a positive $\cos\theta'$ only for $\cos\theta > \beta$ or $\theta < \sqrt{2}\sqrt{1 - \beta} \sim \sqrt{1 - \beta^2} = \lambda/\lambda_0$. Then we get $\cos\theta' = \cos\theta = 1$. Besides, we have

$$\sin^2\frac{\theta}{2} = \frac{\theta^2}{4} < \frac{1}{4}\frac{\lambda^2}{\lambda_0{}^2} < \frac{1}{4}\frac{\lambda}{\lambda_0} = \frac{1}{4}\frac{mc^2}{h\nu}$$

and, therefore, according to the preceding considerations, $\lambda_1 = \lambda$. Hence we obtain $\lambda' = \lambda(2/\sqrt{1 - \beta^2}) = 2\lambda_0 \gg l_0$ and, therefore, $\kappa_1 = 1$. For $\theta > \lambda/\lambda_0$, however, $\cos\theta' \sim (\cos\theta - 1)/(1 - \cos\theta) =$

† Cf. W. Heitler, *Theory of Radiation*, Oxford University Press, 1948.

-1 and λ_1, for a sufficiently large θ, increases to the value λ_0. Therefore we obtain

$$\lambda' = \lambda_0 \frac{1 - \beta}{\sqrt{1 - \beta^2}} \sim \frac{\lambda_0}{2} \sqrt{1 - \beta^2} = \frac{\lambda}{2} \ll l_0 \therefore \kappa_1 = 0$$

In order to evaluate κ_2 we must determine the wavelength λ'' measured in K''. K'' is the coordinate system in which the electron is at rest in its final state. For $\theta = 0$, practically the whole energy is transferred to the scattered photon, in consequence of which, relative to K, the electron is at rest. Thus we have

$$K'' = K \qquad \lambda'' = \lambda \ll l_0 \qquad \kappa_2 = 0$$

For $\theta \neq 0$, relative to K, the electron is moving with nearly the velocity v mentioned above, since the energy of the scattered photon is negligible. Since $\lambda_1 = \lambda_0$, $\cos \theta' = -1$, we have

$$\lambda'' = \lambda_0 \frac{1 - \beta}{\sqrt{1 - \beta^2}} = \frac{\lambda}{2} \ll l_0 \therefore \kappa_2 = 0$$

Thus the result is that the matrix element H_{AZ_1}' in (397) is to be corrected by $\kappa = \frac{1}{2}$, and the element H_{Z_1F}' by either $\kappa = \frac{1}{2}$ or $\kappa = 0$ depending on whether the scattering angle is nearly zero or has a finite value. In any case the second sum in (397) vanishes, since we have seen that $\kappa = 0$ for the emission term H_{AZ_2}'. Thus a photon with $\lambda \ll l_0$ can be scattered only in the forward direction with a probability that is diminished to $\frac{1}{64}$ that of the Klein-Nishina value. The other possibility of a deflection by a finite angle is excluded by the correction factors.

In agreement with our thesis, it can be inferred from this result that it is impossible to distinguish the positions of two particles by means of a diffraction experiment performed with light rays if the distance between them is less than l_0. For such an experiment, a radiation would be required with a wavelength the order of magnitude of which would correspond to the distance to be measured. If the two particles are fixed in space, they cannot react upon a photon with a wavelength very much smaller than l_0 because of the κ factors which make the corresponding matrix elements vanish. If, however, the particles are free, a photon with such a wavelength can only be deflected by an angle $\theta < \lambda/\lambda_0$. On the other hand, a diffraction pattern can only be had if there is a deflection angle θ for which $a \sin \theta = \lambda$ or $\theta = \lambda/a$, which for the case $a < l_0$ is $> \lambda/\lambda_0$.

A second remark concerns the zero-point energy of a cavity radiation. In the present theory, this energy diverges because of the infinity of wavelengths which have to be considered in the evaluation of the energy. Actually, however, waves with $\lambda \ll l_0$ cannot be reflected from the walls of the box in which the radiation is enclosed, as neither free nor fixed electrons are able to deflect a photon by a finite angle. Thus in Section 56 the summation (314) is only to be extended over a domain of wavelengths limited by l_0.

71. *Bremsstrahlung*—**Transverse Self-Energy of an Electron.** It has already been mentioned that the phenomenon of cascade showers can be accounted for only on the assumption that photons of any energy can be emitted by correspondingly fast-moving electrons which are stopped by a nucleus. Therefore it is to be required that the new theory be in accordance with this assumption. In order to show this we consider an electron, the energy $E_0 = mc^2/\sqrt{1 - \beta^2}$ of which may have any value, moving against a nucleus. When passing through the field of the nucleus, it will be deflected and simultaneously it will emit a light quantum $h\nu$. The transition of the system from the initial into the final state is accomplished by means of an intermediate state Z, two different Z states being possible; either the electron is first deflected $(A \to Z)$ and then the transition $(Z \to F)$ occurs, whereupon the quantum is emitted, or the two processes occur in the reverse succession. In any case the possibility of the transition $A \to E$ depends on the matrix element H_{AZ}' or H_{ZE}' which corresponds to the emission of light by a fast-moving electron. We denote the momenta of the electron before and after the emission by $\mathbf{p}_0$ and $\mathbf{p}$ and assume that the initial energy E_0 is very much greater than hc/l_0, so that by the stoppage of the electron a light quantum of a wavelength very much smaller than l_0 is created. The correction factor κ_1 depends on the wave length λ' of the quantum relative to the system K' moving with the initial velocity v_0 of the electron. The velocity v_0 is defined by $mv_0/\sqrt{1 - \beta_0^2} \sim mc/\sqrt{1 - \beta_0^2} = p_0$, so that from (393) we obtain

$$\lambda' = \lambda \frac{2}{\sqrt{1 - \beta_0^2}} = 2\lambda \frac{p_0}{mc} = 2\lambda \frac{E_0}{mc^2}$$

For $\mathbf{p} = 0$ (complete stoppage), the whole energy $c\sqrt{m^2c^2 + p_0^2} - mc^2 \sim E_0$ is transformed into a quantum $h\nu = hc/\lambda$. We obtain then $\lambda' = 2\lambda(hc/\lambda mc^2) = 4\pi\lambda_0$, and therefore $\kappa_1 = 1$ whereas $\kappa_2 = 0$. Thus the matrix element H_{AZ}' or H_{ZE}' is then effective with only half its value, so that the probability is diminished to $\frac{1}{4}$. If, however, the electron is not completely stopped, κ_2 may also be equal to unity, so that the value of κ becomes unity. This is the case if $\lambda'' = 2\lambda/\sqrt{1 - \beta^2}$ is greater than l_0, β now corresponding to the final velocity of the electron. From the energy law it now follows that

$$c \sqrt{m^2c^2 + p_0{}^2} - c \sqrt{m^2c^2 + p^2} = h\nu = \frac{hc}{\lambda}$$

or, if we assume that $E = c \sqrt{m^2c^2 + p^2}$, as well as E_0, is greater than hc/l_0, then

$$p - p_0 = \frac{h}{\lambda}$$

On dividing this equation by $\lambda/\sqrt{1 - \beta^2} > l_0$ or by $\lambda p/mc > l_0$, since $mc/\sqrt{1 - \beta^2} = p$, we get

$$\frac{p_0 - p}{p} < \frac{h}{mcl_0} = \frac{\lambda_0}{l_0} \qquad \text{or} \qquad p > p_0 \frac{l_0}{\lambda_0} \sim p_0 \times 10^{-3}$$

This means, for example, that an electron of 10^{11} ev is slowed down to 10^8 ev. The probability of the creation of a light quantum by such a process is not changed by l_0; therefore we can hold that the theory of *Bremsstrahlung* is practically independent of l_0.

In the preceding considerations we have disregarded the possible influence of l_0 on the deflection of the electron caused by the Coulomb field of the nucleus. This influence cannot be treated with the aid of the developed theory, because the Coulomb interaction does not fit into the mathematical scheme on which the evaluation of the κ is based. If the momenta of the two colliding particles are given by $p_{10}p_{20}$ and p_1p_2 respectively, the interaction V is a certain function of these four momenta which can be transcribed into a matrix. The procedure again is to furnish the elements of this matrix with invariant correction factors the meaning of which is that a diffraction experiment, carried out with material particles, proves as much of a failure in measuring a distance less than l_0 between two particles at rest as the diffraction of light waves. We omit here the details of the theory and find that a particle, when colliding with another of great mass, owing to l_0 is not able to transfer a momentum Δp on the latter of an amount greater than h/l_0. This is the reason why particles with momentum greater than h/l_0 cannot be reflected from a solid wall, since the reflection would be associated with a change of momentum that is excluded by l_0.

The influence of the constant l_0 on the *Bremsstrahlung* resulting from the deflection is unimportant, consisting only in confining the emission to the forward direction.   This direction preference is partially due to the conservation of momentum; hence it has already appeared in accepted theory.   The effect is intensified, however, by l_0 because l_0 limits the amount of momentum transferred to the nucleus.

Hence it turns out that, in the applications of electrodynamics to practical cases, the effect of the constant l_0 is of little consequence and may often be completely neglected.   The only conspicuous effect is that it settles the divergence difficulties.   We have already seen that the zero-point energy of a cavity radiation becomes finite, for the wave-lengths are limited by l_0.   This limitation also settles the divergences that confront us in the higher approximations of the perturbation theory (cf. Section 60).   For example, consider the transverse self-energy of an electron at rest.   This is given by

$$E^{(2)} = \frac{e^2 \hbar}{2} \sum_t \frac{\frac{1}{\nu_t} \int \psi_0^* (\vec{\alpha u_t}) \psi_b \int \psi_b^* (\vec{\alpha u_t}) \psi_0}{mc^2 - (E_b + \hbar \nu_t)} \tag{346}$$

The term is evaluated on the assumption that no photons are in the field initially.   The integrals in the sum are the matrix elements of the interaction H' between the field and the electron, and they correspond to transitions in which the electron passes from rest to motion or conversely, simultaneously emitting or absorbing a photon.   In these virtual processes momentum is conserved, that is, by the emission of a photon the electron obtains a velocity in the opposite direction. Consequently the factors κ_1 and κ_2 vanish for $\lambda < l_0$ so that wave-lengths less than l_0 cannot contribute to the self-energy.   Thus the summation in (346) must be extended only over those wavelengths which are greater than l_0, that is, over a finite number of terms.

Although the l_0 theory removes the divergence of $E^{(2)}$, it does not lead to the correct value of the magnetic self-energy of the electron which is of the order of magnitude mc^2, for in working out $E^{(2)}$ we arrive at about $50mc^2$.   As the sum of the approximations $E^{(2)}$, $E^{(4)}$, and so on, converge very slowly, an agreement of $E^{(2)}$ with the experimental value is not to be expected a priori.

72. **Application to the Nuclear Forces.**   Although the influence of the limiting length l_0 on the electron is confined essentially to removing the divergences arising in the theory, the situation is quite different in the theory of the meson.   The reason why l_0, at least practically, plays such an unimportant part as far as the electron is concerned

(except for the occurring divergences, the incorrectness of the theory would not have been noticed) is that the electron because of its small mass is able to cope with any wavelength however small. In contrast, a heavy nuclear particle on which a radiation of extremely small wavelength is acting is, because of its great mass, hindered from taking on a velocity sufficient to give the factor κ a value considerably different from zero. This must lead to phenomena which cannot be explained without the help of l_0; for this reason in Chapter 9 we had to resort to a "cutting-off" procedure wherein wavelengths less than l_0 are cancelled. However, we shall see in Section 76 that it is not always the short wavelengths with which the theory is unable to cope, but that there are phenomena in the domain of quite normal energies as well which cannot be accounted for without the help of l_0.

We investigate first the influence of l_0 on the potential of the nuclear forces which were determined in Section 64. According to (372) and (373), the potentials arising from the exchange of longitudinal and transverse vector mesons are given by

$$V_{\mathrm{I}} = -2\frac{g^2\kappa}{(2\pi)^3 c}\int d\Omega \int dk\,\frac{k^4}{\kappa^2 + k^2}\,e^{i\mathbf{k}\cdot\mathbf{r}} \tag{399}$$

$$V_{\mathrm{II}} = -2\frac{f^2\kappa}{(2\pi)^3 c}\int d\Omega \int dk\,\frac{k^4}{\kappa^2 + k^2}\,e^{i\mathbf{k}\cdot\mathbf{r}}\left[(\vec{\sigma_1}\vec{\sigma_2}) - \frac{(\vec{\sigma_1}\mathbf{k})(\vec{\sigma_2}\mathbf{k})}{k^2}\right] \tag{400}$$

In these expressions $\mathbf{k}$ multiplied by $\hbar$ denotes the momentum of the exchanged meson, and the integrals relative to $k = 2\pi/\lambda$ are to be taken from 0 to ∞, the result being that V_{II} diverges for $r = 0$ like $1/r^3$. This is prevented by the limit which l_0 imposes on the spectrum. We may assume that the two nucleons are fixed in space by the forces binding them to the nucleus so that they are unable to get into motion by the emission or absorption of a meson. The correction factor κ then becomes zero for any $k = 2\pi/\lambda$ which is greater than $k_0 = 2\pi/l_0$, and thus we need integrate only from 0 to k_0. This also holds if the particles are assumed to be free, since, in this case in which no mesons are initially in the field, the field can be changed only by the emission of a meson and this cannot occur for a wavelength less than l_0. The potentials, therefore, now remain finite for $r = 0$ and V_{I} assumes the value

$$\begin{aligned} V_{\mathrm{I}}(0) &= -\frac{g^2\kappa}{\pi^2 c}\int_0^{k_0} dk\,\frac{k^4}{\kappa^2 + k^2}\\ &= -\frac{g^2\kappa}{\pi^2 c}\left(\kappa^3 \arctan\frac{k_0}{\kappa} - \kappa^2 k_0 + \frac{k_0{}^3}{3}\right) \end{aligned}$$

For $r = 0$, the value of V_{II} depends on the directions of the spins.   For parallel spins, in which $(\vec{\sigma}_1\vec{\sigma}_2) = 1$, we get

$$V_{\mathrm{II}}(0) = -\frac{2f^2\kappa}{3\pi^2c}\left(\kappa^3\arctan\frac{k_0}{\kappa} - \kappa^2 k_0 + \frac{k_0{}^3}{3}\right)$$

For antiparallel spins, $(\vec{\sigma}_1\vec{\sigma}_2) = -3$, so that the factor $-\tfrac{2}{3}$ is replaced by $+\tfrac{8}{3}$.

In order to evaluate the potentials (399) and (400), we introduce the polar coordinates θ and ϕ, taking the direction of $\mathbf{r}$ as the polar axis. We obtain

$$\int d\Omega \int_0^{k_0} dk\, \frac{k^4}{\kappa^2 + k^2}\, e^{i\mathbf{k}\cdot\mathbf{r}} = 2\pi \int_0^{k_0} dk\, \frac{k^4}{\kappa^2 + k^2} \int_0^{\pi} d\theta\, \sin\theta\, e^{ikr\cos\theta}$$

$$= 4\pi \int_0^{k_0} dk\, \frac{k^4}{\kappa^2 + k^2}\, \frac{\sin kr}{kr}$$

If we assume that the spins are parallel or antiparallel to $\mathbf{r}$, we obtain

$$\int d\Omega \int_0^{k_0} dk\, \frac{k^4}{\kappa^2 + k^2}\, e^{i\mathbf{k}\cdot\mathbf{r}}\, \frac{(\vec{\sigma}_1\mathbf{k})(\vec{\sigma}_2\mathbf{k})}{k^2}$$

$$= \pm 2\pi \int_0^{k_0} dk\, \frac{k^4}{\kappa^2 + k^2} \int_0^{\pi} d\theta\, \sin\theta\, \cos^2\theta\, e^{ikr\cos\theta}$$

$$= \pm 4\pi \int_0^{k_0} dk\, \frac{k^4}{\kappa^2 + k^2}\left(\frac{\sin kr}{kr} - 2\frac{\sin kr}{(kr)^3} + 2\frac{\cos kr}{(kr)^2}\right)$$

For spins perpendicular to $\mathbf{r}$ we obtain half of this value.   Using the abbreviations

$$J_1(r) = \int_0^{k_0} dk\, \frac{k^4}{\kappa^2 + k^2}\, \frac{\sin kr}{kr} \qquad J_2(r) = \int_0^{k_0} dk\, \frac{k^4}{\kappa^2 + k^2}\left(\frac{\sin kr}{(kr)^3} - \frac{\cos kr}{(kr)^2}\right)$$

we obtain

$$V(r) = -\frac{\kappa}{(2\pi)^2 c}\,[g^2 J_1(r) + 2f^2 J_2(r)] \qquad \text{for } (\vec{\sigma}_1\vec{\sigma}_2) = 1 \text{ (spins } \| \text{ to } \mathbf{r})$$

$$V(r) = -\frac{\kappa}{(2\pi)^2 c}\,[(g^2 + f^2)J_1(r) - f^2 J_2(r)]$$

$$\text{for } (\vec{\sigma}_1\vec{\sigma}_2) = 1 \text{ (spins } \perp \text{ to } \mathbf{r})$$

$$V(r) = -\frac{\kappa}{(2\pi)^2 c}\,[(g^2 - 2f^2)J_1(r) - 2f^2 J_2(r)]$$

$$\text{for } (\vec{\sigma}_1\vec{\sigma}_2) = -3 \text{ (spins } \| \text{ to } \mathbf{r})$$

The functions $J_1(r)$ and $J_2(r)$ can be worked out by a graphic method. They are plotted in Fig. 5, where $1/\kappa$ is supposed to be less than $l_0/2$. It is very remarkable that in this case, according to Fig. 5, the range of the nuclear forces is given by l_0 rather than by $1/\kappa$. It is readily seen that this is due to the interference of the waves $\sin kr$ and $\cos kr$ over which the integrals J_1 and J_2 are to be taken. Each of these integrals may be interpreted as representing the excitation caused by a wave packet at a distance r. All the waves, $\sin kr$ and $\cos kr$,

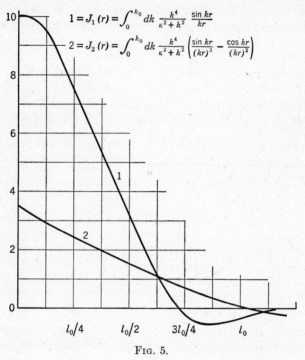

$$1 = J_1(r) = \int_0^{k_0} dk\, \frac{k^4}{\kappa^2 + k^2}\, \frac{\sin kr}{kr}$$

$$2 = J_2(r) = \int_0^{k_0} dk\, \frac{k^4}{\kappa^2 + k^2} \left(\frac{\sin kr}{(kr)^3} - \frac{\cos kr}{(kr)^2} \right)$$

FIG. 5.

of which the packets are composed start from particle 1 with the same phase 0, and their combined effect on particle 2 depends on the phase differences with which the waves arrive at point 2. For a given distance r, we may distinguish waves with $\lambda/2 > r$ and those with $\lambda/2 < r$. The waves of the first kind operate at point r in the same direction so that they reinforce one another, while the latter, which meet in all possible phases, have a zero effect. This means that with decreasing r an increasing number of waves cooperates in the production of V. But, as the wave spectrum ends at a wavelength $\lambda = l_0$ at the distance $r = l_0/2$, all the available waves are already in action, so that with any further diminishing of r the potential can only be changed as far as amplitudes are concerned and not by the number of waves. Conversely, from $r = l_0/2$, with increasing r the potential must diminish rapidly, since, for example, at the distance $r = l_0$, only those waves with $\lambda > 2l_0$ are effective, and the number of these is eight times smaller than that of the waves with $\lambda > l_0$. In this case the potential diminishes to about $\frac{1}{8}$ its initial value, and at the distance $r = 2l_0$ it will be about $\frac{1}{64}$ of the initial value.

So we see that for a sufficiently small $1/\kappa (< l_0/2)$, the range R of the nuclear forces is defined by $l_0/2$ rather than by $1/\kappa$. It is different if $1/\kappa > l_0/2$. In this case l_0 loses its significance, and its place is taken by $1/\kappa$, which now represents the range R. But, as the value of l_0 is probably about 5×10^{-13} cm, the condition that $1/\kappa$ be greater than $l_0/2$ would demand a meson mass m_0 less than 150 electron masses m, whereas actually $m_0 \sim 200m$. Therefore it must be inferred that, in contrast to the generally accepted view, the range R of the nuclear forces has nothing to do with the mass m_0 of the meson but is connected with the fundamental length l_0. This result explains the relation of R to the classical electron radius r_0, which up to now had to be taken as a merely casual coincidence. In reality, both R and r_0 are closely related to l_0. As regards r_0 this can be seen when the κ correction factors are introduced into the quantized field equation (330) in which terms with the Dirac function $\delta(P - P_\kappa)$ occur. These functions, which are zero for $P \neq P_\kappa$, correspond to the point character of the particles and are changed by the κ factors into functions that differ from zero within a region around P_κ, the extension of which is of the order l_0. In other words, the particles appear extended in our theory, although we must not think of the extension in the usual sense of the word because its size is not fixed but depends on the experiment by which it is measured. An extension of this kind was unknown to classical physics, which imagined an electron as a sphere of constant radius r_0. We may, therefore, consider r_0 an inadequate anticipation of the length l_0 and consider as an important success for the theory the fact that it is able to explain the coincidence of R and r_0 as a deeprooted relationship.

73. Nuclear Scattering of Mesons. Magnetic Moment of Proton and Neutron.

In Section 65 we saw that, in the case of the scattering of mesons through nucleons, the vector theory, on the assumption of point-shaped particles, leads to a cross section which increases rapidly with increasing energy and, when compared with the measurements in the region of 10^9 ev, proves to be from one thousand to ten thousand times too great. The pseudoscalar theory is in better agreement with experiment, although its results, being ten to one hundred times too high, are still unsatisfactory. Since we are not sure whether the observed mesons are vectorial or pseudoscalar, at present it is impossible to decide whether the l_0 principle is able to improve the theory. If the mesons were certain to be vectorial, the question must be answered in the affirmative, for, as we shall see, in that case the cross section is diminished by l_0 to the correct value. For pseudoscalar mesons, however, the corrected cross section would be far too small. At the present stage the scattering of mesons, therefore, cannot be used as an argument for or against the l_0 theory, the less so since the scattering process may be associated with a transmutation of the mesons. Notwithstanding this fact, it may be useful for further investigations to know the influence of l_0 on the probability with which a meson of high energy is scattered.

According to Section 65 the process of scattering is achieved in two steps. The nucleon first absorbs a meson, thereby passing from its initial state A into an intermediate state Z, whereupon another meson is emitted in the transition $Z \rightarrow F$. The other possibility that the two processes take place in the reverse order may be disregarded, since a nucleon at rest is unable to emit a meson with a momentum greater than h/l_0. In order to calculate the correction factor κ which belongs to H_{AZ}', we must take into account the recoil the nucleon receives by the absorption. If the momentum of the absorbed meson is given by h/λ, where λ is supposed to be less than l_0, the conservation of momentum requires that

$$\frac{mv}{\sqrt{1 - \beta^2}} = \frac{h}{\lambda} \qquad (m = \text{mass of the nucleon})$$

and hence

$$\sqrt{1 - \beta^2} = \frac{1}{\sqrt{1 + h^2/m^2c^2\lambda^2}} \sim \frac{1}{\sqrt{1 + (l_0/3\lambda)^2}}$$

since $h/mc \sim l_0/3$ if we assume the value 5×10^{-13} for l_0.

For the wavelength λ'' into which λ is transformed by the passage from the original coordinate system K to the system K'' in which the nucleon is at rest, we get

$$\lambda'' = \lambda \frac{1 + \beta \cos \theta''}{\sqrt{1 - \beta^2}} = \lambda \frac{2}{\sqrt{1 - \beta^2}} \sim 2 \sqrt{\lambda^2 + \left(\frac{l_0}{3}\right)^2}$$

Thus, for a wavelength very much less than l_0, we have $\lambda'' = 2l_0/3$. This means that $\int dv \, e^{i\mathbf{k}'' \cdot \mathbf{r}}$ is different from zero but has a small value only, since a considerable part of the wave motion is ineffective. In Code's experiments the energy of the mesons was 0.8×10^9 ev, corresponding to a wavelength $\lambda = 1.7 \times 10^{-13}$ cm; for λ'' we would then have $0.9 l_0$. Using this value, we must determine the value of κ_2 from

$$\kappa_2 = \frac{\left| \int dv \, e^{i\mathbf{k}'' \cdot \mathbf{r}} \right|}{v \left| e^{i\mathbf{k}'' \cdot \mathbf{r}} \right|}$$

using in the denominator the value of $e^{i\mathbf{k}'' \cdot \mathbf{r}}$ at the center of the sphere. By a graphical method we find that $\kappa_2 \sim \frac{1}{4}$; hence $\kappa = \frac{1}{2}(\kappa_1 + \kappa_2) \sim \frac{1}{8}$ since $\kappa_1 = 0$.

The correction factor for H_{ZF}' can be determined in a similar way. Here $\kappa_2 = 0$, while κ_1 is given by

$$\kappa_1 = \frac{\left| \int dv \, e^{i\mathbf{k}' \cdot \mathbf{r}} \right|}{v \left| e^{i\mathbf{k}' \cdot \mathbf{r}} \right|}$$

In the above, $\mathbf{k}'$ is the wave vector of the emitted meson when it is observed in the system K'' of the preceding calculation. $\mathbf{k}'$ corresponds to a wavelength λ' given by

$$\lambda' = \lambda \frac{1 + \beta \cos \theta'}{\sqrt{1 - \beta^2}}$$

if we assume that no energy is lost by the scattering so that the absorbed and emitted mesons have the same wavelengths. θ' is the angle between the directions defined by the incident and the emitted meson. The angle θ' is measured in the system K'', and for $\kappa_1 \neq 0$ it must satisfy the condition $1 + \beta \cos \theta' > 0$ in order that λ' become greater than λ. This means that the angle θ, measured in the initial system K, must be less than $mc\lambda/h$, which is nearly equal to $3\lambda/l_0$. Then κ again becomes $\frac{1}{8}$, and the probability of the transition $A \to F$, which is proportional to the square of $H_{AZ'}H_{ZF'}$, must be multiplied by κ^4, that is, by $1/8^4$. The cross section for vector mesons of 0.8×10^9 ev is then reduced to a value of 0.3×10^{-27} cm, which is in good agreement with the result, 0.6×10^{-27} cm, of the measurements. This would be satisfactory if there were not the possibility of the mesons being pseudoscalar. Then the same factor, $1/8^4$ would have to be applied, with the result that the cross section would become far too small.

There is no such ambiguity in the treatment of the magnetic moment of the proton and the neutron. According to Section 66 this moment comes about by the emission and reabsorption of mesons by the nucleon, only vector mesons being involved since the moment is due to their spin. Since only mesons with a momentum less than h/l_0 can be emitted by a nucleon at rest, the integration in (382) relative to k is only to be extended from $k = 0$ up to near $k_0 = h/l_0$. This limitation of the integral is brought about by the correction factor κ, with the square of which the integrand must be multiplied and which, in the neighborhood of $k_0 = h/l_0$, decreases to zero. The effect of κ can be evaluated by means of a graphic integration, leading to the result

$$\mu_P = 2.4\mu_0 \qquad \mu_N = -1.4\mu_0 \qquad (\mu_0 = \text{nuclear magneton})$$

which as a first approximation are in rather good agreement with the experimental values

$$\mu_P = 2.7\mu_0 \qquad \mu_N = -1.9\mu_0$$

74. Decay of Negative Mesons in Light Elements. It is in the nature of the length l_0 that it generally manifests itself only in experiments dealing with particles of extremely high energy. But, recently, a very striking phenomenon in the region of quite normal energies has been observed. It is inexplicable for the current theory, the only interpretation permissible being that in the interaction between nucleon and meson a limiting constant must be at work. In the experiments of Conversi, Pancini, and Piccioni† the behavior of mesons traversing a layer of matter and being stopped by it was studied. When, by the collisions it experiences, a negative meson is sufficiently slowed down, it is captured by an atom and takes on a motion of revolution around the nucleus. After a very short time it reaches the K orbit, and we should expect that it would be absorbed from this orbit by a proton of the nucleus. We can calculate the probability of the absorption and find that it must take place in an interval of the order of magnitude 10^{-18} seconds which is shorter by about 10^{-12} than the 10^{-6} seconds required by the meson for its decay into an electron and a neutrino. Therefore it should be impossible to observe the appearance of decay electrons. However, experimental results are in sharp contradiction to this expectation. It is true that negative decay electrons are not observed in iron, but, if carbon is used as a stopping material, the number of the negative disintegration electrons becomes nearly the same as that of the positive ones. This means that, for carbon, the absorption probability of a negative meson must be smaller by at least a factor 10^{12} than we should expect according to the theory.

† M. Conversi, E. Pancini, and O. Piccioni, *Phys. Rev.*, **71**, 209 (1947).

As Sigurgeirsson† was able to show, the result holds not only for carbon but also for other light elements with an atomic number Z which is less than 10. With increasing Z the absorption probability gradually increases and reaches the theoretical value when Z is sufficiently high.

A discrepancy between experiment and expectation by a factor 10^{12} creates a very serious situation for current nuclear theories. It is important, therefore, that we come to a very simple explanation of the effect by taking into account the length l_0. Let us assume a pseudo-scalar meson which is moving on the K orbit. We denote the wave function of the meson by ψ and that of the proton belonging to the nucleus by Φ. Then, according to (360), the interaction of the meson ψ and the proton Φ, apart from an irrelevant factor, is given by

$$\int (\Phi^* \vec{\sigma} \Phi) \ \text{grad} \ \psi + \text{conjugate complex} \qquad (401)$$

The problem now is the interpretation of this expression. The current theory considers Φ a function of xyz from which can be evaluated the probability that the particle, represented by Φ, is found at point xyz when an exact measurement of the position is made. But this interpretation is inadequate to the possibilities of a real measurement. Actually there is a limit to the accuracy with which a position can be ascertained, and we must give the function Φ a meaning that takes this limit into account. This is done by defining Φ as a function which determines the probability that the particle is found *in coincidence* with a reference particle to which point xyz is attributed. By coincidence we mean that the two particles, because of a separation less than l_0, cannot be distinguished from each other. This definition attaches an observational meaning to the function without destroying its continuous character. Although the function remains formally the same, it now refers to a point xyz in a way that corresponds to the possibilities of observation. We must not consider the ascribing of definite coordinates xyz to the reference particle a difficulty which seemingly contradicts the principle that an exact measurement of position is impossible, for here our procedure is to be understood in the sense that by means of the reference particle we *define* the coordinate system.

Let us now take as the reference particle that proton P_0 of the nucleus which is situated at the center of the K orbit and to which we attribute the position $\mathbf{r} = 0$. The P_0 is represented by a function

† T. Sigurgeirsson and A. Yamakawa, *Phys. Rev.*, **71**, 319 (1947).

Φ which differs from zero only in the immediate neighborhood of $\mathbf{r} = 0$, so that in (401) we may put

$$(\Phi^*\vec{\sigma}\Phi) = \vec{\sigma}\,\delta(\mathbf{r}) \qquad (402)$$

$\delta(\mathbf{r})$ being the Dirac function which vanishes for $\mathbf{r} \neq 0$ and diverges for $\mathbf{r} = 0$ in such a way that $\int dv\, \delta(\mathbf{r}) = 1$. Conversely, there is, according to the current theory, one and only one particle to which equation (402) applies, so that by

$$\int \vec{\sigma}\,\delta(\mathbf{r})\ \text{grad}\ \psi$$

the interaction of the considered meson with only one proton, situated at $\mathbf{r} = 0$, is described. But, according to our interpretation of the function Φ, (402) applies to any particle which is in coincidence with P_0, that is, which is separated from P_0 by a distance less than l_0. By introducing (402) into (401) we get the interaction of the meson with all these protons. Then (401) becomes

$$\vec{\sigma}(\text{grad}\ \psi)_0$$

the subscript 0 meaning that grad ψ is to be taken at the point $\mathbf{r} = 0$. Now the function of the K orbit depends only on r and therefore, at the point $\mathbf{r} = 0$, grad ψ has the same intensity in any direction and thus $(\text{grad}\ \psi)_0 = 0$. This means that a nucleus, consisting only of protons which are all in coincidence with one another, is not able to absorb a pseudoscalar meson. An absorption other than zero is possible only if the protons of the nucleus do not form a spatially indissoluble unit. The protons which coincide with P_0 lie within a sphere of radius l_0. Because of their own apparent extension, the radius R of the nucleus which is unable to absorb a meson becomes $3l_0/2$. In its dependence on the atomic weight A, the approximate value of R is given by $R = (l_0/2)A^{\frac{1}{3}}$. The value $R = 3l_0/2$ therefore corresponds to $A = 27$, $Z_0 \sim 13$. But it is to be expected that the critical value of Z_0 will be somewhat smaller, since it should not be supposed that the nuclei are exactly spherical.

It should be pointed out, however, that for a longitudinal vector meson the interaction is not determined by $(\text{grad}\ \psi)_0$ but by $(\text{div}\ \pi)_0$, which is not equal to zero. Therefore, for vector mesons a restriction on their absorption should not exist.

Index

Absorption of radiation, 225
Adjunct function, 98
Angular momentum, 49, 98, 170
Antisymmetric state, 140, 150
Antisymmetric tensor, 181

Balmer, 66
Bartlett, 256
Bethe, 254
Bohr's theory, 36, 43, 70
Born, 33
Bose-Einstein statistics, 150, 159
de Broglie waves, 33
de Broglie's equation, 184

Causality, 8, 118
Classical mechanics, 17
Classical theory of radiation, 204
Commutation relation, 103
Continuity equation, 46
Contraction of tensors, 181
Contravariant tensor, 180
Conversi, 287
Correspondence principle, 76
Covariant tensor, 180

Degeneracy, 67
Dirac's equation, 165
Divergences of the theory, 229
Dynamical law, 118

Eigenfunction, 36
Eigenvalue, 36
Electromagnetic field, quantization of, 212
Emission of radiation, 78, 225
Energy, measurement of, 37
Exchange force, 247
Expectation value, 45

Fermi-Dirac statistics, 150, 159
Fine structure, 75
Franck, 37

Fröhlich, 260
Function of matrices, 98
Fundamental problem of matrix mechanics, 111

Geometrical method of wave mechanics, 25
Gerlach, 72
Gordon's equation, 176
Goudsmit, 72
Group velocity, 20

H atom, 62
Hafstad, 245
Harmonics, spherical, 63
He atom, 145
Heisenberg, 3, 6, 30, 83
Heitler, 260
Hermitean form, 106
Hermitean polynomial, 58
Hertz, 37
Heydenburg, 245
Hole theory, 173

Interpretation of matrices, 100
Isotopic spin, 239

Jacobi's equations, 22, 29

Kellog, 251
Kemmer, 232, 255
Klein's equation, 176

Magnetic moment of proton, 266, 284
Majorana, 256
Many-body particle picture, 149
Many-body problem, 136
Many-body wave picture, 154
Matrices, 86
    addition of, 86
    diagonal, 88
    dual, 88
    function of, 98

Matrices, Hermitean, 90
  interpretation of, 100
  multiplication of, 86
  transformation to principal axes, 91
Matrix mechanics, fundamental problem of, 111
Measurement of energy, 37
Mesons, 231
  scattering of, 257
Moeller, 245

Normalization, 42
Nuclear forces, 241
  potential of, 245

Observable, representation of, by matrix, 101
Operator, 53, 56, 110
Orthogonality, 43
Oscillator, 57

Pancini, 287
Perturbation, 127
  of degenerated systems, 130
  of non-degenerated systems, 127
Piccioni, 287
Polarization rule, 79
Potential of nuclear forces, 245
Principle of transformation, 49
Probability amplitude, 54
Probability waves, scattering of, 30
Proca's equation, 184
Proton, magnetic moment of, 266, 284
Pseudoscalar, 183
Pseudoscalar field, 183
Pseudovector, 183
Pseudovector field, 188
Pure case, 40

Quantization, of electromagnetic field, 212
  of scalar field, 194
  of vector field, 199
  of wave fields, 191

Rabi, 251
Radiation, absorption of, 225
  classical theory of, 204
  emission of, 78, 225
Ramsey, 251

Rayleigh's theorem, 15
Rosenfeld, 245
Rutherford's formula, 32

Scalar field, 176
  quantization of, 194
Scattering, of mesons, 257
  of probability waves, 30
Schroedinger's equation, 35
Selection rule, 79
Self-energy, 229
  transversal, 230
Spherical harmonics, 63
Spin, 72, 146, 170
Spinor, 172
State, representation of, by vector, 84
Stationary states, 38
Statistical cloud, 43
Statistics, Bose-Einstein, 150, 159
  Fermi-Dirac, 150, 159
  of measurements, 38
Stern, 72
Symmetric states, 140, 150

Tensor, calculus, 180
Tensors, antisymmetric, 181
  contraction of, 181
  contravariant, 180
  covariant, 180
Time dependence, of matrices, 121
  of probability amplitudes, 55
Transformation, of matrix to principal axes, 91
  principle of, 49
Transition probability, 76
Transversal self-energy, 230
Tuve, 245

Uhlenbeck, 72
Uncertainty relations, 3

Vector field, quantization of, 199

Wave field, quantization of, 191
Wave mechanics, geometrical method of, 25
Wave packets, 14
Waves, de Broglie, 33

Zacharias, 251